W. STORRS LEE was associated with Middlebury College from 1929 to 1955 except for four years in the Pacific in Naval Intelligence. He now lives in Berkeley, California, and summers at Pemaquid Point, Maine. He is the author of *Stagecoach North* (1941), *Town Father* (1952), *The Green Mountains of Vermont* (1955), *The Yankees of Connecticut* (1957). He has crossed the Isthmus of Panama by car, train, and ship. On October 4, 1957 he attended the ceremonies honoring the 200,000th ship to make the transit of the Canal, and the above photograph was taken at the time he went through the Miraflores Locks on the ship as a guest of the Governor's staff.

The Strength
to Move a Mountain

W. STORRS LEE

The Strength
to Move a Mountain

NEW YORK   G. P. Putnam's Sons

© 1958 by W. Storrs Lee

Published simultaneously in the Dominion of Canada by Longmans, Green and Company, Toronto.

Quotations from the following works, further identified under REFERENCE SOURCES, are reprinted by special permission of the copyright owners:

> *And the Mountains Will Move* by Miles P. DuVal, Jr. With the permission of the publishers, Stanford University Press. Copyright 1947 by the Board of Trustees of Leland Stanford Junior University. *Zone Policeman 88* by Harry A. Franck. Copyright 1913, Century Company, reprinted by permission of the publishers, Appleton-Century-Crofts, Inc.

Other quotations for which reprint permissions were granted are identified under REFERENCE SOURCES.

Library of Congress Catalog Card Number: 58-8905

MANUFACTURED IN THE UNITED STATES OF AMERICA

VAN REES PRESS • NEW YORK

To Arthur K. D. Healy

Acknowledgments

AMONG students of the Panama Canal and among those concerned with Canal Zone affairs past and present there are broad areas of disagreement on both political and operational aspects. It would be unfair to allow the reader to infer that those who assisted me in the preparation of this book have given endorsement in any way to my commentary.

I am particularly indebted to the following: Mr. J. Rufus Hardy, Chief, Press and Publications, Panama Canal Company; Captain Miles P. DuVal, Jr., former Captain of the Port, Pacific Terminal, and author of several excellent volumes on the Canal; the Honorable Maurice H. Thatcher, Zone civil administrator, 1910-1913; the late General James G. Steese, former Canal maintenance engineer; Admiral Leo Bachman, United States Navy; Captain Andrew Gray of the United Fruit steamship service; Mr. E. C. LaClair, official photographer for the Panama Canal Company; William G. Arey, Jr., public relations officer, Panama Canal Company; Miss Jane Latta, Publications Division, United Fruit Company.

A special note of gratitude is due the librarians of the University of California where much of the research for the book was done; to Colonel Hugh M. Arnold, Acting Governor of the Canal Zone, who, with his staff, was most hospitable during a visit to the Zone in October, 1957; and to my wife Mary Louise for research and patient collaboration in the preparation of the book.

Contents

Sixteen pages of illustrations will be found following page 160.

Foreword

"SOMETHING WORTH BRAGGING ABOOT"

HALF a century ago the Panama Canal in-the-making was the wonder of the world—an engineering colossus that would dwarf all the ancient and modern wonders—"the most noteworthy contribution toward the material improvement of the world ever made by the Teutonic race."

That was before the skylines of Chicago and Manhattan were punctuated with spectacular pinnacles of steel and concrete, before Hoover Dam, Grand Coulee, and Bonneville walled back small inland seas, before TVA and the St. Lawrence Seaway, before the era of eight-lane throughways, skyways, and the Golden Gate Bridge, before the incredible construction miracles of World War II.

The importance of Panama has not diminished in those fifty years, but so many other man-made miracles have been crowded onto the continents that the Canal has long since lost its preeminence as the earth's major tourist attraction. When the great ditch was empty of water and the concrete walls naked, the sight was stupendous, the awe-inspiring grandeur too magnificent to comprehend. Now the real wonder of the Canal is submerged, concealed behind the unimposing control towers or inside the giant walls where acres of intricate machinery have been functioning with scarcely an interruption since 1914. Transit through the locks is made so smoothly, so effortlessly that a spectator unfamiliar with the hidden workings sees little to marvel about, and the ride through the Cut where terrifying slides and upheavals kept engineers on edge for decades is no more exciting than a river-boat trip down the Hudson. To inured globe-trotters the slow, eight-hour passage across the Isthmus can be rather tedious.

From the Caribbean a ship noses past the twin cities of Colón and Cristobal into the channel leading to Gatun Locks. Great gates swing open and close; in three steps the vessel is magically lifted eighty-five feet to the level of a broad inland lake that bridges the American continent at its narrowest point. Skirting little exotic islands and jungle peninsulas, the ship winds across the lake for twenty miles, then at a dawdling pace moves majestically through the nine-mile Cut in the Continental Divide, pauses at Pedro Miguel for the first Pacific lockage, at Miraflores for two more steps down, and in a few minutes is sweeping past Balboa toward the open Pacific. Altogether from deep Atlantic to deep Pacific the trip is only fifty miles, instead of ten thousand around the Horn.

Seamen in their sixties and seventies still remember when they had to take that long way around, when the distance by water from New York to San Francisco was over 13,000 miles rather than some 5,000, when the passage to Ecuador was 7,000 miles longer than it is now. Old men—the veteran diggers of the Panama campaign—remember when the terrain through which the waterway was to pass was a swampy morass, the bed of turbulent rivers, and impenetrable hillside jungle. But almost everyone else has forgotten. People back home, and the new generation, take the Canal for granted, as though it had always belonged to the geography of the Western Hemisphere.

It's our Canal. We built it. But we built it on foreign soil—as the French built Suez on foreign soil. The private corporation that dug Suez and operated it for nearly ninety years lost their canal; even the statue of builder Ferdinand de Lesseps was ignominiously torn down and destroyed, and the fact that Egypt could abrogate her treaties and repossess Suez introduced for the first time a shade of uncertainty regarding the permanence of American rights in Panama. It raised a confusion of questions on the fallibility of basic political pledges on which continued canal operation depended.

Actually there was little similarity between the original Panama and Suez pledges. In 1854 the Government of Egypt granted de Lesseps the right to form a private company which would dig the canal, control it for 99 years after its opening, and yield to Egypt 15 per cent of the net profits. By an international agreement of 1888, the canal was to be a neutral passage open in times of war or peace to all commercial and military traffic without distinction of flag—and if Nasser had been less impatient, Suez in another decade, would have reverted automatically to Egyptian ownership, without an international scandal.

The Panama Canal Zone, on the other hand, was a grant in perpetuity for which the United States made a cash payment and agreed to an annuity of $250,000—subsequently raised to $430,-000 and $1,930,000. Over this narrow strip of land, which sliced the Republic of Panama in half, Uncle Sam was to maintain sovereignty as supreme as in any American territorial possession.

The ninety-nine-year agreement between Egypt and de Lesseps' Universal Suez Maritime Canal Company was no less inviolable than the tight treaty between Panama and the United States, but Nasser took the liberty of abrogation, and if Egypt could get away with it, why couldn't the Government of Panama?

Even before the seizure of Suez, the propriety of national control over a vital waterway had been questioned. Had a single country the moral right to regulate the passage between two oceans? At Potsdam President Truman ventured an off-the-cuff proposal that all focal waterways be placed under the jurisdiction of the United Nations. The suggestion sounded good—notably to the Soviet Union. Communist propaganda mills started churning, vicariously supplying Central Americans with the courage to

11

challenge and embarrass their Yankee benefactors. Though rational Panamanians were well satisfied with American management of the Canal and knew that they had neither the capital nor the skill to operate it permanently, extremists hinted inconsistently of both nationalization and internationalization. The precedent set by Egypt—with the support of Russia—egged them on. Then came a haughty announcement that "the Republic of Panama means to resume complete sovereignty over the Panama Canal and over the land known as the Canal Zone."

The statement was attributed to the United States' good friend President Ernesto de la Guardia and he summarily disclaimed it. "The nationalization of the Panama Canal is not a public issue in Panama," he wrote. "In a world subject to bitter rivalries between great powers, Panama could not realistically think of operating and protecting the Panama Canal alone. In the case of the original Panama Treaty, its clauses were considered to be perpetual by its authors, and yet they have suffered various fundamental modifications. Treaties are written by men, and only God makes eternal things."

To such a reasonable and even-tempered philosophy no one could take exception, but in view of the epidemic of doubts and suspicions, an unequivocal reassertion by the United States of its long-range Isthmian policies and plans would have been reassuring. No such reassertion appeared. Although a few Washington principals were gravely concerned about affairs in the Canal Zone, collectively the American people weren't particularly interested. They had never lavished a display of pride or sentiment on the Canal, and now they were unaware that before a definite policy assertion could be made, a great many conflicts in military and engineering doctrine had to be squared away; a fundamental argument had to be settled on whether the Canal should be maintained by the United States primarily as a public utility in the service of world commerce or as an indispensable accessory in a system of national defense.

On these two divergent concepts disagreements had mounted,

colored by army and navy school-tie rivalry, political opportunists at odds with idealists, openhanded economists at odds with the conservatives. There were those who wanted to scrap the present Canal and replace it with a sea-level ditch that would cost billions; others who insisted that an enlarged lock-lake canal would be far superior and ultimately more navigable; still others who maintained that the present waterway with a few improvements would be adequate for many decades.

Then the old arguments for a shipping lane across Nicaragua or across some other part of Central America were being revived. Fifty years ago fantastic plans were drawn up for a railroad large enough to portage the greatest ocean liners overland on flatcars; less fantastic now seemed ideas for a forty-mile conveyor belt stretching from ocean to ocean, for super-highways through the jungle and over the Cordillera, for coastal super-ships loaded with freight cars which would roll off the decks on the Atlantic side, cross to the Pacific, and roll onto sister transports on the Pacific side. Advocates of one plan were slow to yield a point in favor of the advocates of another. A procession of Congressmen and engineers was once more trudging over the terrain, mediating, investigating, and making recommendations. Until they could reach some agreement, it was impossible to draft an enduring Isthmian policy.

Anyone familiar with world transportation problems conceded that the Panama Canal was in urgent need of renovation and enlargement, if the demands of steadily increasing traffic were to be met. The annual tonnage passing through the locks was close to fifteen times what it was during the first twelve months of their operation—when slides were still hampering transit—and in the last decade shipping had more than doubled, reaching an annual total of fifty million tons. In oil alone five million tons were being transported in a year from Atlantic to Pacific ports. Panama was, indeed, a commercial crossroads of the world, yet no major alteration had been made in the thoroughfare since the days of Taft and Teddy Roosevelt. Month after month tonnage records for corresponding periods were being broken; month by month the problem of congestion was growing more serious—particularly during the weeks when one lane of locks had to be closed for cleaning and overhauling. Every transit spilled some 52,000,000 million gallons of water from Gatun Lake into the oceans—a two-day supply for a city the size of Boston—and in an abnormally dry season the reserve in the Lake was becoming dangerously low. Moreover, designers of ocean Queens, aircraft carriers, and tankers were no longer limiting the dimensions of their ships to fit the 1000-foot length and the 110-foot width of the Panama locks.

From the beginning, interests of defense and interests of commerce were not always compatible; appropriations for military bases came more readily than appropriations for expansion of shipping facilities. The initial cost of the big ditch ran to $375,-000,000—in days when raw labor was demanding twenty and thirty cents an hour, and when billion dollar figures were discussed whimsically. Many times that first investment went into defense of the Canal during the four decades after its construction. Guarding the waterway during World War II was a thousand-mile ring of sea and air bases. Implausible sums were poured into fortifications, air fields, and naval facilities—from which there were no returns in tolls.

Then the blast at Hiroshima echoed the warning that the locks and dams were as indefensible as the streets of Manhattan, Detroit, or San Francisco. In the post-war years the seacoast guns were scrapped, airfields abandoned, barracks deserted, important property restored to Panama; for a time it looked as though even the transcontinental railroad might be given up. Taking advantage of diplomatic fumbling and the indecision in Washington, Panama appeared to be contesting the validity of the old Canal treaty while making new financial demands.

"Do we face the possibility, in effect, of having to buy back the Canal every once in a while?" queried a disturbed Congressman in the summer of 1957.

The atomic age and the postwar years disrupted Zone equilibrium, brought a confusion of plans for coping with a new order and brought, too, the riddle of whether modifications in the Canal should be considered primarily in terms of national defense or in commercial enterprise.

Largely as a defense measure, a Third Locks Project had been started in 1940, and a total of $75,000,000 spent on the venture before it was abandoned in 1942, when the need for men and materials was more critical elsewhere. The Project was never revived, for the congestion of World War II traffic demonstrated that it was perhaps not the right answer.

In 1943 Miles P. DuVal, Jr., Captain of the Port at the Pacific terminal, came up with a bright idea for operational improvement of the Canal. He wanted to remove the Pedro Miguel Locks altogether, to construct all three Pacific locks in continuous steps at Miraflores, provide an anchorage there on an extension of Gatun Lake, raise the maximum lake level from 87 to 92 feet, widen Gaillard Cut, and build a set of larger locks at each end. Labeled the "Terminal Lake-Third Lock Plan," it was forwarded by the Secretary of the Navy to the President and was the kick-off for a new "battle of the levels" almost as bitter as the controversy of 1906.

Two years later the dropping of the first atomic bomb introduced a pressing question of security for the Canal. Could it be protected from atomic attack or refashioned to be less vulnerable? Congress called upon the Governor of the Panama Canal to make a comprehensive investigation of means for increasing the capacity as well as the security of the waterway, to restudy the Third Locks Project, and to look into other possible routes. An expert staff of some two hundred, representing every applicable branch of science and engineering, went to work on the assignment, and in 1947, in one of the most meticulous engineering reports ever written, spoke for converting the present passage into a sea-level canal. The deeper ditch, they concluded, would be less destructible under atomic attack, would solve some of the

15

navigational problems, and more than double the transit capacity.

The engineers estimated that it would take 37,000 employees ten years to dig a channel across the Isthmus 600 feet wide with a 60-foot low-tide depth. It would be five miles shorter and save four hours in transit. Taking into consideration the new science of soils mechanics and new earth-moving techniques, the experts no longer feared disruptive earth slides; the disparity in tides, which have a range of twenty-two feet on the Pacific side against twenty-two inches on the Atlantic, would be licked with a tidal lock; gigantic dams and diversion channels would take care of the rivers which now empty into Gatun Lake. During its construction the only interruption in normal canal traffic, according to the plans, would be seven days at the end of the project while Gatun Lake was being emptied and land plugs removed.

But the job was going to be very expensive, costing nearly two and a half billion—later revised to over three and a half billion. Recalling that the original Canal cost more than twice the first estimates, captious Congressmen guessed that the tab for a sea-level project might well run to ten billions, and statistics showed that the cost of even a three-and-a-half-billion-dollar ditch could never be amortized. The ultimate question was whether or not the American taxpayer was going to be induced to ante up for a gamble that definitely could never pay off—excepting conceivably in terms of wartime logistics or a peace-time standard of living. Moreover, the surveys for the sea-level route were made by a new generation of young engineers who could claim little or no experience with the uncertainties of Isthmian terrain. Was their judgment on cost and construction problems reliable?

"I cannot believe that any committee of Congress, if properly advised, can be induced to recommend a sea-level canal at Panama," stormed George M. Wells, a seasoned engineer who had struggled with unpredictable earth movements on the Isthmus from 1904 to 1916. "The unnecessary waste of unknown billions of moneys, the certainty of temporarily losing the existing passageway between the oceans with prolonged interruption to commerce, and finally, the futility of it all, if ever completed, in comparison with the existing canal, just does not make sense."

For a decade other reports and counterreports, investigations and counterinvestigations accumulated. "The existing lock canal across the Isthmus of Panama is destructible by nuclear weapons, either through enemy attack or sabotage," summarized a registered lobby committee of the National Rivers and Harbors Congress in 1956, slighting the fact that for forty years a few well-placed sticks of dynamite could have put the Canal out of commission indefinitely. "A continually available ship channel connecting the Caribbean Sea with the Pacific Ocean is essential to the security of the United States; . . . by conversion of the lock canal to a sea-level waterway the hazard of prolonged closure can be reduced to a minimum; . . . further delay in accomplishing such conversion is highly inadvisable."

Taking the opposite bench, and quoting authorities on nuclear weapons, Representative Willis W. Bradley, a distinguished retired naval officer, retorted: "Any canal would be critically vulnerable to the atomic bomb, regardless of type; a sea-level canal would be in the same security class as a lake canal; . . . the atomic bomb is irrelevant as a controlling factor in the planning of operational improvements for the Panama Canal."

And representing the anti-internationalists, Maurice H. Thatcher, former civil administrator for the Zone and ex-Congressman, pleaded: "It will be a sad day, indeed, that on which the great ocean link is taken from the jurisdiction, control and operation of the United States and turned over to any other organization or power. . . . Our people taxed themselves to build this, the greatest industrial enterprise of history; and our Government has maintained and operated it with great success ever since its completion. American lives, American leadership and skill, and American treasure went into the successful effort. . . . I would oppose the indicated suggestion or movement as one of monumental stupidity and evil. . . . Not only would our land greatly suffer, but at some time of crisis perhaps with fatal effect, and the cause of free peoples would everywhere be imperiled."

No resolution of the controversy is in sight, and while the battle of the levels goes on, the Board of Directors of the Panama Canal Company, U.S. governing authority for the Canal, continued to be faced with the problem of increasing traffic, long delays in lock operation at the Pacific end because there was no mooring space above Pedro Miguel, and because all shipping in the opposite direction had to wait while the largest vessels passed through the narrows of Gaillard Cut.

To cope with the congestion, the Directors had four-year plans, with a twenty-million-dollar price tag, calling for the widening and deepening of sections in the Cut, improvements in lighting to permit safer round-the-clock transits, moorings north of Pedro Miguel, and new towing locomotives. These alterations would take care of all anticipated traffic for a decade or two, would increase the dependable capacity of the Canal by 25 per cent, and could be financed from current operating funds, but they were only a temporary solution pending the answering of billion-dollar policy questions in Washington.

The time had come for an informed public interest in affairs on the Isthmus, and an informed reaction. But needed first was a reassessment of the significance of the American accomplishment a half century ago. Before objections are expressed to handing over the Zone to another authority, before reluctance is shown toward the spending of millions or billions on modernizing the Canal, the stake we have there should be reexamined, the early sacrifices recounted, the Culebra background reexplored, the forgotten story of the building of the Canal exhumed.

Along with instances of exemplary beneficence, the examination will bring to light some imperious tactics which we prefer to consider outmoded—most conspicuous of which is the manner in which we "took" the Isthmus. But that one indiscretion should not be permitted to color the whole. Roosevelt was acting for the good of mankind; he knew it. And the intervening years have

18

failed to prove him far wrong. The Zone was "taken" in an era of power politics when it was still an accepted principle of international law for "civilized" states to intervene in the affairs of backward countries. The acquisition of Panama was in no way out of step with the times; in fact, the maneuver was carried out with more grace and tact than was common among the other great powers in the early 1900s.

"Under the treaty with Panama," William Howard Taft reminded an informal audience at New Orleans in 1909, "we are entitled to exercise all the sovereignty and all the rights of sovereignty that we would exercise if we were sovereign, and Panama is excluded from exercising any right to the contrary of those conceded to us. Now that is a ticklish argument, but I do not care whether it is or not. We are there. We have the right to govern that strip and we are going to govern it."

That was the spirit of our imperialism. We can deplore it, we can be embarrassed about the aggressiveness of our fathers, but it is too late to retract. Attempting to make amends for their tenacity then, by turning over the Canal to another authority now, carries as much logic as our volunteering to return California and Texas to Mexico because of our former obstreperousness, Puerto Rico to Spain, or the Hawaiian Islands to the heirs of Queen Liliuokalani.

The 1914 triumph over Panama mountains, mosquitoes, and sliding mud was one of the greatest of American conquests. It was a battleground that should rank with Valley Forge, Gettysburg, Belleau Woods, or Guadalcanal, but it has never been honored with any such distinction. The construction of the Canal as a world utility was perhaps the most noble benefaction in the history of the United States, yet neither the benefactors nor the beneficiaries regard it as such. To be sure, the liberality was not without self-interest. It benefited the commerce of Lima and London, Trieste and Tokyo on equal terms, but it also made Oregon apples cheaper in Rhode Island and Rhode Island textiles cheaper in Oregon.

When pressed for his reaction after making the grand tour of the Canal in 1914 in unbroken silence, a Scottish engineer finally allowed: "At last you Americans have done something worth bragging aboot!"

Panama was the spectacular demonstration to the world of American initiative and know-how. Experiments successfully tried out on the Isthmus were later applied with equal success in World Wars I and II—technical experiments with big machinery; logistical experiments with the movement of masses of men, with commissaries and living quarters; political experiments in dealing generously with foreign peoples; sociological experiments with "field" churches, "field" schools, and Y.M.C.A.s. Panama set a pattern that was to be followed nearly half a century later in the conduct of occupation forces and in Point Four programs. It marked a turning point in our history. With Panama America took the lead in man's attempt to reorder the geographical conditions of creation.

The digging of the Canal was a drama of conflicting forces and personalities. In the cast of great performers were Ferdinand de Lesseps, mastermind in a merging of waters in another part of the globe, the tireless promoter who liked to refer idealistically to the Isthmian undertaking as "The Panama Crusade"; Theodore Roosevelt, the headstrong, dynamic "American" who saw in the cut through Culebra a new destiny for his country; Bunau-Varilla, the informed, brilliant French engineer and clever strategist; the indomitable John F. Stevens, who could sway men with a colorful phrase as well as with an unconventional idea—the basic architect of the Canal; Dr. William Gorgas, the humanitarian with the courage to defy slow death on the Isthmus; George W. Goethals, the man who stuck with the job to the bitter end, to be popularly tagged the "hero" of Panama. Backstage was a corps of diplomatists, Congressmen and statesmen vying for position as prompters, occasionally fumbling the script, giving the wrong cue and stepping into the limelight themselves; upstage an important group of engineers who really knew how the act should go, knew their lines, but didn't always have a chance to speak them; downstage an army of laborers from every corner of the globe, sweating it out, symbolically playing bit-parts they didn't understand, but all contributing to the drama that was going to make headlines in their home papers for a long time to come. And the setting was the most dramatic thing of all—two oceans separated by a narrow neck of jungle, the tropical torrents and awful heat, the mountains of mobile mud.

It was a great performance. The Scotsman was right. It was "something worth bragging aboot."

W. S. L.

The Strength
to Move a Mountain

"I TOOK THE ISTHMUS,
STARTED THE CANAL"

THE off-season run on Winchester rifles extended all through the summer of 1903. It was a spotty, unaccountable trade. A sports shop in New Orleans was cleaned out. Hardware dealers in out-of-the-way towns had to place new orders. In New England, in New York, in cities along the Atlantic seaboard a stranger with a foreign accent dropped in at gun stores, paid cash for a dozen Winchesters, and ordered them shipped to—of all places—Morgan City, Louisiana. A single big purchase to a town was the rule, and the purchases were widely enough dispersed so that a clerk in one store never had reason to compare his sales with those in another. It never crossed the mind of the man behind the counter that he was supplying an arsenal for a revolution in Panama.

Then just before dawn one morning late in August, a derelict schooner that had been tied up for weeks at a ramshackle wharf of Morgan City put out into the Gulf. She was low in the water, had a surly, pick-up crew of Spaniards and half-castes, a skipper who didn't talk, and a top-heavy deck cargo of Southern pine. Nothing particularly unusual about her; it was the kind of vessel, the kind of cargo, and the kind of crew that was commonplace in the sleepy fishing and lumber port between New Orleans and Galveston. The Customs House officials cleared her in routine fashion for Progresso, Yucatan; her papers were in order, her declared cargo was lumber.

Only the silent captain and a few of the well-paid crew knew that the schooner had stowed below decks a stand of 4000 Winchesters and 1,500,000 rounds of ammunition—"enough rifles and cartridges to oppose any army in Central or South America." And the skipper alone knew that before they touched Yucatan, they were to pick up a steamship from Kingston and transfer the arms and ammunition for shipment to Colombian rebels at Porto Bello, a few miles east of Colón.

Revolution was brewing again in Colombia—a country that could ill afford another civil war, for the government at Bogotá had barely established an uneasy peace after the last revolt, which had cost the lives of 100,000 men and boosted the national debt to $800,000,000. But this was a revolution with a difference. The Panama Canal was at stake. After nearly a quarter of a century of trial and error, the French had thrown in the sponge and offered to the Americans for $40,000,000 their concession, their abandoned equipment and their modest ditch. It was a deal, provided the prospective customer could come to terms with Colombia on a price for rights of transfer. Teddy Roosevelt and a lot of other Yankees wanted very much to take advantage of the bargain. For three-quarters of a century scarcely a U.S. Congressional session had adjourned without a heated debate on ways and means of acquiring rights for a trans-Isthmian canal. The Nicaragua route had long been preferred in Washington, but it looked now as though Panama might be a better gamble. T.R. was getting ready for his re-election campaign of 1904, and it would be a feather in his political cap to have a canal agreement to boast about.

The unhappy province of Panama was eager for the United States to move in, but mother Colombia was balking. Periodically Panama had been an independent country, but for fifty years she had been tied to the apron strings of Colombia, enduring humiliations and oppressions dictated by Bogotá, treated with the indifference of a stepchild, as though she were worthy only of being a provider for the national treasury. Reduced from a state to a "department" and robbed of any significant political voice, she was obliged to accept the government officials appointed for her. The one enviable asset Panama possessed was geographic—the narrow stretch of land between the Atlantic and the Pacific. In her own good time Colombia intended to capitalize on that geography to replenish the empty coffers of the federal treasury, even though it meant pauperizing her subjects in Colón and Panama City.

The Panamanians well knew what Colombia was up to. Congress was in special session at Bogotá during the long summer of 1903 and the canal was the principal subject on the legislative agenda. The lawmakers were stalling on any deal with the United States because they were satisfied neither with the terms of the proposed American treaty nor the price offered; moreover the canal concession granted more than two decades before to France would expire in another year. If they held off long enough it would be forfeited; Colombia would automatically fall heir to the three-hundred-million-dollar French investment and could sell the works on her own conditions to the highest bidder. Germany, for instance, might be ready to bid considerably more than the United States.

On August 12, 1903, the Colombian Senate summarily turned down a United States offer of $10,000,000, maintaining to the last that proposing such a meager cash payment was nothing more than "the attempt of a stronger nation to take advantage of Colombia and rob her of one of the most valuable sources of wealth which the world contains." Rejected with it was the Hay-Herran treaty for the canal rights, which Washington had approved six months before.

Rebels in Panama had anticipated the rejection, as had President Roosevelt and the Department of State. T.R. lost his temper. "Those contemptible little creatures in Bogotá," he called the august body of Colombian senators. "Inefficient bandits. Foolish

27

and homicidal corruptionists! Cut-throats of Bogotá! Those jack rabbits!" The rebels in Panama took no exception to the President's evaluation, but were less outspoken. Discreetly they laid careful plans for secession. The big difference between this rebellion and the others that occurred in Panama almost as regularly as church festivals was that at least tacit support could be counted on from the big sister nation to the north.

The general public in the United States was as blithely ignorant of what was going on behind scenes during the early autumn months of 1903 as were the clerks who sold the Winchester rifles in July. Scarcely a thought was paid to the shuffling of warships toward Central America. A revolution was fortuitously stirring in the Dominican Republic too; Nicaragua allegedly was about to attack Honduras, and Guatemala was said to be in a state of unrest. The reports offered plausible excuse for fleet movements. Newspaper readers who scanned inside pages could note that the cruiser *Boston* had been ordered from San Francisco to San Juan del Sur; that the *Baltimore* was hurriedly dispatched from Hampton Roads to the Caribbean, although an enlightened analyst might well question the necessity of sending a cruiser to referee a Santo Domingo squabble. The *Dixie* was circuitously routed from Guantánamo to Puerto Plata—by way of Kingston, Jamaica. Under an inconspicuous heading "Movement of Naval Vessels" appeared all too casually the information that the *Osceola* was sailing from Key West to Jamaica; the *Atlanta* was en route to Guantánamo; the *Marblehead,* the *Concord,* and *Wyoming* had put in at Acapulco.

On the other side of the globe in Kobe, Japan, where Admiral Robley Evans was readying his Asiatic fleet for maneuvers in the Philippines, secret orders were suddenly received to proceed to Honolulu with three battleships and four cruisers as soon as coal could be taken on. The Admiral didn't learn until years later that the purpose of his junket was to stand by at Pearl Harbor in case his services were needed off Panama. Both the Atlantic and the Pacific fleets were converging on the Isthmus. And, as if to allay any suspicions, the mighty new battleship *Maine*—much too obvious a threat to send to a Central American fracas—moved from Newport News to Martha's Vineyard.

Then on October 31, from Kingston came the giveaway: "The United States gunboat *Nashville* sailed from here this morning under sealed orders. Her destination is believed to be Colombia." The following day, under a "Panama, Colombia" date line, appeared the incidental intelligence: "News has been received here from Barranquilla on the Atlantic side of Colombia, that a formidable revolutionary movement is to be inaugurated very soon. The liberals are said to have received munitions of war from the Government of Venezuela." Simultaneously the State Department announced that its Minister to Colombia would soon return to the States on a "leave of absence"; it meant that a mere Secretary of Legation was to remain in charge at this critical moment. Yet not one of these news stories conveyed any significance to the ordinary newspaper subscriber.

"I took the Isthmus—" gloated Theodore Roosevelt long after the event, "I took the Isthmus, started the Canal."

But the land-grab wasn't as simple as that. Groundwork was laid by a handful of Americans with business interests in Panama. A Frenchman named Philippe Bunau-Varilla was in on it. A canny New York lawyer and a shrewd Columbia University professor stood in the background. Wall Street and the Bourse were involved, along with accomplices in the State and War Departments and a host of willing conspirators in Panama.

Nor did the Roosevelt claim go unchallenged. A dozen principals insisted that they were as fully entitled to the dubious honor of taking the Isthmus as was he. In particular the self-applauding Bunau-Varilla was reluctant to let anyone rob him of credit due. "To realize the Panama Canal and to vindicate the honor of France," he averred unblushingly, "I was constrained to make myself responsible for the creation of a new independent state in Central America."

The Columbia professor of international law and diplomacy, John Bassett Moore, had carefully reviewed an old treaty of 1846 between the United States and New Granada (Colombia) and advised the President that the United States was in a position "to demand that it shall be allowed to construct the great means of transit which the treaty was chiefly designed to assure." And the New York lawyer, William Nelson Cromwell, counsel for the Panama Railroad as well as the French Canal Company, without bothering to furnish the source of his intelligence, had managed to plant in the New York *World* a provocative item alleging that Panama was ready to secede and enter into a canal treaty with the United States. "President Roosevelt is said to strongly favor this plan," he added. There was no White House denial.

The intrigue was concealed in enough smudge to brush off on any claimant eager to have his share. The cat was coming out of the bag by November, and people with nice principles were beginning to wonder. To the editors of the New York *Times,* who were single-mindedly contending for a canal across Nicaragua, it was "a miserable business," from which they warned, Americans must "either withdraw at once or, shutting our ears to the voice of conscience and to the reproaches of civilized mankind, plunge on in the path of scandal, disgrace and dishonor. Revolt . . . has been altogether too openly encouraged and foreshadowed in this country to permit any further dalliance on our part with the abandoned Panama Canal unless we have come to such a pitch of shamelessness that we are willing to give the world the right to say that we have for our own selfish ends despoiled a sister republic."

What the United States was doing to Colombia in 1903 would a half-century later have put the United Nations into an uproar and invited condemnatory notes from all the prime ministers of the world. But the age of imperialism and gunboat diplomacy was still thriving, and the American intervention produced scarcely an international ripple. No one of importance listened to the pitiful protest of Colombia as voiced by her Consul General in New York: "The men who came here to plan the revolution were without exception foreigners. . . . If the United States would keep its hands off for fifteen days, the Colombian Government would have no trouble in reducing the rebellious State to ready obedience without firing a single shot and without any bloodshed whatsoever. This so-called revolution would not have started at all if there had not been ample assurance of the backing from this government beforehand. The interference practically puts an end to the Monroe Doctrine. South American countries will consider from now on that there is danger from all the grabbers, but the greatest dread will be of the United States which we have always called our elder sister among the republics and regarded as our protector."

America was on the glory trail, intent on liberating Panama from the insufferable oppression of Bogotá.

But Commander John N. Hubbard wasn't in search of glory on the evening of November 2, 1903 when he piloted the United States gunboat *Nashville* into Limon Bay and dropped anchor off Colón. They were familiar waters to him, for he had spent a dull week there during the middle of October—in fact, had put out only seventeen days before, and couldn't comprehend why he was kept shuttling back and forth across the Caribbean. Usually the gunboat carried a squad of a dozen marines, but at Kingston the *Nashville* had reportedly been converted into a troop carrier with 260 men crowded aboard. And Colón duty was so thoroughly detested by the crew that six of them had gone AWOL in Jamaica as soon as scuttlebutt got around that they were to head back south.

Like other Americans, Hubbard had only the faintest inkling of the international intrigue in which Panama was encompassed. He wasn't at all sure of what was expected of him. He had much less confidence in his own intuition than had the Assistant Secretary of the Navy, who in reply to a reporter's query about the character of instructions given to the *Nashville's* captain confided:

31

"Oh, we simply expect our forces there to maintain order and keep the railroad open to traffic. They have had experience on the Isthmus to guide them. They can be trusted to do what is wise and right. We shall not allow fighting anywhere we can stop it."

The Captain knew that warships were frequently sent to Colón for stand-by duty during the recurrent revolutions. He knew that the Americans had built a railroad across the Isthmus, and that the road had to be protected, but it had also been drilled into him that in return for the right of way, the United States had a long-standing agreement to preserve and defend Colombian sovereignty. He was confident that the breakdown in negotiations for canal rights would not be allowed to affect that agreement.

Commander Hubbard had not been informed that Roosevelt was interested in promoting a revolt in Panama, nor that only three weeks before the President had slyly commented, "I should be delighted if Panama were an independent State, or made itself so at this moment." No one had even bothered to inform the Captain that a whole armada of eight other warships was to be engaged in Operation Panama. His sealed orders merely advised him to proceed at full speed to Colón where he could expect further instructions by cablegram.

But there were no messages for the *Nashville* in Colón. The skipper was on his own to do what was "right and wise." Crowds were milling about the streets in a holiday mood, and they seemed unaccountably jubilant over the return of the Yankee gunboat. Aside from that, the city was as quiet as they had left it on October 17. The railroad property was secure, trains had been running on schedule; there was no disturbance in or near the station, no gun play anywhere. Casual reconnoitering revealed the usual waterfront loungers, the promenading in the Spanish quarters, the avenues of squalid Negro huts all tightly shuttered against the "foul" night air. From the bars surged a normal ruckus. Excited talk on the street corners had replaced most of the cheap music and gaiety, but it was nothing to be alarmed about.

Commander Hubbard saw no reason for maintaining a street patrol. Obviously consular intelligence had misjudged the seriousness of the political situation on the Isthmus. After the exciting dash from Jamaica, with the anticipation of a free-for-all, everyone on board the *Nashville* was disconcertingly let down. The Captain set the watch and turned in, oblivious of the cablegram that had been drawn up for him in Washington: "Maintain free and uninterrupted transit. If interruption is threatened by armed force, occupy the line of railroad. Prevent landing of any armed force with hostile intent, either Government or insurgent, either at Colón, Porto Bello, or any other point. . . . Government force reported approaching Isthmus in vessels. Prevent their landing if in your judgment, this would precipitate a conflict."

Through the night bluejackets paced the deck, swatting mosquitoes and looking into a quiet harbor of a quiet city. Toward morning the silhouette of a steamship loomed up from the east, slowly made its way into the harbor, and with much clanging and shouting, anchored a few hundred yards from the *Nashville*. In the darkness it was impossible to identify her, but there was nothing out of the ordinary about a night arrival. At times Colón was a busy port where the coming and going of ships could be expected at any hour. Then before it was light, fishermen began assembling on the beach, and with fluttering sails, pirogues shadowed past the gunboat, their dark crews flinging unintelligible insolence at the watch.

But as dawn broke, the ship that came in during the night began to look more ominous. She was a gunboat, not a trader. Commander Hubbard was summoned. Oh, yes, the *Cartagena*. He knew all about her—the best-armored warship in the Colombian Navy, recently purchased from the Sultan of Morocco. And as he surveyed her through his binoculars, he was not a little alarmed. She was crawling with troops getting ready to disembark. Undoubtedly the anticipated arrival of the *Cartagena* had something to do with the *Nashville's* being sent back to Colón.

Immediately he ordered his gig and boarded the *Cartagena*. He paid his respects to the captain, exchanged salutes with the senior army officer, General Tovar, and a host of other officers, looked about and returned to the *Nashville*. It was just a routine movement of regulars, the Tiradores Battalion, brought in to replace the garrison at Panama City, he was told—obviously nothing that a foreign power had any reason to oppose.

From the deck of the *Nashville* Hubbard watched the gunboat tie up at the Colón piers. The disembarkation was more like an excursion than a military operation. Wives and women accompanying the soldiers added spice and entertainment to the junket. Except for the bright uniforms and the arms, there was nothing martial about the landing. And as soon as the last of the troops, women and household goods were down the gangways, the *Cartagena* sounded a cheerful blast, took anchorage farther out in the harbor, and lay there as lifeless as a deserted hulk.

Bloody conflict for Panama was building up. Commander Hubbard had the guns and the men to stall it, but he still saw no signs of disturbance. He had no orders.

Theodore Roosevelt's inspiration for intervening in Panama as a means of getting a canal may have originated with the counsel of Professor Moore or with attorney Cromwell; it may have sprung from the advice of Bunau-Varilla. In any case, the Frenchman claimed to have thought of it first. Philippe Bunau-Varilla was such an ardent canal fanatic that even he once admitted: "The rumor is current in Paris that I have gone crazy." A proud graduate of the French military engineering academy, the École Polytechnique, he had been caught up in the wave of idolatry lavished on Ferdinand de Lesseps, and had dedicated his life to the cause of canals and worship of the builder of Suez. De Lesseps had seldom permitted facts, figures, or conscience to deter his ambitions and he had an irrational aversion to engineers and the realities they posed, but engineer Bunau-Varilla was enough of a visionary to please the archpropagandist for canals. At the age of twenty-six, because he happened to be on the scene at a moment when there was a dearth of French engineers, he had for a brief period served as director general of the Compagnie Universelle du Canal Interocéanique de Panama—the biggest engineering job that had ever been assigned to one man.

The Compagnie Universelle had failed, but the failure served only to sharpen Bunau-Varilla's enthusiasm for Panama. He devoted all his energies to salvaging what was salvageable from the magnificent fiasco, fought tirelessly the plan Americans favored for building a canal across Nicaragua, in wordy cablegrams that cost up to three or four hundred dollars apiece, urged Bogotá officials to endorse the Hay-Herran Treaty, and poured forth a stream of eloquence on the grand and noble conception of a Panama route that would benefit all mankind. As an engineer he was interested in redeeming his professional honor, determined to prove that a canal, as he and de Lesseps envisioned it, could be cut across the Isthmus; as a very wealthy capitalist he was also interested in redeeming the stock he had invested in the French enterprise—stock that would be worthless unless the United States' offer of $40,000,000 was made good.

Bunau-Varilla fancied himself the rightful heir to the de Lesseps mantle, and as the world's foremost promoter of canals, he was familiar with every phase of Panama history. During the summer of 1903, while the Colombian Congress was massacring the Hay-Herran treaty and hopes for redemption of his reputation and investments were fading, he reread the Treaty of 1846 between Colombia and the United States. That treaty specifically granted the Americans a right of way across the Isthmus "upon any modes of communication that now exist or may thereafter be constructed," in return for which the United States guaranteed that "the free transit from the one to the other sea may not be interrupted in any future time." Clearly, concluded Bunau-Varilla, the words referred to a canal as well as a railroad. Ergo the United States already possessed the right and duty to construct a waterway, regardless of what government controlled the Isthmus. The area could be occupied by force of arms, or, better still, the secession movement of Panama could be encouraged; perhaps the United States would accept the new republic as a protectorate, with the canal rights tied into the bargain.

Coming from a private citizen of a foreign country, the idea contained some highfalutin intrigue, but nothing that the energetic Frenchman couldn't handle with ease. After repeatedly warning the President of Colombia by cable that Panama was considering secession, he touched off a campaign on September 2, 1903, in his brother's newspaper *Le Matin,* virtually declaring that the Americans were negligent in not exercising the canal rights already possessed under the Treaty of 1846. He referred to the revolution which was "smouldering in the State of Panama," and accused Colombia of overstepping her property rights by "barring the road to progress." In a tangle of periphrastic ranting, he asserted that Colombia was defying "the superior law of the necessity of the circulation of the human collectivity," and bluntly added: "It is this superior law which President Roosevelt will enforce and which it will be his next step to enforce."

A copy of *Le Matin* was dispatched by the first mail to the Chief Executive of the United States. Bunau-Varilla didn't expect a reply, but he was so confident that the explosive would raise Roosevelt out of his executive chair that he took passage across the Atlantic to witness the repercussions. He arrived in New York on September 22—just in time to give a lift to the lagging spirits of the conspirators from Panama.

Things weren't going too well for the rebels at that point. They had an ample supply of arms and munitions, but they needed a navy, they needed heavy guns, they needed money—at least six million dollars, they reckoned. Most of all they needed the unqualified backing of the United States. A little junta had been meeting regularly and surreptitiously in the electric light plant on the outskirts of Panama City, taking stock of the situation, and had at length reached the conclusion that an official delegate would have to be sent to New York and Washington to draw up some sort of provisional treaty. One of their recruits, Captain J. R. Beers, freight agent for the Panama Railroad, had already made the trip and talked men he claimed were key supporters into verbal promises of assistance. "Nothing is easier. They promise to obtain whatever we ask for," was the message he brought back. Now an emissary had to go north to get something more tangible than promises. All fingers pointed to Dr. Manuel Amador Guerrero, the seventy-year-old idealist and physician who had gradually assumed the leadership of the revolution.

The doctor was too frail, too modest, too soft-spoken to head any insurrection. Scheming didn't come naturally to him. Panama needed a swashbuckling zealot, a table-pounding fanatic, not a doddering old man with poor eyesight, uncertain legs, and bony fingers that refused to curl into an effective fist. But the doctor was the one man whom everyone trusted, a man with no personal political ambitions, a man of cool dignity; and he it was who had to make the trip to New York.

No more courageous ambassador of a government-in-being or to-be ever sailed past the Statue of Liberty. Amador was sure that Uncle Sam would gladly lend him six million and sign a provisional treaty with a state that didn't exist. Confidently he strode into the legal suite of Sullivan and Cromwell, with the intention of dropping the whole problem in the lap of William Nelson Cromwell, the lawyer to whom everyone took any scheme relating to canal stockholders or the Panama Railroad. Cromwell had influence in high places and Amador was confident he would be thrilled to learn the latest intelligence regarding the projected revolt, ready to procure the essential capital, and somehow able to swing the weight of Washington to the cause of Panamanian freedom. Of Cromwell's support there could not be the slightest doubt; Captain Beers had assured him of that.

The doctor naïvely unfolded the plot of Cromwell, trustfully enlightening him on every detail, even to the names of fellow conspirators, and was thrilled with the attorney's response. Cromwell had the eagerness, the wisdom, and the worldly experience, thought Amador, to accomplish what neither he nor any member of the junta could possibly maneuver. With the support of a man like that, the success of the revolution was foreordained. The doctor did not realize that he was dealing with one of the shrewdest manipulators in the United States—a man who could "smile as sweetly as a society belle and at the same time deal a blow at a business foe that tied him in a hopeless tangle." He was completely taken in by the gracious manner, the obvious enthusiasm, and the captivating smile.

Cromwell was not exaggerating his devotion to the cause of Panamanian independence; it would be immensely profitable to him to swing the Revolution and get his cut of the $40,000,000 that would be paid as a result to his clients, but he was banking on a more sophisticated candidate for the leadership than Manuel Amador. His name was José Gabriel Duque, native of Cuba, naturalized United States citizen, publisher of the Panama *Star and Herald,* and controller of Panama's lucrative lottery—one of the most influential men on the Isthmus, and he had arrived from Colón on the very ship that brought Amador.

No sooner had the doctor left Cromwell's office, glowing with optimism and anticipating a follow-up conference a few days later, than Duque was summoned and presumptuously offered the presidency of the Republic of Panama if he would stage the revolution. On the spot, Cromwell phoned the State Department and made arrangements for his presidential nominee to confer with Secretary Hay.

But the cunning attorney had gravely misjudged his candidate. Instead of jumping to the bait, Duque promptly reported the plot with all its ramifications to the Colombian legation in Washington, and the Minister lost no time in spreading the alarm. Bogotá was informed, private detectives were put on the trail of Amador, and Cromwell was notified that if he participated in any conspiracy against the Government of Colombia or was known to associate himself with the revolutionists, the property of both the canal company and the railroad he represented would be confiscated immediately. The master of intrigue had been treated to his own art of double cross, and in order to avoid further evidence of contamination he was obliged to make immediate preparations to leave New York on "urgent business" in Paris.

When Amador—totally unaware of what was going on behind his back—returned to the office of Sullivan and Cromwell for his second appointment, the attorney's door was closed. No, a secretary informed him, Cromwell would not be able to see him that day or at any time in the immediate future. He was leaving for Paris. The astounded doctor was not exactly ejected from the office, but he was peremptorily dismissed—and then further confounded when, in the corridor outside, he came face to face with one of his most contemptuous enemies from Colombia. Instantly he realized that Bogotá spies had caught wind of the plot; that his movements in New York were being closely scouted; that he was in trouble, his fellow patriots in trouble too. To Panama he cabled the single word *"Desanimado"*—"Disappointed."

Amador had staked everything on Cromwell. He was beside himself, ready to give up the conspiracy on the strength of one cold-shouldering. He was as confused as were the narrators who tried to give chronology to his next move. None of them could agree with another on his itinerary. One plausible story takes him to the Manhattan branch of the Piza Lindo Bank of Panama, where he poured out his troubles to an old Panamanian friend, Joshua Lindo, bewailing the apparent hopelessness of the cause."

"There is only one man who can help us," sighed Señor Lindo, according to this account. "Bunau-Varilla."

"But he is in Paris," the doctor moaned.

"Yes, and if he were summoned, he couldn't come in time."

Then the miracle occurred. The telephone rang. Lindo listlessly reached for the receiver and held it to his ear for a moment.

"Santa María!" he suddenly shouted into the phone—and then in an excited aside: "Amador, it is Bunau-Varilla! He is here!"

Within half an hour the doctor and the canal promoter were warmly gripping hands in Room 1162 of the Waldorf-Astoria.

But that wasn't at all the way Bunau-Varilla remembered it. Amador had already tapped on the door of Room 1162 twice and left several calling cards before he was admitted. The Frenchman, who accepted the distress of others with uncommon resignation, took the trouble to record their exchange verbatim:

BUNAU-VARILLA: With your imprudence you have indeed brought yourselves to a pretty pass.

AMADOR: Alas! The case is much worse. . . . The cablegram "Disappointed" which I sent after realizing my failure, has leaked out. . . . It is incredible, it is monstrous. I have been exposed unwittingly to the danger of giving up my friends to death.

BUNAU-VARILLA: Calm yourself, my poor doctor, you are the victim of your own heedlessness. And to extricate yourself from the extremely painful situation in which you and your friends are plunged you must appeal to reason and not to passion. Tell me what are your hopes and on what are based your chances of success. Tell me, all calmly, methodically, precisely.

AMADOR: There is today only a weak garrison in Panama. Moreover, these men who have been living for many years on the Isthmus have ceased to count as foreigners to us. Our emotions, our aspirations are theirs. Then General Huertas, a valiant soldier, who has his troops well in hand, is himself shocked at the way Colombia is behaving toward Panama. The revolution would today meet with no obstacle. But the Colombians have the command of the sea; their ships' crews are loyal. We must first, therefore, acquire a fleet. . . . Besides that we want arms. Our first envoy, Captain Beers, had been assured . . . that the United States would give us all the money we needed to buy arms and ships and to pay the troops.

BUNAU-VARILLA: How big a sum do you consider necessary?

AMADOR: We need six million dollars.

BUNAU-VARILLA: My dear doctor, you have expressed the situation to me and you have come to ask for advice. I answer: Let me think it over. At first glance I see no way out of the labyrinth which imprisons you. Tomorrow perhaps I shall find one.

"The old doctor went out," concluded Bunau-Varilla, "having recovered his composure. He had grasped in his extreme need the open hand of a friend. He held up his head, sure henceforth of being led in a safe way."

Room 1162 of the Waldorf-Astoria became "the cradle of the Panama Republic." The revolution was definitely to be. Cautiously Amador cabled another word to the conspirators two thousand miles south: *"Esperanzas"*—"Hopes."

Bunau-Varilla took over in a bigger way than the fumbling doctor dared dream. He consulted assistants in the State Department; he saw Secretary Hay; he had an interview with the President and got the assurance that the United States would "not be caught napping." He talked with bankers and lawyers and with Professor John Bassett Moore, Columbia's authority on international law; it was through Moore that he learned how deeply President Roosevelt had been impressed by the article in *Le Matin.* The President had discussed it with the professor. Bunau-Varilla was everywhere at once, and he didn't need the assistance of the bumbling emissary from Panama. Amador was left in the background, summoned only when a messenger was needed.

On October 13 he was called to Room 1162 and briefed on developments. "There is no subsidy to be hoped for from the United States," Bunau-Varilla announced with finality. "Her honor forbids her from taking part in the revolution. It is for us to act. When we have acted, they will be able to protect us."

Amador's face fell. "But General Huertas' troops have not been paid for a long time, and no revolution can be made if——"

"Yes indeed," replied Bunau-Varilla, "but it is not necessary

41

to have six million dollars for that. They are five hundred. Give them twenty dollars each. That makes ten thousand dollars."

"That is not enough."

"Let them have forty dollars each. That makes twenty thousand dollars."

"Still insufficient."

"Let us say two hundred. That makes one hundred thousand dollars. That will be enough, I suppose?"

Amador agreed that it would do, but he was in a quandary about the six million dollars needed for the gunboats.

"Instead of purchasing warships for millions of dollars," replied Bunau-Varilla testily, "it is better to create conditions on the Isthmus such that the American fleet will have to fulfill her duty in case of revolution. The American ships and the American army can not intervene except along the railroad line of transit, but to protect traffic is to protect the whole population of the new republic."

The doctor began to comprehend the size of the plot and counterplot that were being spun by the wily Frenchman. His head swam. He was no longer in a position to ask for favors or counsel. He was taking orders.

At 8:00 A.M. on October 20, just before boarding the *Yucatan* for his return to Panama, Amador made a last call at Room 1162. The new Panamanian flag was unfurled for his inspection: a duplicate of the American emblem, except that yellow stripes had been substituted for white, and two yellow suns substituted for the stars. He didn't like it, but out of respect for Madame Bunau-Varilla, who had done the hemming, he kept his silence.

In a package deal he received everything that would be needed for the perfect revolution: a code for secret correspondence, a plan of military operations, the promise of a private gift of $100,-000 to defray immediate expenses, and finally a message to be sent to Bunau-Varilla as soon as independence was proclaimed. That message was an invitation requesting the recipient to accept an appointment as Panamanian Minister to the United States.

The master strategist was taking no chances; as Minister he would assume the prerogative of drafting the terms of a treaty for United States acquisition of a zone for the Panama Canal, and incidentally dictate the terms that would be most favorable to holders of stock in the old French company.

Bunau-Varilla had thought of everything—almost everything. He had provided the conspirators with a primer of military action, written their speeches and a constitution, given them a flag to haul up at the proper moment, and set November 3 as the date of revolt. All they had to do was follow his instructions to the letter, and success was certain. He had talked to the right people in Washington, and without getting a single unstatesmanlike comment from any of them, knew exactly what they would do. As the first evidence of his insight and persuasive genius, the *Nashville* arrived in Colón on schedule.

II

"BUT IT IS THE HOUR OF SIESTA"

In all his meticulous planning, Bunau-Varilla slipped up on one detail. He failed to provide the revolution at the right moment—failed to impress upon Dr. Amador the importance of stirring up something that at least looked like insurrection for the Americans to quash upon their arrival. Moreover, the French sage neglected to anticipate that the junta might not be as enthusiastic about his program as he was.

Even Dr. Amador, who knew his people well enough to expect a certain amount of resistance, did not foresee the stony opposition he encountered. The conspirators were keenly disappointed in the accomplishment of their envoy. They had been confident he would secure warships, a reassuring treaty, a loan of six million; and all he managed to bring back were a portfolio of Bunau-Varilla's documents, promises of "benevolent neutrality," and a conditional agreement from the Frenchman to advance $100,000 in bribes for the troops. They heartily resented the interference of Bunau-Varilla, his audacity, and his dictatorial attitude. And as for his decreeing that the revolution had to come off on November 3—that was outrageous. Seven days! Impossible! It would take weeks to complete preparations.

The plan would have been discarded if the doctor hadn't painted a very bleak picture of their alternatives. They were in a perilous predicament. Accepting Bunau-Varilla's scheme now

45

was a matter of life or death for them. Colombia would be sending troops—and a firing squad—any day. They couldn't afford
to delay.

In the end they asserted their independence of Bunau-Varilla
by postponing the revolt one day and by rejecting the flag. Then,
as if these two trifling compromises made all the difference, they
dropped their opposition and adopted an air of grim urgency.

Some three hundred members of an augmented fire brigade in
Panama City were conscripted as a home guard, and it was agreed
that the blowing of fire bugles at 2:00 A.M. on November 4 would
be the signal for revolt. Ample stores of Winchester and Mauser
rifles mysteriously appeared. The engine house was converted
into an armory, and arms and ammunition were cached there in
quantity. The garrison was won over with promised bribes of
fifty dollars per man. Along the line of the railroad, arms were
stashed at strategic points. To several hundred trusted section
hands of the railroad, rifles were issued for the defense of Colón.
And as though the flag continued to be a paramount problem,
they commissioned a local señorita to design and stitch a more
fitting emblem than Madame Bunau-Varilla's.

There was still a disconcerting number of loyalists to reckon
with. A war on the Costa Rican border was invented, and one
of Huertas' companion generals, whom nobody trusted, was bun-
dled off to conquer an imaginary foe. That put the population of
the capital pretty solidly in the hands of the rebels, even to the
Governor. But Colón swung over less readily; that city was inter-
larded with dissidents, and the Prefect complicated affairs by
rallying a few Colombian faithfuls who would have to be dis-
posed of when the opportune moment arrived.

Then three gunboats from Colombia, the *Bogotá*, the *Chucuito*, and the *Padilla*, unexpectedly steamed into Panama Bay.
At first glance they looked like a formidable threat, particularly
the *Bogotá*, which had been purchased in Seattle, Washington,
only a year before. She had displacement of 1400 tons, a fairly

heavy sheathing of armor, and a battery of one fourteen-pounder, six six-pounders, and two rapid-fire machine guns.

But all that the warships wanted was coal.

"Coal? What for?" queried the Yankee foreman in charge of the bunkering station operated by the Panama Railroad.

"Well, confidentially, they'd been ordered to Buenaventura to pick up auxilliary troops for a campaign on the Isthmus."

"So? Probably in a hurry, too. It's a crying shame, but the bunkers are fresh out of coal. Just enough to keep the trains running. Another shipment might be coming through any day now. Possibly the fifth or sixth. Might be a week."

No pleadings were warm enough to budge the foreman.

The warships dropped anchor in the Bay, and in a few hours the skippers and crews of the *Padilla* and *Chucuito* had all but sworn allegiance to the Republic of Panama—when and if she came into existence. But no such luck with the *Bogotá*. She had a taut American-trained crew that wasn't to be swayed. Menacingly she sat in the Bay, just out of range of the guns on the sea wall, her own fourteen-pounder leveled at Panama City. But nobody took the *Bogotá* very seriously. At worst she would be only a nuisance.

By November 2 the conspirators were almost ready. The weight of firepower and the weight of loyalty were decidedly in their favor. In a street battle they couldn't lose, and when the *Nashville* appeared in Limon Bay, the last anxiety for coastal security at Colón was dismissed.

PERSISTENT RUMORS HAVE BEEN CURRENT HERE THAT A MOVEMENT IS ON FOOT LOOKING TO THE INDEPENDENCE OF THE ISTHMUS, wired a correspondent to New York that afternoon. THE GOVERNMENT, HOWEVER, IS APPARENTLY NOT ALARMED, AND SO FAR AS IS KNOWN, NO STEPS WERE TAKEN TO QUELL ANY ANTICIPATED DISTURBANCE. And a man at the rewrite desk took the liberty to add shrewdly for the benefit of the American public: "We seem to have been better advised than the Colombian government and to have acted more promptly."

If the rebels had taken the initiative and fired a single shot to resist the landing of General Tovar's troops on the morning of November 3, Commander Hubbard would have been obliged to rush his bluejackets ashore, and a bloody battle for Panamanian independence would have started then and there; but the junta had fixed the hour for an uprising at 2:00 A.M. on November 4, and it occurred to no one in Colón that there could be any flexibility in that deadline. So the comic plot of revolution was allowed to expand.

To would-be insurgents, the arrival of the *Cartagena* was a calamity, and the failure of the *Nashville* to halt the landing was a Yankee double cross. They didn't know that Commander Hubbard had no orders and didn't perceive that the Americans couldn't take up arms until there was a semblance of rebellion to put down. In all the bungling no one even thought to pass the word of the new crisis to the proper officials in Panama City.

But Colonel J. R. Shaler, superintendent of the railroad, kept his head. When the landing started, he knew that very shortly the Colombian officers would be demanding transportation across the Isthmus. He was familiar with the rules and regulations set down years before in the Colombian concession to the Panama Railroad: "The Company binds itself to transport gratuitously and without the Government having to pay anything either for freight or for any other cause, the troops . . . destined for the immediate service of the Government of the Republic of Colombia."

There was only one way to forestall the trans-Isthmian invasion: get the trains out of the railroad yards. So while the troops were leisurely disembarking, Shaler was shunting his rolling stock down the tracks toward Panama City—empty. He kept one locomotive and a parlor car at the station, and soon had General Tovar, his three fellow generals, and their staff of a dozen other officers deferentially escorted aboard it. There would be a slight delay, he explained, in providing cars for the troops. Colonel Torres was designated to remain behind in charge of the privates.

There was an exchange of salutes, and General Tovar and his staff were on their way across the Isthmus to garrison headquarters.

It wasn't until ten o'clock that Commander Hubbard at last received his orders: "Maintain free and uninterrupted transit. . . . Prevent landing of any armed forces. . . ." Cohorts of the Colón Prefect had somehow managed to stall on delivery of the cablegram until rescue forces arrived. It was exactly ten o'clock when Manuel Amador received a phone call from Colonel Shaler, divulging the news of the landing, explaining the precautions he had taken, and informing the doctor that the generals were en route to Panama City, due to arrive there at eleven.

Dr. Amador hung up the receiver. He had just an hour in which to save himself from a firing squad, to save an unborn nation, and to salvage plans for a canal destined to reorder the path of commerce for the world. He scribbled some hasty notes and sent off a boy to summon his fellow conspirators.

Amador was stunned. It wasn't the facing of the firing squad that tortured him most. He was an old man with rich years behind him. He had ushered countless souls into life, but he wanted his crowning achievement to be in statesmanship rather than in medicine; he wanted to bring birth to the Republic of Panama, to free the state of further distress from an overbearing parental government, and most of all to see the dream of the ages come true—a canal across the Isthmus.

He tried to collect his thoughts and survey the situation objectively. One hour was much too short a time in which to reshape all the plans they had worked out. He couldn't move that quickly. He had made a grim mistake in taking on the leadership of the insurrection. They had gambled on completing the coup before the arrival of the troops, gambled on the Americans' preventing the landing—gambled and lost.

The minutes of Amador's hour of grace ticked off: ten minutes, fifteen minutes, twenty. Inexplicably the waiting brought a calm to him. Perhaps all was not lost. "It must be a bloodless revolution," he recalled Bunau-Varilla's insisting. "Bloodshed will produce an unpopular cause, will alienate the sympathy of America."

Slowly the key conspirators filed in, excited and out of breath —men slated to head the executive council of a provisional government, the judiciary, the police force, the fire brigade—and Governor Obaldia. But not all of them came. Sensing that something had gone wrong, a few of the less stout-hearted sent word that they were too busy, were indisposed, could not be inconvenienced. They were backing out. General Huertas begged off with the plausible explanation that he must assemble his men to receive the generals. Loyalty was one of the variables that had to be taken into account in any Central American political jugglery, but Amador was sure that he could count on the allegiance of the garrison, for the men now had a much better chance of getting overdue wages from Panama than from Colombia.

"We must strike at once," announced an impetuous council member, as soon as Amador had explained the situation.

"Strike at whom? We have less than a half-hour," the doctor chided.

"It's a choice of putting our lives in their hands or getting rid of them first," the councilman replied.

"Do away with them quickly." "Hang them." "Arrest them." "Drug them," came the responses.

"We cannot begin with a massacre," Amador insisted, "if we are to look for assistance from the United States."

"Assistance? How can we expect American assistance? They did not stop the landing of Tovar's troops."

"Until there are signs of disorder on the railroad line, they cannot help us," Amador reminded his inquisitors.

"Then let us provide disorder at once. Tomorrow will be too late. How soon will the reinforcements arrive here?"

"They must not arrive. They will not arrive. They will remain in Colón. Colonel Shaler will see to that. He assures us. No transportation will be made available," Amador reported.

"Amazing!" "Magnificent!" "A master stroke!" chorused his associates.

"The men are separated from their command. We have only the officers to reckon with for now. Fifteen officers. But quite enough to constitute a firing squad," summarized a judge-to-be.

"Our only hope is to rely on General Huertas," ventured Amador. "I think he will take suitable measures. It will be worth his while. Let us receive the officers with proper military honors and watch for the right moment to act."

It was necessary to leave the argument there. The train was due, and they could not afford to be conspicuously absent from the reception. There wasn't time to work out a scheme worthy of incorporation in Bunau-Varilla's masterful plot. Bowing to expediency, they decided to delay making any drastic move until later in the day. The officers would be received with civility, as if no revolt were stirring. After that, they would let circumstances dictate procedure.

At eleven o'clock the train puffed into the dingy Panama station. A military band was pumping away at a triumphal march. From the background came wave on wave of lusty cheers barked by a carefully indoctrinated claque. With disarming smiles and gracious aplomb, Governor Obaldia and all the officials of Panama City awaited their turn to extend formal greetings. The generals stepped down, glittering with medals and gold braid, arrayed in plumage, bristling with swords and side arms. Any uncertainties they had anticipated regarding their reception dissolved in the flow of flattery.

But the warmest of the welcoming fell to Esteban Huertas, a boy-sized general who in sheer arrogance more than made up for his diminutive stature of five feet, six inches. Bedecked in full-dress uniform, built-up boots, and gaudy headgear, he looked the part of a Napoleon, and indeed had the temerity to rank himself just above Bonaparte and George Washington. He had the insolence, the composure, the brazen self-esteem to play the part of suave host. With respectful bows, heel-clickings, and buttery

51

speeches, the generals were shown the homage they lived for, and then were ceremoniously conducted under honor guards to Government House.

"You will please to take us at once to inspect the city fortifications on the sea wall," blandly ordered General Tovar.

"But it is the hour of siesta," protested young Huertas without a trace of insubordination, knowing full well that even this group of fifteen officers, if given a chance to take over the modern guns commanding the city and the harbor, could start a civil war. There was enough treachery in Huertas to recognize treachery in his superiors.

"It is the hour when men should rest and not exert themselves," he reiterated graciously. "Besides, you are dressed in close-fitting uniforms. For the present, let us dine and unbend. When the siesta is over, then we will inspect the fortifications during the cool of the day. Your men will doubtless have arrived from Colón by that time. I will first facilitate any disposition you wish to make of your gallant soldiers. It will be my extreme pleasure then to conduct you to the sea wall."

It was too inviting a postponement to be dismissed by any officer with a trickle of Spanish blood. The courtesy was accepted; an elaborate luncheon was spread, and over the glasses any suspicion of duplicity that General Tovar may have entertained was gradually dispelled. It became increasingly evident to the guests that the reports of unrest in Panama were exaggerated. Huertas and the hospitable Governor had made a hit.

But late in the afternoon, conversation once more returned to the men left behind in Colón. They had not arrived, nor had any word been received from them. "Was it not strange that no message had come to explain the delay?" queried General Tovar.

The General's question was well-founded. Camped in the hot, filthy streets of Colón, forty miles from Panama City, the little army of invasion was getting restive and ugly, and the complaints of wives and camp followers were not diminishing the embarrassment of Colonel Torres. But the Colonel's embarrassment was mild compared to that of the American navy commander. Hubbard had come ashore upon receipt of his orders. He was at his wit's end to know what to do. He had not resisted the landing and was now powerless to act. With his forces overwhelmingly outnumbered, he could not take the risk of attempting to drive the Colombians back to their transport.

"I demand that a special train be provided," the Colonel finally flung at the railroad superintendent.

"Certainly," replied Shaler. "A train will be placed at your disposal as soon as the cars return from Panama City. But the Company has an inviolable rule that all transportation of passengers must be paid in advance. You will make arrangements for that?"

The superintendent took a long chance on the Colonel's ignorance of rail regulations for transportation of troops, as well as on the size of his purse, and the bluff paid off. To be sure, the generals had departed with all the funds. Railroad fare for over 450 men would total some two thousand dollars in gold. The Colonel, of course, carried no such amount, nor had he the means of securing it.

"No money, no trains," responded the railroad official resolutely, adding a word of apology. Nor was telegraph service available to the stranded Colonel. No, it was too dangerous to march down the tracks. That was forbidden. He was indeed sorry.

So the defenders of the Republic of Colombia had no choice but to accept the imposed holiday in the streets of Colón.

Off to New York went the factual report from a *Times* correspondent: "The streets of Colón today present somewhat the same appearance as during the days of the late revolution. Several hundred troops who arrived this morning on the Colombian gunboat *Cartagena* with their wives are squatted on the street corners. The battalion consists of 450 soldiers well supplied with

53

ammunition. General Tovar left for Panama this morning, but the troops will remain here."

From Washington orders were cabled to the *Dixie* and *Atlanta* at Jamaica to proceed to Colón at once; for the *Boston* at San Juan del Sur, Nicaragua, to head for Panama City; for the *Baltimore* to skip Santo Domingo and proceed to Colón. Shore leave at Martha's Vineyard was canceled for all men attached to the battleship *Maine,* and she was shortly ordered to Colón too— "not because there is any particular necessity for the presence of the big battleship, but the Navy is deficient in squadron movements and the Navigation Bureau desires to remedy this deficiency whenever practicable. . . . The cruise to the Isthmus will be beneficial to discipline."

Admiral Coghlan was needed in Limon Bay as over-all commander of fleet operations, but his flagship *Olympia* was tied up for repairs. Impatiently T.R. ordered out his presidential yacht *Mayflower,* and with instructions that it be "pushed to her utmost speed," sent the Admiral off to Colón, carrying the vacationing Consul General of Panama along as passenger. Prying Manhattan reporters invaded the office of Sullivan and Cromwell, keenly aware that these background participants could throw light on what the Panama assault was all about. But Cromwell was in France, and a partner coldly replied: "You may quote me to the extent of saying that I have nothing to say." And a full hour before real revolution broke on the Isthmus, overeager officials at the State Department in Washington, wondering why things weren't developing as fast as anticipated, jumped the gun and cabled the American Consul's office in Panama: UPRISING ON ISTHMUS REPORTED. KEEP DEPARTMENT PROMPTLY AND FULLY INFORMED.

At Government House in Panama City, General Huertas had extended the siesta as long as he dared. The effect of his garrulous cordiality was wearing off, and once more the guests were showing impatience to get to the fortifications on the sea wall, with or without their men.

Huertas desperately needed a word of counsel from his fellow conspirators before he made another move. Excusing himself for a moment, he went to the door, hoping that he might by chance encounter one of them. He closed the door behind him, and out of the shadows leaped Dr. Amador. The General asked one question.

"Do it!" implored the excited doctor in a whisper. "Do it now!"

The generals buckled themselves into their uniforms, ready for the march to the sea wall, while Huertas ordered out his men and dictated what their part in the rebellion was to be.

A column of Panamanian troops, fully armed and with rifles loaded, marched into positions on either side of the generals, as if to form an escort to the fortifications. Huertas gave the order, and instantly a hundred rifles were leveled at the astounded officers.

"Take the prisoners to police headquarters," barked the pompous little commander.

From Tovar came impassioned demands for release, from the other generals threats and caustic warnings of retaliation, but not an officer drew a sword or reached for side arms. They were quickly disarmed and led off to jail like common miscreants. Behind them, under arrest, marched Governor Obaldia, who had volunteered to submit to a show of incarceration to symbolize the overthrow of the last gubernatorial appointment of Bogotá.

With all the parading of fallen generals through the city, the imminence of revolution was no longer a secret to the citizenry. During the afternoon the junta had officially advanced the hour of revolt to eight o'clock that evening, but impetuous Panamanians were in no mood for a delay of three hours. If there was to be a fight for freedom, they wanted to be in on it; they wanted arms now. No bugle-blowing from the brigade was necessary to give an alarm. Hastily the firemen proceeded to issue arms to trigger-happy insurrectionists—some three thousand of them. The revolution was in progress.

Suddenly the Colombian flag over Government House fluttered down. In its place rose a strange emblem of four squares, blue and white fields to the left, white and red to the right; centered in the lower white square was a blue star, in the upper white a red star. The cheering was hilarious. That flag, reckoned an ungrateful junta, should put the interfering Bunau-Varillas in their places.

"Viva el Istmo libre! Viva Huertas! Viva el Presidente Amador!" the rebels shouted, milling through the streets. In minutes the arms-toting insurgents had grown into a defiant mob, crowding about police headquarters, completely out of control.

"Viva el Istmo libre! Viva Huertas!"

The rifles became toys for celebration rather than weapons of attack—to the peril of spectators and comrades at arms alike. The crackling of rifles all but drowned out the cheering. It was well that the generals were safe within the protective confines of the Panama jail.

The three Colombian gunboats in the harbor still had to be taken into account. Bribes had been deposited with the crews and commanding officers, and it was hoped that the *Bogotá* would come around. But when the prearranged signal for revolt was flashed to the ships, the *Padilla* and *Chucuito* remained silent; the commander of the *Bogotá* sent word that unless the generals were released the city would be bombarded.

The generals remained behind their bars, and timid citizens took cover. At ten o'clock a salvo of half a dozen shells burst over the city. One of them exploded near the military barracks, killing a Chinese shopkeeper named Wong Kong Yee; another landed on the hind quarters of a donkey; the others went wild. After this show, the *Bogotá* mysteriously steamed out of the bay, "but as she has very little coal on board," flashed a report to the States, "she will not be able to go very far." The next morning the

Padilla and *Chucuito* casually anchored under the guns of the sea wall and hauled down the Colombian flag. Informed of the shelling by the *Bogotá* but not of her departure, the Navy Department issued the threat: "Should the commander of the Colombian gunboat *Bogotá* fail to observe the admonition of Vice-Consul Ehrman to desist from firing on the city of Panama, the *Nashville* will take her three-inch gun across on the railroad from Colón and sink the *Bogotá,* which the expert gunners of the *Nashville* would regard as an easy matter."

Checkmate in Colón came less precipitately. When Colonel Torres learned of the imprisonment of his superiors and of the revolt at the capital on the morning of November 4, the real purpose of his being denied transportation became shockingly clear. He resented the duping more than the denial of the privilege of waging war with Huertas. In a rage he sent word to the American consul that unless the generals were released by two o'clock that afternoon, he would kill every American in the city. Then he prepared to take over the railroad by force.

At last Commander Hubbard could spring into action. He limbered up his guns, leveled the starboard battery at the *Cartagena,* and cleared the decks. Taking the hint, the Colombian gunboat weighed anchor and steamed out of Limon Bay. To the Prefect of Colón the Commander sent a judiciously worded note:

Sir:
The condition of affairs at Panama, I am advised, is such that any movement of the Colombian troops now at Colón to that neighborhood must bring about a conflict and threaten that free and uninterrupted transit of the Isthmus which the Government of the United States is pledged to maintain. I have therefore the honor to notify you that I have directed the Superintendent of the railroad that he must not transport on his line any troops either of the Government or of the Opposition Party. Trusting that this action on my part will meet with your cordial acquiescence . . .

57

At one o'clock the Commander was summoned ashore for a council of war with the United States Consul, the Vice-Consul, and Colonel Shaler. Quickly it was decided that the stone railroad station should be turned into a fort, and women and children should take refuge on the German *Markomannia* or the American *City of Washington,* both conveniently tied up at the Colón piers. By two o'clock refugees were flocking aboard the ships, barrels of a few hundred rifles were protruding from the windows of the station, and fifty marines were strategically dispersed behind cotton bales on top of freight cars.

Colonel Torres made a thoughtful survey of the situation and defaulted on his ultimatum. An hour later he sauntered into the railroad station to explain that he had nothing but the most friendly respect for the Americans; all he really wanted was to get orders from his superior officer, General Tovar.

Fair enough. A courier was provided a special train and guaranteed safe conduct to Panama City.

At five-thirty, still waiting to hear from Tovar, Colonel Torres came up with another proposition. He would withdraw his troops to Monkey Hill outside the city, provided Hubbard would get his men out from behind their cotton bales and send them back to the *Nashville*. The Commander took him up on the deal. Within two hours Colón was almost back to normal and a correspondent for the New York *Times* cabled home optimistically: THE OPINION OF EVERYBODY HERE IS THAT THE ISTHMIAN CANAL IS NOW ASSURED. . . . COLONEL TORRES AGREES, IF GENERAL TOVAR SO ADVISES, TO EMBARK THE TROOPS NOW AT COLÓN ON THE ROYAL MAIL STEAMER *Orinoco,* SAILING FOR CARTAGENA TOMORROW. THE PRESENCE OF THESE TROOPS HERE IS NOW THE ONLY DIFFICULTY IN THE WAY OF THE PROVISIONAL GOVERNMENT. IF GENERAL TOVAR CONSENTS TO THE PROPOSITION, IT WILL MEAN THAT THE BLOODLESS REVOLUTION OF TWO DAYS HAS BEEN SUCCESSFUL, AND THE REPUBLIC OF PANAMA IS SUPREME ON THE ISTHMUS. THAT WILL MEAN THE CONSTRUCTION OF THE PANAMA CANAL.

At Panama City late in the afternoon Dr. Amador guided

Colonel Torres' courier to the calaboose and to General Tovar's cell, but the doctor did the talking. He offered to release Tovar at once, disarmed, provided he would return to Colón and see his men aboard the *Orinoco*. The General declined, and the interview was over.

That left the decision entirely up to Torres.

Someone remembered that there was $140,000 of depreciated Colombian currency in the Panama treasury, worth at least $50,000 in gold. Torres was offered $8,000 of it if he would take off quietly and peaceably. Eight thousand gold dollars was enough for a life endowment. With a happy dream of escaping to Jamaica and a life of luxury, he accepted it, and on November 5 led his forces up the gangway of the Royal Mail steamship *Orinoco*. The amiable Colonel Shaler was so pleased with the easy riddance that he sent aboard a few cases of champagne as a *bon voyage* gift. But Torres' acceptance of that was a fatal error. Under the influence of the champagne, he let slip some hint of the bonus he had received, and the troops had enough alcoholic fortitude to mutiny and rob their commanding officer of every last peso. The Colonel vanished as mysteriously as the gold. General Tovar and his staff were perhaps spared a similar fate, for they missed the *Orinoco* and were transferred under guard to the jail at Colón, where they waited in ignominy for the next ship out; and to deprive them of any temptation to solicit sympathy from the municipal government, the fence-sitting prefect was arrested and ushered across the Isthmus to the cell vacated by Tovar. Colombian resistance was broken. The barricades came down and the cotton bales were toted back to the warehouses. The railroad station was put in order and transportation service restored. In effect the Revolution was over.

To the blaring of bands, to fusillades of gunfire and hilarious Spanish cheers, the citizenry of Panama City thronged into Cathedral Plaza at three o'clock on the afternoon of November 4 for the proclamation of independence. Huertas was the hero of

59

the hour. He arrived enthroned in a great chair draped in royal velvet and borne aloft by his faithful soldiers—every one of whom had received fifty gold dollars in the payoff. On his right walked the American Consul, carrying the American flag; on his left Manuel Amador, bearing the new Panamanian flag.

"The world is astounded at our heroism," declared Amador. "Yesterday we were but the slaves of Colombia; today we are free." His words were lost in the huzzas and rifle salutes. "President Roosevelt," he continued, "has made good. Long live the Republic of Panama! Long live President Roosevelt!"

"Viva el Presidente Roosevelt! Viva el Presidente Amador! Viva Huertas! Viva el Istmo libre!" echoed the crowd.

Then in a ceremony calculated to justify the "spontaneous movement of the inhabitants of Panama," an edited version of Bunau-Varilla's Declaration of Independence was solemnly presented: "Long is the recital of the grievances that the inhabitants of the Isthmus have suffered from their Colombian brothers. . . . In view of such notorious causes, they have decided to recover their sovereignty and begin to form a part of the society of free and independent nations. . . . At separating from our brothers of Colombia, we do it without hatred and without any joy. Just as a son withdraws from his paternal roof, the Isthmian people in adopting the lot it has chosen have done it with grief, and in compliance with the supreme and inevitable duty it owes to itself —that of its own preservation and of working for its own welfare. . . ."

Panama was an independent nation, and if only Wong Kong Yee had been watching the fun somewhere else on the evening of November 3, the joyless separation would have come off without the shedding of a drop of human blood.

At 6:40 P.M. on November 6, the French coordinator of the insurrection plans received an approximation of the message he had penned a month earlier: *The junta of Provisional Government of Republic of Panama appoints you Envoy Extraordinary and Minister Plenipotentiary to the Government of the United*

*States of America with full powers for political and financial
negotiations.* Paris was immediately exercised over the conduct
of the engineer whose sanity had recently been questioned: *Attention is called to the fact that it is probably unprecedented for
a French citizen to be selected to represent a foreign Government
without first consulting the Government to which the appointee
owes his allegiance or without the Government being asked
whether, in the event of his accepting the agency, he would not
thereby forfeit his French nationality.*
Simultaneously the United States extended official recognition
to the new republic—before many a resident of Panama knew
he was the citizen of an independent nation, before Bogotá had
any clear conception of what had transpired at the Isthmus, before those messengers of peace, the *Maine,* the *Marblehead,* and
the *Mayflower* had arrived to forestall further controversy.

THE PEOPLE HERE ARE FRANTIC WITH DELIGHT AT THE UNITED
STATES' RECOGNITION OF THE DE FACTO GOVERNMENT OF THE
REPUBLIC OF PANAMA, cabled a reporter. ALL DURING THE DAY
FIREWORKS WERE EVERYWHERE EXPLODED. . . . ALL CLASSES
OF THE POPULATION GO ARM IN ARM, AND THE ENEMIES OF YES-
TERDAY ARE TO BE SEEN EMBRACING EACH OTHER. TO THIS PIC-
TURE THERE IS NO SHADOW. Indeed, there were at the moment
few political shadows, for every last municipality in Panama soon
overwhelmingly endorsed the action of the junta. At least one
Central American nation had rallied to a cause with unanimity.

Explained the United States Secretary of State, sorrowing for
the misfortunes of the disrupted Republic: "The Colombians have
practically abdicated their former authority and withdrawn their
military forces, leaving the people of Panama free to act for
themselves; . . . in these circumstances the obligation of the
United States to preserve order and protect property made it in-
cumbent to recognize the de facto government. . . . With the withdrawal of the Colombian officials, the Isthmus was left entirely
without a government, unless that established by the secessionists
could be recognized, and this step seemed necessary for the trans-

action of the routine business of the United States on the Isthmus. It must not be lost sight of that the treaty [of 1846] is not dependent for its efficacy on the personnel of the signers or the name of the territory it affects. It is a covenant that runs with the land, the name of New Granada has passed away; its territory has been divided. But as long as the Isthmus endures, the great geographical fact keeps alive the solemn compact which binds the holders of the territory to grant us freedom of transit."

Not every American swallowed the explanation without protest. "Perhaps the most sensational aspect of the revolution is the fact that the affair seems to have been plotted in New York," editorialized one New York newspaper. "Our interference is equivalent to the denial of the right of the Colombian Government to put down an insurrection within its own borders. Plans of the insurgents were known in New York more than two months ago. It is to this country that the authors of the plot naturally turned for help. . . . If the Government of the United States were bent on convincing an unthinking world that the revolt in Panama was undertaken solely to secure the construction of the Panama Canal on terms acceptable to our own Government, it could hardly act or talk in a way different from that it has adopted. . . . It is plain that the dominating thought in the mind of our Administration has little to do with the rights or wrongs of the little community of Panama and still less with the rights of the Federal Government of Bogotá."

The man who was to become first President of Panama, Manuel Amador, hurried to Washington with a fellow delegate to discuss a canal agreement with the United States, but he arrived a few hours too late. Philippe Bunau-Varilla had already signed, sealed, and delivered a treaty that took into consideration his interests and the interests of the big brother nation. Neither Panama nor Colombia would ever forget or forgive.

But Panama got the $10,000,000, plus an annuity of $250,- 000. General Huertas received $30,000 in Panamanian silver and $50,000 in gold, his junior officers $10,000 each. Colombia

had to wait until 1921 for a United States apology and the appeasement offering of $25,000,000, and refused to recognize her Isthmian offspring until four years after that.

The $40,000,000 due the French canal company went to J. P. Morgan and Company for distribution, and how that pie was cut became one of the best-kept secrets in financial history. Cromwell submitted a bill for legal services totaling $800,000, including a contribution of $60,000 to the Republican National Committee, while the cut for Bunau-Varilla and his associates was modestly estimated by his enemies as high as $16,000,000. Congressional investigations went on for years, as documents and data piled up—documents much too ambiguous and confused to comprehend. The case was never cracked. In December, 1908, a tireless news ferret threw up his hands and announced: "The documents in question throw no conclusive light on the question of who got the $40,000,000."

Shocked by the "indecent haste" with which the President recognized the new republic, a heavy-conscienced United States press shyly fretted: "It does seem as if Mr. Roosevelt might have waited six days." With less shyness a commentator added: "For almost a year Roosevelt's mind had apparently been made up: the Canal must be built across the isthmus. . . . Acting with a haste unparalleled in American history and unwarranted in international law, he immediately recognized the new republic and promptly concluded a treaty with it on terms most favorable to the United States."

Privately the President explained: "Some people say that I fomented insurrection in Panama. . . . While I was President I kept my foot down on those revolutions so that when the revolution referred to did occur, I did not have to foment it; I simply lifted my foot."

III

"A SHELL OF RUST
COVERED WITH PAINT"

THROUGH political finesse and down payment of ten million dollars, the United States acquired sovereignty over one of the most unattractive pieces of real estate in the Western Hemisphere. It was a stretch of snake-infested, insect-ridden jungle, roughly forty miles by ten reaching from the Atlantic to the Pacific, landscaped with bottomless swamps and mud flats, crossed by a sag in the Continental Divide, and crisscrossed by lazy streams which could rise during a half-hour cloudburst from trickling brooks into rampaging sluices forty feet in depth.

Mosquitoes swarmed down upon their human prey in clouds. Colonies of omnivorous ants could strip a tree or the bones of a man in a few hours. Ticks and redbugs gnawing under the skin were a pestilence. Tarantulas, scorpions, and poisonous snakes were everywhere—brought out of hiding particularly after a good rain. Even Bunau-Varilla, who thrived on living dangerously, was respectful of the wild life he encountered while serving as engineer for the French canal builders. He loved to repeat the story of his venture in an overloaded native canoe during a Chagres flood. Swirling brown water was lapping the gunwales of the craft in which he was navigating to high ground, and the dozen passengers were under warning from the boatman not to move a muscle or the boat would overturn and they'd all be fed to the crocodiles.

"Mais je ne peux pas nager," whispered a scared surveyor squatted tensely on the thwart beside Philippe.

"Have no fear," reassured the chivalrous Chief Engineer. "I am a strong swimmer and can easily buoy you to the nearest treetop."

Then the would-be rescuer looked more closely at the branches in which he expected to take refuge. "On the general green color of the tropical foliage, a zone of about a yard above the water was black. Leaves and branches were simply concealed by enormous spiders of the Tarantula series—millions and millions of spiders chased by the inundation. But suddenly my thought was diverted by wild cries from the Negro who was steering the boat. 'Knock it down! Knock it down!' I could scarcely turn my head for fear of capsizing the canoe. I distinguished, however, a coral snake about two feet long swimming toward the boat. In an instant it had boarded and its head was in my left-hand coat pocket."

The famed engineer and the dozen passengers were saved from certain drowning by the cool action of a companion from behind who happened to be gripping a furled umbrella. Calmly he lifted the umbrella between the gunwale and the pocket, let the snake coil around it, and then dropped both overboard.

Snakes, tarantulas, crocodiles, and slinking cats had long held possession of the Isthmus and yielded it with reluctance.

Over this sorry plot of 436 square miles, just nine degrees north of the equator, the United States held completely sovereign powers—free to fortify and populate with military forces as it saw fit, free of immigration and importation restrictions, free of taxation. Included in the grant were an offshore extension of three nautical miles into both oceans, the islands in Panama Bay, all railway and canal rights, and any lands in the Republic lying outside the Zone needed for the construction of a canal or for its auxilliary works. Unfortunately Panama City and Colón retained their newly-acquired nationality, but they fell under the arm of United States control for enforcement of proper standards of health and order, and those two conditions could cover almost any anticipated jurisdictional squabble. As landlord, Panama agreed to become a protectorate of Uncle Sam, and after nine years—the estimated time required for the completion of the canal—would charge an annual rental of $250,000.

"I wanted, above all, to avoid any sharing of sovereignty in the Canal Zone—a radical innovation in international law," affirmed Bunau-Varilla. "I decided to grant to the United States, in the interior of the zone, all rights, powers and authority that she would have if she were sovereign, to the entire exclusion of the use of any such rights, powers and authority by the sovereign Republic of Panama." No agent could have worked out a better arrangement for his client.

For the United States it was the bargain of the century, despite the nature of the terrain. It was the most coveted stretch of shore property anywhere in the Americas, containing the shortest right of way from the Atlantic to the Pacific, and as the Colombian congressmen had all too monotonously reminded their customers, "one of the most valuable sources of wealth which the world contains," yet that strip of land was a nightmare even to the boldest of engineers daring to dream of a ditch across it.

Soft clay silt lay everywhere. In the rainy season from May to December, it formed vast quagmires as treacherous as traps of quicksand—clay so sticky that it tried a man's patience to dislodge a lump of it from his shovel, so soggy that it flowed like pudding down an embankment, so heavy that accumulated excavations weighted down the earth on which it was dumped, displacing the subsoil in slow, unpredictable upheavals. In the brief dry season the clay baked hard, but from the pulverized surface a mere stir of air picked up a cloud of swirling dust, while a steady trade wind blew up a yellow blizzard of the stuff, gagging, blinding, suffocating to those who had to labor in it.

Over the centuries erosion had carried vast acreages of the clay into the sea to create mangrove swamps and low-tide mud flats along the shore. On the Atlantic side there was an average tide of less than two feet, so that relatively little of the silt was left exposed, but the maximum Pacific range of twenty-two feet converted half the harbor at Panama into a broad plain of fetid mud at low tide.

Then the most uncongenial feature of the Isthmus was the stigma white visitors had given it as a plague spot of hideous disease—a place where "life dies and death lives." There was something sinister about the area in the way it harbored pestilence. "When the trade winds die' out, and the hot sultry air of the isthmus ceases to move," a lay visitor explained, "a white mist will sometimes rise out of the swelling ocean and hover like a fog over land and sea. The white mist is the precursor of fever and sickness, and those of the isthmus who know remain within doors, unwilling to meet the ghost of the ocean half way. In the early days . . . the white mist that rose from the disturbed soil of the isthmus was far more disastrous in its killing effects than the mists of the ocean. It rose from the soil like incense from a brazier. It carried with it from its underground prison all the poison of putrefaction, and wherever it enclosed its victims, there fever and death followed. . . ."

The "ghost" was more than a legend. Tough laborers, grim French superintendents, men of science vouched for its existence.

All this the United States had taken on in its bargain with Panama: the "ghost," the clay silt, the coral snakes, the treacherous rivers, the mangrove swamps, the tidal flats, the gap in the Continental Divide—as well as the sovereignty. It was a strange topsy-turvy land, where even the sun rose incongruously in the Pacific and set in the Atlantic. People back in the States who were so enthusiastic about uniting two oceans couldn't get it through their heads that a ship would never sail through the Canal from the Caribbean toward a setting sun. The land link between North and South America sprawled east and west, and if a ship passage were ever cleared, navigation from Colón would actually be to the southeast rather than to the northwest.

For centuries explorers had been poking into gulfs and estuaries looking for a water route through the continental barrier. Some twenty different passages across the Isthmus had been plotted, but Panama was at last settled upon as the most likely, for here the Chagres River and its tributaries on the Caribbean side cut nearly two-thirds of the way across the Isthmus, and in the highlands almost met the headwaters of the Rio Grande, which flowed into the Pacific. Since the early years of the sixteenth century the route had been a thoroughfare for explorers, traders, and speculators, and long before that it had been used by native Indians as a pack and dugout trail.

It was on this route that an American corporation built a forty-seven-mile railroad between 1849 and 1855 at an average cost of $150,000 a mile. It was over the same route that de Lesseps, refusing to recognize the obstacles that his engineers enumerated, set out to construct his sea-level canal twenty years later. Millions of dollars in gold had been packed over the trails en route from Peru to Spain during the sixteenth century; more millions were freighted over the rail line after the California gold rush; and then during the last two decades of the 1800's golden millions came back from Europe to pour into extravagant failures of engineers trying to do what an American canal commission was now honor bound to complete.

From the railroad builders and the French canal builders, the United States was inheriting vast quantities of obsolete tools and machinery, but the priceless inheritance was a knowledge of the anguish, of the blunders, and the failures that others had met and that need not again be repeated. In itself that knowledge of the trials and errors was worth incalculable millions.

The railroad had been a great success; it paid handsome dividends, thanks to extortionate freight rates and the one-way fare of twenty-five dollars per person, but the cost of laying those two streaks of rust over the stretch of less than fifty miles was an awesome figure in finance as well as in loss of human life. The fable that there was a "dead man for every tie" made a capital story, but some stickler for fact had spoiled it by counting 140,-

000 ties and less than a thousand graves. Nevertheless the mortality rate was enough to give pause to any laborer eager to make his pile in the Zone.

Originally it had been estimated that the cost of the railroad might run as high as a million dollars and that it could be completed in three or four years. It cost $8,000,000 and took almost a decade. The jungle seemed to grow back as fast as it could be cut away. Men had to contend with "noxious snakes and every species of wild beast," but the mosquitoes and sand flies were worst. Cholera and malaria, jungle fever and yellow fever, each took their toll. Terrain that first looked like an easy conquest turned into a slough that swallowed up endless loads of fill. There were places like Black Swamp, a stretch of silt and water interrupting the right of way for more than half a mile, under which engineers could nowhere find bottom at 180 feet.

Recruiting of labor had been a perennial occupation calling for artful persuasion. Hardy Caucasians often were the first to succumb to tropical maladies, and indolent Negroes proved more productive workmen in the end. A thousand Chinese coolies were brought in, but they were found to be so subject to fits of despondency in the enervating climate that scores took solace in suicide. In turn laborers were recruited from Ireland, Hindustan, England, France, Germany, Austria—an army of seven thousand —and disease was so prevalent and desertion so common that hordes of Jamaicans had to be imported as replacements. The turnover was proportionally as great among white-collar supervisors as among the laboring classes. Even the railroad presidents were not immune to disease and discouragement; it took a succession of four of them to finish the road.

In all of the Isthmus it was found that there was nothing of value that could be used in railroad construction. Local cross ties were tried, but they had rotted at one end of the line before the last of them was laid at the other. All had to be replaced with hardwood ties shipped in from Colombia, Canada, and the United States. Everything had to be shipped in—lumber, girders, cement,

food, living quarters—everything from toothbrushes to turbines.
There were accidents and washouts, train wrecks and disasters. Before the line was half completed a train on a trial run
struck a bull on the tracks and plunged over an embankment,
injuring most of the passengers and killing two. A magnificent
bridge over the treacherous Chagres was all but completed when
a sudden freshet swept down the valley, carrying away one span
and damaging the rest, so that the entire structure had to be
rebuilt.

Gangs of robbers and murderers roamed through the wild
country creating a menace to life and property, until one "Ran"
Runnels, an experienced Texas Ranger, persuaded the railroad
and the government to let him try eliminating the outlaws by
methods he had learned back home. With a nondescript posse
of Mexicans, Chileans, Negroes, and Orientals under him, he
cornered criminals of every shade and strung them up in batches
of thirty and forty along the sea wall at Panama City. Professional banditry began to lose its popularity.

Before it was started, the railroad was visualized as a unit
proposition, not to be opened until the whole line was completed,
but the California gold rush changed all that. A tide of emigrants
poured onto the Isthmus demanding transportation over completed portions of the road, so the whole undertaking was reordered as an income-producing venture while it was in the
process of construction. Traffic congestion became a major deterrent to progress. In 1852 eight companies of United States infantry demanded the same service. They were carried part way
across and left on the upper banks of the Chagres to complete
the trek afoot, by dugout, or by mule pack. Cholera and jungle
fever claimed so many stragglers that eighty of the seven hundred
died before they reached California. Yet during the last four
years that the road was under construction, 196,000 transients
paid fares for the transcontinental trip and the Panama Railroad
had netted over two million dollars on the traffic.

Always there were the optimists and the overeager promoters

to contend with—men who were certain that the road would be in operation long before there was plausible reason for such hope, men who had something to gain by drawing trade to the Isthmus. Even the Panama *Star* climbed on the promotion bandwagon and urged travelers to try the new route: "As to all the nonsense about malaria, fever, pestilential swamps and the thousand other ills that are charged to the Isthmus, we repeat again, they exist no more than in any other tropical climate. . . . Prudence and ordinary precaution are all that is required on the part of unacclimated passengers."

The doctors and engineers had learned that *extraordinary* prudence and precaution were called for in Panama. That knowledge was included in the invaluable legacy of experience inherited by the Americans from the railroad pioneers of the 1850's, but its sum was modest compared to the legacy handed down by the pioneer canal builders of the 1880's and 1890's. Indeed, it was only by political accident that the Yankees weren't the debtors instead of the legatees, for if they had obtained the coveted canal rights first, they would undoubtedly have failed too.

In 1825 the Republic of the United States of Central America made overtures to Washington for aid in constructing a canal. Fortunately nothing came of it. In 1839 President Van Buren sent a corps of surveyors and explorers down to look over the site. That effort didn't pay off either. Three decades later, in 1869—the same year that the Suez Canal was opened—the Americans had whipped up enough enthusiasm to draft a diplomatic agreement with Colombia for rights to build a canal. The Colombian Senate rejected it.

Then the United States Congress appointed a commission to investigate other possible routes for a waterway between the Atlantic and the Pacific. The investigations were still going on sporadically while de Lesseps, thriving on his Suez reputation, was stirring up interest in France. In fact, Congress was so disturbed by all the eagerness exhibited during the spring of 1879 at a Congrès International d'Etudes du Canal Interocéanique in

Paris that a threat was issued to the world, declaring that any attempt on the part of European canal builders to defy the Monroe Doctrine would be regarded as a "manifestation of an unfriendly disposition toward the United States."

But de Lesseps and his Compagnie Universelle du Canal Interocéanique de Panama weren't to be scared off. It was Adolphe Godin de Lépinay, the talented French chief engineer of bridges and roads, a man familiar with every feature of the Isthmian terrain, who proposed at the Congrès International a lock canal for Panama, using the impounded Chagres as a "water bridge" across the Isthmus. Essentially de Lépinay's plan was the one later adopted by the Americans, but de Lesseps refused to listen, and instead went on to his magnificent fiasco.

At the first meeting of the Compagnie Universelle in the summer of 1879 he grandly promised that ground would be broken for the Panama Canal on January 1, 1880. True to his promise, he was at Panama on that New Year's Day. A shovel in one hand and a pickax in the other, he boarded the tender *Taboguilla,* along with a train of distinguished guests, and headed for the mouth of the Rio Grande, where ground-breaking ceremonies were to be held. The party was in a gay mood, and the popping of champagne bottles kept it that way. But someone had miscalculated on the tides, and by the time the *Taboguilla* reached the mouth of the river, acres of mud flats barred the approach to the designated spot. Over the side went a member of the crew to scoop up a champagne box of silt. Then, in a fetching bit of make-believe, the pickax was placed in the hands of de Lesseps' young daughter, Mlle. Ferdinande, and she daintily pitched the point into the box.

"By the authority of the Republic of the United States of Colombia," de Lesseps pontifically declaimed to a suddenly sobered audience, "with the blessing of the Monsignor, the Bishop of Panama, in the presence of representatives of all governments and of those of the United States of Colombia, with the assistance of the members of the technical commission charged with the

73

investigation of the Universal Interoceanic Canal, Mlle. Ferdinande de Lesseps, on this first day of January, 1880, has made the first stroke with a pick at the point determined upon for the beginning of the maritime canal on the coast of the Pacific."

The sham and the celebrating went on for days, with a succession of band concerts, fireworks, bullfights, and banquets. To any heckler with the effrontery to inquire how particular obstacles were to be met, de Lesseps had the stock answer: "The Canal Will Be Made. The Canal Will Be Made."

At the culminating banquet a correspondent for the New York *Herald* was named as spokesman for the United States. "Let the work go on!" he cried. "M. de Lesseps is indeed the man who will carry it on with energy. In doing this he will add another laurel to the crown which he has already won and at the same time he will show to the world the grand spectacle of joining commercially the turbulent Atlantic and the calm waters of the great Pacific."

Even at that early date a sharp observer was skeptical of the "diplomatic smile" which de Lesseps wore, his "winning manners," his "magnetic presence." "When he spoke, the hearer would not fail to be convinced that whatever he said was true—or at all events that he believed it to be true. . . . But he did not possess the administrative abilities required for so great and so difficult a work; he was too old, too eager, too vain of the glory it would add to his already great reputation; too easily imposed upon; . . . too ill a judge of character; . . . he lacked practical knowledge and was always wrongly advised."

French peasants, charmed by his eloquence, didn't see him in that light. At Suez he had wrought a glorious miracle; at Panama he could do the same. Every loyal Frenchman was sure of it. Suez was paying off; so would Panama. Give de Lesseps a free hand, give him freely of hard-earned sous, and he would perform a second wonder for the glory of France, and incidentally convert their sous to francs. They dug deeply into their pockets and turned over their life savings to him. The peasants had no way of knowing that the jungles of Panama presented an entirely different kind of challenge from the sands of Egypt.

De Lesseps was to be provided unstintingly with every product of France, whether he needed it or not. He and the unwieldly bureaucracy he built up about him were taken advantage of by manufacturers of every article a factory could furnish in quantity. His own agents traveled about Europe scouring warehouses for useless supplies which trusting, uninquiring investors in the provinces paid for. Panama became the dumping ground for accumulated stocks that were unsalable even in France.

Fifteen thousand kerosene torchlights were delivered early at the Colón wharves for festive processions which would commemorate the completion of the canal. Far back into the hills of Culebra, miles from navigable water, were dragged a flotilla of portable iron steamboats, to be left in the jungle awaiting the day when they could be floated on the canal. Snow shovels—snow shovels by the thousand—were stacked in the congested warehouses of the tropics. From Belgium came locomotives by the dozen, requisitioned by official agents and delivered according to specifications, only to collect rust on improvised sidings or in mud up to the axles because agents had specified the wrong gauge. Shiploads of cement solidified in open storage areas exposed to rain and sun.

Dock supervisors were so overwhelmed by the deluge of materials that they hastily signed delivery papers as shipmasters dictated. Anything to get one ship out of the way, so that another could take its place at the pier. From the holds of colliers skippers delivered a few tons of coal and quickly departed with receipts for the whole cargo; a week later the same ship would appear again to unload another fraction of her cargo and get another receipt for the whole; the process was repeated again and again.

While contractors waited in desperation for construction supplies that had been ordered and reordered, cargoes of wine arrived almost daily to clutter wharves and warehouses. The thirst of bibulous thousands was phenomenal, but even that thirst

75

couldn't begin to deplete the reserves. "Nothing like the supply of liquor which the French poured out upon the Isthmus during the years of their occupation was ever seen there before, or has been seen since," alleged an interested gourmet. "It was well-nigh unlimited in quantity and was sold to everybody for prices at which it had been bought in large quantities wholesale in France. Nothing was added for transportation across the ocean or to defray the cost of handling. Champagne flowed like water. . . . The ingredients for a genuine bacchanalian orgy being supplied, the orgy naturally followed."

Money was squandered lavishly on personnel and services. Three men were hired to do the work of one, and all were richly compensated. Salaries for chief officials ranged from $50,000 to $100,000 per year, with additional travel allowances running as high as $50 a day. Almost a million dollars went into elaborate stables, carriages, and horses for top employees. More than five and a half million were poured into a single group of luxurious hospital buildings, and there were several such institutions. Another five million were expended on preliminary office buildings and residences. The Victorian mansion for the director general cost $150,000, his bathhouse $40,000, his private railroad car $42,000, and since no equipage becoming his rank could be found on the Isthmus, a commission of seven assistants was sent to New York at the expense of the company to find a suitable carriage and horses.

The extravagance was incredible, staggering, senseless. Everyone in France or Panama with something to sell wanted to get in on the bonanza while the money held out. When a forty-thousand-dollar structure was called for, an eighty-thousand-dollar edifice was erected, but rake-offs in the process of construction brought the total cost to $160,000. In the path of the canal was a thirty-acre plot of swampland owned by a stubborn Panamanian who had been witnessing the flow of French francs. Its only possible use was as a breeding place for alligators and malarial mosquitoes. The evaluation of $10.00 an acre was preposterous, so the French agents offered $100.00 an acre—$3,000 for the worthless plot. The owner declined. The price was advanced to $1000 an acre. The owner was outraged. When the Colombian courts finally handed down a verdict, the owner received his demand in full—$300,000.

Again and again tireless President de Lesseps toured Europe and America trying to raise subscriptions that would match the magnificent waste, and he was successful for a time. From chief engineer to the humblest laborer the personnel was in a constant state of flux. In 1887, when it became obvious that money wouldn't hold out for a sea-level canal, plans for a lock type were adopted. But it was too late. The bubble burst on December 14, 1888, when the Compagnie Universelle went into receivership. The Isthmus was thrown into a turmoil, and the Americans offered little solicitude, for New York capital was going into a competing canal that would be cut across Nicaragua. On May 8, 1889, the Maritime Canal Company of Nicaragua came into existence, and exactly a week later all work on the Isthmus was suspended. In Paris the fiasco brought a series of court trials for corruption and malfeasance, which lasted for years and all but brought on a collapse of the Government of France.

A French commission went to Panama in 1891 to assay the equipment and to make a tour of the ruins. Outside of Panama City they found towers of Belgian and French dredges rotting in detached and partly filled channels that had once been sections of the sea-level canal. Farther east "an almost continuous line of villages for laborers that were never occupied, storehouses, sidings filled literally with miles of dump cars, locomotives and other machinery . . . stacks of Decauville railroad track and the small iron dump cars to fit them." In another area, almost buried in the jungle, was a line of steam cranes; on a siding, "60 clumsy locomotive boiler steam drilling machines with the drill frames rigidly attached alongside the boiler." They had never been used, never fired up, and were utterly useless for work on the Canal. The commission discovered, too, that the fraud was still going on, for $20,000 a month was being spent in daubing paint over the rust to give the machinery a presentable appearance. A mechanical engineer examined a typical piece glistening with new paint. The door fell off in his hands, and the boiler was so scaled with rust that a blow of his fist could punch a hole through the plates. It was nothing but "a shell of rust covered with paint."

Not yet ready to give up, the French formed a new corporation in 1894—Compagnie Nouvelle du Canal de Panama. Some of the usable machinery was put back into operation; channels that had filled in were re-excavated; and a few million more cubic yards of earth and rock were taken out of Culebra Cut. But the Compagnie Nouvelle was never in sight of victory. It served principally to keep nominal control of the canal concession granted by Colombia.

Altogether the French companies had issued securities totaling over half a billion dollars—and half of it was squandered. Millions had gone to the French press for what were naïvely referred to as "reading notices—articles, apparently editorial, lauding the enterprise to the skies, and indulging in extravagant prophesies as to its success, which were, however, really contracted for as paid puffs." More millions had gone to bankers to keep them "friendly to the enterprise and willing to gull the hundreds of thousands of small investors." And still other millions were expended "to keep government officials and members of the Chamber on the right side."

The record of fraud, corruption, and exorbitance was part of the legacy which the United States bought with their $40,000,-000. With government ownership substituted for private enterprise, there should be no excuse for anything resembling a repeat performance.

"We inherit a graveyard of many wrecked hopes and lives, with their monuments strewn from the Atlantic to the Pacific in the shape of decaying relics of an earlier engineering period," editorialized the *Scientific American* in 1904. "There is no richer

78

digging in the ruins of an ancient Rome or Pompeii than along the deserted route of the canal."

"In nothing was the French Company more extravagant than in purchasing supplies for the Isthmus," the editor continued. "There was machinery by the scores and thousands of tons, large, small, and medium sized, costly machinery and antiquated types of no real value at all; machinery that was to be used, and machinery intended for waste; machinery that was as much out of place in that far-away corner of the earth as steam radiators in the Desert of Sahara. Why this endless amount of machinery was shipped there, no one could explain; but it was all accepted, paid for, and then left to rot in the hot moist climate. There were locomotives, scoops, buckets, steel rails, and machine tools by the acre from all parts of the earth."

American "excavators," going to the scene with something of the spirit of archaeologists digging in Rome and Pompeii, found that vast quantities of surplus machinery had been used as foundation material for expensive homes. They estimated that single houses rested on fifty thousand dollars' worth of engines, tools, and apparatus. Machines not in use at the moment had been handier than rock for fill; they had been dumped into the soft silt and an umbrella of cement poured over them, but even with such foundations large houses had settled into the soil until only the upper stories protruded.

In uncovered storage areas, they found where machinery had buried itself of its own weight, sometimes ten or fifteen feet beneath the surface. "Unearth it and you find it as soft and porous as cheese." Equipment like huge iron anchors, steel buckets, and cast-iron scoops had disintegrated in the moist climate, retaining its original shape and appearance, yet it crumbled to the touch. "With a penknife it can be cut and pared as easily as an apple."

At Colón on the coast and at Empire in the interior were the two largest supply dumps. Here inventory takers found machinery scattered over miles of land—"the graveyard of France's past ambitions." They explored ground littered with "millions upon

79

millions of useless, rotting, neglected property . . . sadly out of date and fit only for the junk pile . . . miles upon miles of steel rails piled six feet high, sinking slowly into the soft soil and rusting in the moist atmosphere . . . rows upon rows of car wheels —wheels which represent huge expenditures, but which were apparently simply dumped there and never used . . . machine shops filled with huge steel hammers and giant turning lathes— falling apart of their own weight . . . a dozen rows of locomotives —small in size and weight and scarcely adapted to the work required of them, standing half-sheltered under sheds that are themselves hardly able to stand up under their aged and weakened rafters. . . . The hand of neglect appears stretched over the whole length and breadth of the Isthmus."

In 1904 the Zone, as taken over by the new tenants, resembled a far-flung battlefield from which a defeated army had made a hurried retreat, leaving the weapons of assault on the scene of the disaster. The jungle had crept back to wrap steam shovels in a camouflage of green creepers and lush bamboo; earth had slid down the steep embankments to bury lines of dump cars; ocean tides and the wash of the Chagres had refilled the channels and locked barges in sucking jaws of silt.

But regardless of the graft, the extravagance, and the purple propaganda, the French men of science had achieved a pioneer triumph in attempting the most colossal engineering feat ever undertaken by man. The job, as they visualized it, was more than half done. They demonstrated that they could have finished it, given less overbearing management, a less sophisticated system of auditing, and more funds honestly applied to the work at hand. Without their faltering start to point a different way, the United States might easily have plunged into a confusion of errors no less formidable. In a premature attempt to persuade the world that Americans were incapable of exhibiting such awkwardness, home journalists outdid themselves in discrediting the French vision and the French accomplishment.

The Compagnie Universelle established the base of operations

—a sprawling plant of 2145 buildings; they made methodical, intricately recorded surveys of the whole area, worth all of two million dollars; in the hard, expensive way, they discovered the kinds of machinery that were ineffective, and devised ingenious equipment that was effective; they dredged deep-water channels into both the Pacific and the Atlantic and made a good start at establishing port facilities; they learned that a sea-level canal was less practical than a lock canal; they cut the beginning of a canal most of the way across the Isthmus, lowered the Divide over 160 feet at its highest point; and although the Americans decided to alter most of the course for the canal, the French route proved invaluable for cheap transportation of materials as far as Gatun on the Atlantic side and almost to Miraflores on the Pacific.

When tempers had cooled and American engineers soberly went about the business of making an appraisal of what they were getting for the $40,000,000 payment, they found that almost half of the eighty million cubic yards that had been excavated was useful, that some fifteen hundred of the French buildings could be renovated, and that several million dollars' worth of equipment could be utilized. All this was worth close to $3,000,000 more than had been paid for it, and the lessons painfully learned by the French were gratis. It was not a bad bargain.

IV

"TELL THEM I AM GOING TO MAKE THE DIRT FLY"

FROM the White House was emanating the doctrine of Vigorous Endeavor, Great Dreams, Manly Virtues, the Strenuous Life. The President's sleeves were rolled up, the pressure was on. Roosevelt was girding the nation for action. Emphasis on haste had become the religion for a whole new national cult. America was picking up speed.

The idealism of impatience and urgency was echoed from soap box and pulpit, from commencement platform and editorial column. Roosevelt scripture was quoted as text: "For us is the life of action, of strenuous performance of duty; let us live in the harness, striving mightily; let us rather run the risk of wearing out than rusting out." "Believe in going hard at everything, whether it is Latin or mathematics, boxing or football." "It is only through strife, through hard and dangerous endeavor, that we will ultimately win the goal of true national greatness." "Great action, action that is really Great, can not take place, if the man has not in his brain to think great thoughts, to dream great dreams."

The dream of Panama had just the right dimensions to excite the cult. For them there could be no delay in pushing the canal across the Isthmus, showing France and the world what American energy and efficiency could accomplish. Let other nations

83

talk about it, but let America—the land of action—do it. The Canal would be a dramatic reaffirmation of the Monroe Doctrine; it would keep South American trade in the home hemisphere, provide a cheaper route to the gold and sunshine of California, give the coastal shippers a new lease on commercial life. That forty-mile ditch could make the United States the greatest nation on earth.

To the west, Japan was flexing her muscles; to the east, Germany was playing Goliath. Their ambitions could be cut down to size by this great expression of American enterprise. Within the decade, war with Spain had demonstrated the pressing demand for naval flexibility: the tide of battle hung in the balance while generals and admirals waited for the *Oregon* to steam all the way around South America from San Francisco to Cuba—13,400 miles. The Canal could have eliminated nearly 9000 of those perilous miles. That was too close a shave to risk again. There was a terrible need for haste.

Men of America thought they knew something of the dangers of wielding a pickax in the fever-ridden jungles of Panama, and they were ready to face the hazards as a patriotic privilege. It was not very different from responding to the call of the colors, though the weapon was a shovel rather than a rifle. The chances of survival were about the same, and the objectives were comparable. Aspersions once cast at the French for their readiness to sacrifice life and property in the cause of national achievement were forgotten when the cause changed its nationality. The Americans now were prepared to engage in a majestic battle for the exaltation of their own country and for mankind. "It is only through strife, through hard and dangerous endeavor, that we will ultimately win the goal of true national greatness."

Roosevelt was looking toward that goal, but there was a multitude of obstructionists—men who deplored the ignoble way in which he had appropriated the Zone, statesmen who lamented his "indecent haste," "his rashly vigorous administration," "these wild and whirling times" into which he was plunging everybody,

84

elders who felt it their duty to restrain "the hustling youth playing football with international law."

But the "hustling youth" wasn't one to be halted by insult. People could chew him out as much as they wanted, if they'd let him go ahead. "Instead of debating for half a century before building the canal, better to build the canal first and debate me for a half-century afterward."

The Hay-Bunau-Varilla Treaty had to be approved by the Senate before it would be effective, and two months after it had been endorsed by Panama, respected legislative prophets were still predicting that the American Democrats would amend and clip it beyond recognition, that the debate would go on for an entire session, that the Treaty would never be approved. Yet the President pushed through a ratification on February 23, 1904. Less than a week later he whipped out his list of appointments for an Isthmian Canal Commission—the men who would establish the policies and oversee the construction—and called for an immediate Senate confirmation. Caught up in the lickety-split race, the lawmakers obediently gave in. Roosevelt rushed off wires to the seven members, giving them just four days to drop their personal affairs and get to Washington for a conference. Their homes were in New York, Detroit, New Orleans, and San Francisco, but they made the deadline.

"What this nation will insist upon is that results be achieved," he drove home to the team of distinguished professional men assembled at the White House. "The utmost practicable speed" was the President's theme. "Push the work rapidly and at the same time with safety and thoroughness."

These were men not used to the Dutch-uncle treatment. They were gentlemen in the habit of telling others how things were run—a college professor, civil engineers who had made names for themselves in major construction wonders, a rear admiral, a major general. But as if there existed a national emergency in which all the old amenities were suspended, they took the hectoring in good grace. They were told that they were the best engineers and executives for the job to be found in the country, and that achievements consistent with their reputations were expected of them; resignations were in order from any who failed to live up to the charge. No time was to be lost in getting to their posts and seeing that the popular demand for results was fulfilled. In the appointment of subordinates there was to be no political favoritism; capability, competence, and energetic leadership were the qualities to be sought. The best available sanitation experts were to be secured and careful attention given to health measures, and they were never to lose sight of the cause of previous failure—the matter of finance. The most rigorous attention was to be given to the supervision of every expenditure.

They buckled into their armor and went forth dedicated to a crusade, led by the dauntless old campaigner Rear Admiral John G. Walker, whose experience of nearly fifty years in the Navy had failed to rob him either of his Yankee energy or the nasal twang picked up in New Hampshire as a boy. He had acquired a reputation for being a go-getter in fearless attacks on Confederate shipping during the Civil War, in maneuvers off South America during the late 1880's, in sailing the flagship of the North Pacific Command during agitation over the annexation of Hawaii in 1894. Politically he was the most powerful man in the service, with a long record as Chief of the Bureau of Navigation, and he knew something about canals, too, for he had been one of President McKinley's appointees to investigate the Nicaragua route, and for three years President of the Isthmian Canal Commission that had finally recommended Panama.

Every member of the Commission was a strong-willed individualist no less domineering than Admiral Walker himself: men like William Parsons, who had engineered the New York subway system; William Burr, Professor of Civil Engineering at Columbia University; and General George W. Davis, who could boast of virtually no formal education, but who had pulled himself up by his own boot straps to become officer in charge of constructing important forts in Texas and Utah, assistant engineer for the

Washington Monument, general manager of the Nicaragua Canal Contruction Company, Military Governor of Puerto Rico. Davis was now governor-designate of the Panama Canal Zone.

In his eagerness to assemble the most distinguished brain trust available, Roosevelt seemed to have overlooked the simple truth that too many good cooks could make any dish indigestible. Moreover, the Commission was loaded in favor of a sea-level canal, although public sentiment had swung overwhelmingly toward locks.

Impelled by the explosive enthusiasm of the President, the Commission was on its way to Panama before the end of March, 1904, and just before sailing they persuaded Colonel William Gorgas, the army physician who had distinguished himself in the fight against filth and mosquitoes at Havana, to go along with them as sanitary officer. En route down the coast, before they had laid eyes on their battleground, the Commission members decided unanimously that a prominent railroad engineer back in Chicago, John F. Wallace, should be their field general.

As past president of the American Society of Civil Engineers, Wallace was held in highest respect by his profession, and in rugged individualism he could match any member of the commission. To demonstrate his individualism, he had even passed up a degree at Monmouth College, doggedly refusing to take a required course—to the mortifying embarrassment of his father, who was president. But in the practical world, his aggressive independence paid off as he moved through the Midwest and Northwest from big railroad engineering jobs to bigger. He worked on Mississippi bridges at St. Louis and New Orleans, constructed terminals at Chicago, New Orleans, and Memphis, and won popular fame on the side in supervising the transportation facilities for millions crowding into the Chicago World's Fair. To be sure, he had no frontier experience involving anything like mountain, forest, and jungle, but the Commissioners were confident that a genius with such rare talents could quickly make up for this shortcoming. As soon as the ship docked at

Colón, an invitation to join the crusade as chief engineer was dispatched to Wallace.

For several of the Commission members the arrival was an introduction to the new United States acquisition, and it was a shattering experience. Colón was an incredible desolation of filth and squalor—"as though Nature had made the city with a blot and no one had been able to erase it." Ten thousand people were crowded into what had once been a swampy mangrove island, and nine thousand of them lived in shanties built on piles. The ground was so low in the shanty town that at high tide the hovels were surrounded by water and could be approached only over rickety boardwalks, which were forever spilling unsteady pedestrians into the mire. There were but two almost civilized sections of Colón: commercial Front Street, overlooking the piers and the Bay, always teeming with a confusion of humanity, hawkers, and delivery wagons; and Cristobal, a peninsula at the south end of Front Street, which the French had built up from mud dredged out of the canal. In Cristobal, virtually a separate village, the de Lesseps company had established administration buildings, a hotel, and a handsome mansion for the resident director. Into this mansion the Commission members moved. It was to be their headquarters and their living quarters.

In Washington, Senator Morgan had described the inhabitants of Panama as "the remnants and off-scourings of all creation—Italians, Spanish, Americans, Central American Negroes, Jamaican Negroes, Japanese, called there to furnish labor for the French Canal." The fastidious Parsons decided that the Senator hadn't said nearly enough, as far as Colón was concerned. Rotting piers strewn with debris and neglected equipment, the turmoil of commerce, and the tidal swamps were a match for the human mélange.

Guided by a half-dozen military officers and subordinates, who had arrived before them as vanguard, and by the one-man Chamber of Commerce for the Isthmus, Tracy Robinson, former editor of the Panama *Star and Herald*, the Commission members

88

lost little time in setting out for Panama City or a tour of their domain. But what they saw from the train windows was as depressing as the squalor of Colón. Here and there they could catch a view of the abandoned French ditch, blocked by intrusions of silt and by sunken dredges. From the jungle protruded gaunt arms of cranes festooned with rank vines. On rail sidings were strings of cars that had been rusting to the tracks for a decade. They passed through village after village of deserted labor camps with broken windows, smashed doors, and gaping roofs. Scores of sprawling shops and warehouses appeared in no better condition. The desolation and waste were staggering.

Compared to the rest of the Isthmus, Panama City was a haven of order. It had an air of gentility, was picturesque and cosmopolitan, still retaining the flavor of old Spain. There were palm-shaded plazas and parks, the four-story Hotel Central where the politicos and general populace gathered for their drinks, their dances, and their gossip, the cathedral and a half-dozen other ornate stone churches, a lively public market, the sea-wall promenade overlooking the ocean, narrow streets with overhanging balconies—all a "strange mingling of the fifteenth century with the twentieth." But to anyone arriving from the North, Panama was a city living on sedatives, unhurried, lazy, sleep-swollen. The only display of real animation came from the little horses that drew cabriolets over the rough cobblestones at a frantic pace. Bouncing and swerving through the crooked, crowded streets, the Commissioners were rushed about the city on a sight-seeing tour as if horses and cab driver alone appreciated the urgency of their mission.

After seeing Panama City, they couldn't quite understand why they had to be put up in Colón. But back in the de Lesseps mansion the seven members gathered in an air of gloom to weigh their great undertaking. The purpose of the visit to the Isthmus was only to make a quick survey, to get an over-all conception of their problems. Any momentous decisions such as the type of canal to be constructed—whether it was to be sea-

89

level or high-level—would have to wait for a long time. The most important thing at the moment was to get the digging started somewhere—anywhere—to satisfy the public eagerness for immediate movement of mountains.

A train trip through Culebra next day gave a ready answer to that. Laborers for the Compagnie Nouvelle were still puttering there, gangs totaling as many as seven hundred, biting into the hills with antiquated machinery, going through the motions of digging for the sole purpose of technically retaining the French concession until the long-drawn-out legal proceedings of transfer to the United States were completed. Men were drilling by hand, shoveling by hand, making dents in the hills—a process that could go on at that rate for a thousand years without bringing the waters of the Atlantic any nearer to the Pacific. But it was clear that no matter what kind of canal was finally settled on, the cut through the Cordillera was necessary. Culebra was the place to get things under way. Any number of men could be set to work there, and, given more adequate machinery, they would soon put to shame the efforts of the French.

In the sweltering heat of Cristobal the seven members of the Commission with half a dozen assistants pored over maps; discussed mosquitoes, yellow fever, and privies; made guesses on how much French machinery might be salvaged, on how many cubic yards actually had to be excavated, and on how long it would take. When they reached a stalemate on the seeming impossibility of the whole project, Admiral Walker drolly repeated the story of Spain's Philip II, whose engineers listed so many insurmountable problems that the King abandoned the idea of a canal, with the handy explanation that it was "contrary to the Divine Will to unite two oceans which the Creator of the world had separated; to attempt so impious a deed would surely provoke some appalling catastrophe."

It was essential that they make a rough survey of the settlements along the line of the Canal. They took a special train from Colón, and with Tracy Robinson and their military escort as guides, worked over the Isthmus village by village. The route, they soon concluded, would be divided roughly into four sections if they wanted to consider a lock canal: the four-mile cut across the lowland from Limon Bay to Bohio; a stretch of twenty-five miles along the Chagres Valley to Gamboa that would be submerged under a broad inland lake; the nine miles of Culebra Cut through the Divide; and the six-mile descent from Pedro Miguel to the Pacific. If it were a sea-level canal, there would be no such divisions; it would all be a unit—one vast cut, creating the "Straits of Panama." There was no question about it, the Straits was what they wanted.

Repeatedly on the tour they were astonished at the size of establishments built by the French, spaced every few miles along the whole line; the ruins of a dynamite depot at Mindi, so ideally situated in the hills that Colón would be shielded from an accidental explosion; district headquarters and a sprawling machine shop at Bohio, where the landscape was scarred by attempts of the Compagnie Nouvelle to build a dam; a complete rum distillery at Frijoles; a repair shop and spoil dump at Tabernilla; a labor camp at San Pablo, where Catholic missionaries years before had operated a great plantation; some of the largest repair shops of all at Gorgona. Above Culebra Cut the shops and labor camps were more concentrated; engine houses at Las Cascadas big enough to accommodate dozens of locomotives, administration buildings, shops for mounting and repairing every kind of equipment at Empire, and more like them at Culebra, Paraiso, Pedro Miguel, and Miraflores. At Ancon Hill above La Boca was a palatial hospital and a huge farm with stables for several hundred horses, carriage sheds, sick bay, and blacksmith and horseshoeing shops.

On their scouting tours, the Commission members saw a bewildering amount of waste and desolation, but closer scrutiny showed that there were untold quantities of equipment that could be salvaged. In fact, without adding a shovel or a crowbar, there was no reason why a few thousand men couldn't move in the next day and be put to work. Only vaguely were they disturbed by the disruption that big-scale canal building would bring to the native settlements. For instance, if a dam were constructed at Gatun, the lake it created would drown a dozen ancient villages like Ahorca Lagarto, Bohio, Buena Vista, Frijoles, Tabernilla, Gorgona, and Matachín, while Gatun itself, the busiest inland village on the Isthmus, would be buried under a mountain of fill.

Gatun was an amazing little port. Located on a peninsula jutting out into the Chagres, and bisected by the French canal, it had a church, a dozen stores, and close to a hundred native huts. From Gatun came tons of bananas to be shipped to New Orleans and Boston. The trade reached back into the valleys for thirty miles; down every navigable stream came fleets of cayucas, loaded with the green stalks, to tie up at the cluttered Gatun water front. As many as nine carloads of bananas pulled out of the railroad station at the end of a good market day. But despite the commerce, the town had changed little in the half-century since California-bound argonauts bought eggs there at four for a dollar and rented a hammock exposed to the insects and the rains for two dollars a night. Gatun would become only a memory if the dam were built there.

The Commissioners were intrigued by the bits of historical background dropped by Tracy Robinson. Bohio was once a soldier's home—Bohio Soldado—and the "Soldado" had become lost in the shuffle of centuries. Tabernilla had been known for its "little tavern." Obispo meant "bishop"; Gatun, "cat," from the feline Chagres; Paraiso, "paradise." Pedro Miguel, abbreviated by the West Indians to "Peter M'Gill," originally honored Saint Peter Michael; Emperador similarly had been distorted to "Empire." And Ahorca Lagarto actually meant what it said, "Hang the lizard"; in 1549 a regiment of Spaniards wearing emblematic lizards on their helmets and breastplates were rushed by native *cimarrones* with the war cry *"Ahorca lagarto,"* and the name had stuck for three and a half centuries.

92

Altogether there were twenty-seven villages and flag stops scattered along the rails between Colón and Panama. They resembled one another only in the clusters of native shacks and shanties constructed of everything from palm thatch and cane to odd pieces of sheet roofing pilfered from the ample stores of the Compagnie Universelle. Overshadowing the hovels in almost every settlement were the imposing French shops, warehouses, and residences. Among all the twenty-seven villages, Culebra alone was still occupied by canal laborers in 1904. There the gangs still working the Cut lived in disorder and filth. Even those seven hundred men might be rejuvenated under efficient American management.

In all the parleys at Colón, no decisions were made—no significant decisions on policy, procedure, or route. After all, they reasoned, Congress would have to pass on the type of canal, and in the meantime they would be hiring specialists to come up with recommendations that in due time would be placed before them for mature judgment. It was their function to weigh the decisions of others, to listen to many sides, to check the caprice of subordinates. They could put a lot of men to work in Culebra Cut; they would get a chief engineer on the job and start assembling engineering parties. For the present, that was about all that could be done.

The septemvirate hurried back to Washington at the end of two weeks, duly impressed with the mighty responsibility resting upon their collective shoulders. Representing their interests in Panama, they left Dr. Gorgas to carry on his sanitation surveys and Mark Brooke, a young lieutenant two years out of West Point, to take care of political exigencies. The push was on. The President expressed his pleasure with the prompt preliminary surveys, and before the Commission could catch a breath, he was ticking off another schedule of events to give them food for thought.

On April 28 Congress was at last cudgeled into appropriating the $40,000,000 for purchase of the French rights. Mark Brooke got the word in Panama late in the evening of May 3, and as though there were not a moment to spare, at seven-thirty the next morning, spruced out in his second lieutenant's dress uniform, he assembled a few dignitaries at the Grand Hotel. Assuming the importance of a viceroy, he signed a forty-million-dollar receipt to the Director General of the French Company. France was officially out, and the United States was in. Brooke read off a proclamation that he considered suitable to the occasion and promptly ran up the Stars and Stripes on the hotel flagpole.

It was an event that Central Americans would have turned into a two-day fiesta with dignified ceremonies, parades, speeches, and open bars, but in all the haste, President Amador wasn't even invited. The perfunctory transaction was over in a few minutes, before most Panamanians were stirring on the sultry May morning. All the disappointed populace could do was give the day a label and harbor a permanent grudge against a stripling officer who had cheated them out of a holiday. "Acquisition Day" it was called, and May 4 went on the calendar in red letters to commemorate a great event and a celebration that wasn't.

For Panamanians, *mañana* was soon enough to go to work; the celebration came first. But with callous disregard for Latin American sentiment, the Yankees went about things as though they were trying to accomplish what should have been done yesterday. Mark Brooke's oversight was only an introduction to the foreign neglect of sentimental solemnities.

There weren't enough days in the calendar to allow for amenities, though the Roosevelt program of urgency furnished excuse for a fiesta every week during 1904. On May 7 the Panama Railroad became the property of the United States Government, except for a few hundred shares of stock owned by private individuals. Two days later the whole Isthmian Commission was placed under the supervision of Secretary of War William Howard Taft. On May 17 Major General George W.

Davis took over the government of the Zone, and on June 1 John Wallace officially stepped into the post of chief engineer.

The acceleration of events was bewildering to slow-moving Latins but not fast enough for Americans. They wanted something more than announcement of plans and appointments. Before United States citizens had finished their condemnation of the President's impetuous action, they themselves had become infected with his fervor and were crying for more visible signs of canal building than were apparent. Already eight months had passed since the Revolution, and not a single steam shovel had been shipped south! If mountains were to be moved, why weren't men working at least on the foothills? What was holding up progress? The hustling youth in the White House suddenly had to defend himself against accusations of both action and inertia. To a group of Yale professors who still challenged the legality of his aggression in Panama, he evasively flung back: "Tell them that I am going to make the dirt fly on the Isthmus."

Overnight that retort did more to subdue the foes of Roosevelt policies on the Isthmus than all his speeches and explanations. Flying dirt at Panama was just what the public wanted. The idea raced across the country in the form of a rallying cry, a call to arms, the catch phrase of a campaign—"Make the dirt fly at Panama." It was a password on the streets, a chestnut for political oratory, a headline for countless editorials.

With the cry still ringing in his ears, John Wallace arrived at Colón on June 29. He had a mandate from the people to make the dirt fly, and a determination to build the canal or die in the attempt. Actually he had premonitions that the job might turn into a death-dealing proposition, for in his cumbrous assortment of luggage were included two handsome metal caskets—one for himself and one for his wife—in which they could be shipped back to the States, in case——.

He had been warned about yellow fever, plague, and malaria, about the mosquitoes *Stegomyia* and *Anopheles*. Death on the Isthmus could come quickly and in unpredictable ways. All these

95

forebodings were in Wallace's mind, but, to all appearances, he cast aside the hazards in his assignment and plunged headlong into the work cut out for him.

Secretly he wanted a sea-level canal, and he intended to settle for nothing less, regardless of what the public had in mind, but that argument could wait. The imperative thing now was to stir an eagerness in Panama, to get the dirt flying. So five days after his arrival, the whole Zone turned out for a frenzied celebration of its first Fourth of July—to inaugurate the great undertaking before them, to honor the man who was to do the supervising, and to make up for Mark Brooke's mistake. There were games, excursions, band music, and picnicking—American style—and after that everyone was in a mood to take up his tools.

In the days and weeks ahead Wallace directed the renovation of the palatial Ancon Hospital; new hotels for employees were started at Corozal and Culebra; carpenters were set to work on scores of delapidated shops, utility buildings, and laborers' quarters; jungle was cut away to get at abandoned machinery; and as workmen poured in from the West Indies they were sent down the rail line to make the dirt fly in Culebra Cut.

"The construction of the Panama Canal calls for the largest number of men that were ever employed at one time on any modern or medieval peaceful enterprise," the American public was informed. And the assembling of that working force had to start almost from scratch—a force that would eventually total nearly fifty thousand, but, because of the constant turnover, would involve the recruiting of perhaps a quarter of a million. The group of seven hundred inherited from the French regime were "not only incompetent, but altogether too small to be regarded as even a nucleus . . .—Negroes from the islands of the Caribbean Sea well-known for their indolent habits engendered by the lassitude of a tropical climate." But, regardless of the "indolent habits," thousands more of them were soon streaming down the piers at Colón.

96

Generally they were set to work in gangs of thirty or forty, under American bosses. Foremen, engineers, mechanics, steam-shovel operators, carpenters, plumbers, steam fitters, with few exceptions, were all Yankees, and there was one of them for every ten common laborers. In squalid huts or ramshackle sheds built by the French, those new arrivals from the West Indies put up with living conditions fully as primitive as what they had known in the islands, and the Americans often endured housing that was little better.

For a time the empty wards of Ancon Hospital were used as dormitories for the skilled white-collar class. A clerk assigned there in July, 1904, recalled that his "de luxe" quarters had "thirty single iron beds of French make, ranged hospital style, a row on each side of the room. One straight-backed chair was made to do duty for the entire bunch, and this useful article was generally found in the morning alongside the bed of the one who was last in at night. We had but one kerosene lamp and this was usually empty. There were no mirrors, and the fortunate possessor of an individual looking glass was to be envied. Some combed their hair and shaved with the aid of the swinging glass windows backed up against the wall. There were but two wash-stands for all of us, but thanks to the French, there were a couple of pretty decent shower baths. We lived in constant dread of the scorpion who seems to have a penchant for buildings long unused, and for going to sleep in our clothes or shoes. One morning one of these fellows, which have a stinger where their tail ought to be, dropped from the ceiling to the wash basin, where I was performing my ablutions. One another occasion I shook one out of the fold of my collar where he had been enjoying a quiet snooze."

The men cheerfully put up with conditions as they found them, but it was necessary to arrive at Panama well fortified with a hardy constitution and a pioneer spirit. Their first job was bringing a semblance of order to the chaos. The job at Gorgona was typical. Gorgona—or Bas Matachín, as it had long been

97

known to the natives—was almost in the dead center of the Zone. On a plot of three acres between the Chagres and the railroad line was a jumble of buildings standing almost wall to wall, a total of 36,750 square feet of floor space; machine shop, car shop, foundry, storage sheds, a power plant with three thirty-five-horsepower engines, and a half-dozen buildings used as mechanics' quarters. The sheds were filled to the rafters with old locomotives, cranes, excavators, and a hundred carloads of tools and spare parts.

Gorgona had been one of the main repair centers for the Compagnie Universelle, but it had been closed and shuttered for years. The roof leaked and the rafters sagged. Before a door could be opened it was necessary to cut away trees and brush that blocked it. The rail yards were overgrown with bamboo and scrub. Walls had to be reinforced before the locomotives that supported them could be removed. Yet within a few weeks after the natives with their machetes and the American with their wrenches had moved into Gorgona, rebuilt locomotives were coming off the jacks. From the limitless supply of spare parts anything from a wheel to a whistle could be replaced. Journals were cleared, fire boxes repacked, frozen steam gauges replaced; and when the boilers were fired with coal that had been seasoning in bins for a decade, the locomotives miraculously ran.

Six months after Wallace's big push started, the United States Minister to Panama, John Barrett, took it upon himself to chronicle "the great progress being made along the whole line of the Panama Canal from Colón to Panama." For the popular *Independent* magazine, read by everyone in search of unbiased news commentary, he wrote an article extolling the accomplishments of his good friend John Wallace.

"This distance of approximately forty-five miles grows busier every day," Barrett eulogized. "Some 5000 men are now working for Uncle Sam and that number will be doubled. . . . So pronounced and so extensive have been the improvements made by Chief Engineer Wallace in the past half year that they seem almost incredible. . . . Hundreds and hundreds of acres, grown up with luxuriant and rank tropical vegetation, have been cleared away in order to get at hidden machinery, to make surveys, and to utilize old railroad tracks or lay down new ones. Over twenty-five miles of railway lines built by the French, and unused for eighteen years, have been restored, after much repairing, so that they are practically new. Fully five miles of new tracks have been put down to facilitate the work of canal construction."

He pointed out that three hundred of the French buildings had been repaired and were ready for occupancy: that a large dormitory with dining and social halls, recreation rooms, and baths was going up at Culebra, as well as twenty small homes for married couples; that the hospital had accommodations ready for two hundred patients with forty "trained American female nurses in charge," yet remarkably enough, there had been only eighteen cases of yellow fever in six months, only three deaths. The sanitary corps was doing a praiseworthy job of cleaning up Colón and Panama.

"There is at the present time," he assured timid State-siders, "no more danger from yellow fever in Panama than there is from pneumonia and grippe in the United States."

Barrett knew that the people were most interested in the digging, and he gave them the statistics. "The work of actual excavation under the masterhand of Chief Engineer Wallace is going apace. Nearly 3,300 cubic yards of earth and rock are being taken out each day. . . . Some 1200 men are employed at Culebra Cut alone."

He pictured three huge new American steam shovels, each digging a thousand cubic yards a day, and a battery of rebuilt French excavators doing from four hundred to eight hundred yards per day; noted, too, that 250 mechanics in the machine shops at Gorgona were rebuilding four French locomotives and fifty dump cars every month to add to the earth-moving equipment; and he ventured the prediction that a hundred of the old puffers and a thousand dump cars would soon be in service.

99

44658

"Most of the data gathered," he concluded, giving a little free publicity to Wallace's ideas, "warrant the opinion that a low-level canal can be constructed at such a conservative increased cost and extent of time over a high-level route that the American people, in their desire to have the best thing done, will support the President and Congress in an eventual determination to select the low level scheme. . . . Barring some great physical cataclysm or unexpected political delay in the United States, a low-level waterway can be opened for larger vessels in ten years."

In view of the remarkable progress reported, it was time for the Administration to demonstate its interest with a dramatic appearance, so Secretary of War Taft was assigned the honors and late in the year arrived on the scene, not only to inspect the wonders that Wallace had wrought in so short a time, but also to kill a number of Panamanian rumors about the political and economic intentions of the new tenants. He was given an extravagant welcome in Colón, the ovation of a hero in Panama City; at a dinner in the Grand Central Hotel his address was interrupted time and again with applause and cheers, and at an open assembly in Cathedral Plaza, where he ended a flow of oratory with *"Viva la República de Panama!,"* he was "acclaimed with a universal frenzy of enthusiasm, until the fronds of the towering palms and the gray façade of the old Cathedral seemed to vibrate together with its tumultuous stress."

His five-day visit was a round of conferences and conclaves, banquets and balls, receptions and picnics, excursions and guided tours of the Zone. Then he hastened back to Washington to make a progress report almost as flowery as John Barrett's. It was now taken as a foregone conclusion that the Canal would be a success. Things were moving. Dirt was flying.

V

"NOBODY'S HERE FOR HIS HEALTH"

SOMEBODY wasn't telling the truth about Panama. As evidence of bungling, discord, and penny-wisdom piled up in 1905, it looked as though both the Secretary of War and the Minister to Panama would have to trim the extravagant superlatives they were using to describe achievements on the Isthmus. The man on the scene knew that "great progress" was not being made "all along the line of the Canal."

Fired with enthusiasm for the part he was going to play in digging the Big Ditch, a young rookie swung onto the four o'clock train at Colón, bound for Culebra Camp. He was a graduate of a good Georgia technical school, lacking in experience but wise enough to disregard the flow of gossip he had been overhearing in Colón all day while waiting for the train—dissentious hokum about poor food, bad management, shoddy treatment.

Why didn't those men get a job with the United States Government working on the Canal, where they could be sure of good lodgings and steady work? He'd been tempted several times to tip them off. Culebra was the place. A rundown seaport like Colón, of course, would be sheltering the loafers, the dregs of humanity. But Culebra and Panama City—they were different. He knew because he'd just come from the States, where he had been reading about the tropical paradise of blue seas, lofty palms,

101

lush vegetation, and Caribbean romance, about the fine hotel accommodations and congenial companionship, the broad beaches, tennis courts, recreation rooms, and libraries. The employment agent in New York had vouched for it all, stressing particularly the crying need for surveyors like himself, the golden opportunities waiting for young men who wanted to make names for themselves in the great national engineering enterprise.

"From here on, you'll spend most of your time wanting something to eat. You'll not hanker after fashionable boulevards so much," one of the old wartheads at Colón had responded when the neophyte had tried to make a cheerful joke out of the ankle-deep mud in the streets. Old gloom monger! Everybody in Colón except the naked black kids seemed to be gloomy. He was glad to be leaving the filthy place behind.

The outskirts of the city flashed by the car window—ugly warehouses, glimpses of the abandoned French canal, shacks on stilts with a dozen expressionless faces crowding the doorways, acres of swamp and acres of discarded machinery. Then the jungle closed in, and he was rushing through an exciting tunnel of greenery—the last lap on his long journey to Culebra.

But even on the train it was annoying to have to listen to the snatches of conversation all around him, more of the talk he'd heard in Colón: facetious remarks regarding delays in shipments of dynamite, lumber, repair parts; cynical speculations about when the work was going to start; monotonous queries on how Jones was, whether or not Frank had the fever. Was Sam Craig dead yet? Had they buried Hank Billings? Eggs gone up to a dollar and a half a dozen; everlasting preoccupation with food—dirty bread, no butter, no cheese, no milk, no ice, no fresh vegetables. Why didn't they all get jobs with the Government? That guy Wallace needed men.

The train finally pulled up at a grimy shed labeled "Culebra," and the enthusiast from Georgia got off. He spotted a few bedraggled palms that fell short of what he had imagined, but the hotel was undoubtedly some distance from the clutter of bunkhouses he saw on the hillside. He elbowed his way through a snarl of very black Negroes and swarthy, sweat-soaked Europeans to inquire about directions to Culebra Hotel from the stationmaster. The official pointed toward a rambling bunkhouse.

At that instant the rookie's vision of a Panama paradise vanished. Like hundreds of other American dupes, he never recovered from the shock.

He lugged his valise up a steep path of mud—red, gummy clay that sucked at his shoes with every step. The "hotel" was a filthy barracks swarming with mosquitoes and flies. The veranda floor was plastered with mud. There were no screens on the windows. The dining room was a smelly mess hall with long, littered tables, where several hundred workmen were swilling a supper of corned beef and cabbage.

According to promises in New York, his private quarters were to be furnished with "a single bed, mattress, lamp, two chairs, a dresser, table, washstand, a bowl, and a pitcher." In a room already occupied by seven others, a sloven darkie pointed out a cot and a box he could have. That was all. He wandered out back of the hotel to survey the recreational facilities. The dingy café and bare reading room were both deserted; the one kerosene lamp attracted so many moths and mosquitoes that it was impossible to approach it, much less sit down with a magazine.

There was no refuge, no escape from the mosquitoes, no place to spend the long evening except under a blanket. And his crowded room was a poor excuse for refuge. To provide ventilation the partitions were left open above, and the noise of scores of men drinking, gambling, and brawling echoed through the entire building. One by one the roommates thundered in, treating the newcomer as impersonally as they regarded each other. It didn't matter particularly who occupied cot number 8. Somebody else might be there tomorrow. "Who died today?" seemed to be the standing joke, and "Nobody's here for his health!" the stock justification for putting over a fast one on the management.

They swore at the mosquitoes, God-dammed the superintendents, and spent their loftiest profanity on the man who was slow about turning out the kerosene lamp.

The crowning blow came to the young surveyor the next morning. Instead of being sent out with a chains-and-transit group, he was informed that surveyors were a dime a dozen at Culebra. They didn't need any surveyors. He was assigned a job as foreman for a gang of Barbadians working a shovel pit.

To any aspiring recruit the broken morale, the total lack of organization, the endless waiting, the waste of time were unpardonable. As the United States public had been told, steam shovels were at work in Culebra Cut—three of them. Sporadically they grubbed at the embankments, the great maws gorging and disgorging, but half the time they were idle. The operators waited, the shovel crews waited, the dump crews waited—waited for empty cars to return, waited for traffic on the congested rails to be unsnarled. The shovels were idle because there weren't enough cars to load, because the empties were tied up on the side tracks, because there wasn't enough track in the right place, because there weren't enough track foremen, and if there had been enough foremen, their superintendent would have been too busy somewhere else to put them to work. Wherever one looked, digging operations were bogged down or proceeding at a snail's pace.

Nor was Culebra the only trouble spot. Panama City and Colón were supposed to be getting a new water supply. Open ditches crisscrossed the cities everywhere, impeding traffic and making convenient gutters for private sewage disposal. Half-filled with green slime and caving in a little more with every downpour, the Isthmians waited for pipe to be laid in them. Natives were inured to unsanitary and unsightly conditions, but they resented the way the Americans had dug these yawning trenches for people to fall into and then gone off and forgotten them. Meantime there was a water shortage in Colón. Cisterns were dry and the Panama Railroad Company was peddling water through the streets for five cents a gallon. A bucket a day to a family, that was the limit, regardless of the size of the family. One bucket.

The slowdown was as apparent in construction work. Tales had been spread abroad about the hundreds of renovated French buildings. Many had been repaired and made habitable, but scores of others were in a state of semidemolishment. One could never tell whether the men working on a structure were in the process of razing it or rebuilding it. Rotted floors were ripped out, only to uncover decayed joists, termite-hollowed studding, and weakened crossbeams. Then there was no lumber with which to restore the wrecked building. The shortage of carpenters was critical, but those on duty couldn't be kept busy for lack of boards and two-by-fours.

The universal cry for lumber was providentially answered early in March, 1905. Twelve million feet of lumber that had been on order from Seattle for nine months arrived at the Pacific port, La Boca, all at once. The Bay of Panama was filled with ships burdened with lumber, and there was no place to unload or stack twelve million feet. At best the wharf at La Boca could accommodate three ships at a time. Three freighters tied up, and the slow process of carting off every plank by hand began. At that rate the unloading could take weeks. Ships in the Bay transferred their loads to lighters and rafts. The lighters were drawn in as close to shore as possible and gangs of Jamaicans were ordered to wade into the shin-deep mud and bring the lumber in on their heads. In water up to their chests, they struggled ashore with a few planks at a time, dropped them on the muddy banks, and went back for more—a vast army of Negroes slowly plodding back and forth across the mud flats. Rafts piled high were moored along the shores of the Rio Grande and left there to tug at lines as the tide rose and fell its twenty feet. Then an unexpected freshet put the river on a rampage, tearing the rafts loose and sending them to sea. For days those

105

that didn't disappear over the horizon were a menace to traffic in the narrow, crooked channels of the Bay. Most of the rafts were eventually rounded up, but expensive driftwood from Washington girdled the shores at high tide for miles.

When the last of the ships was unloaded, La Boca was rimmed with the helter-skelter piles, unsorted and the worse for handling. It was a nuisance to freight hands filling requisitions for delivery inland to sort the stuff; so, as a foreman explained, "Orders were filled from the pile nearest the track without regard to what was asked for. It was not measured, but loaded on the cars and *weighed*. Dressed or undressed, it did not matter which. And when the architect ordered two-by-fours he was liable to get six-by-sixes." At building sites the confusion mounted.

In such a chaos, morale steadily deteriorated. Plans were constantly being changed. All orders seemed to be signed by "acting" officials. A man never knew at the end of one day whether he would have the same boss the next. Good men were suddenly dropped and incompetents put in their places. "There were those who argued that the Canal would never be finished, that the Washington people were keeping up a show of doing something for the graft they got out of it, and the men in charge at the Isthmus were 'railroaders' sent down on purpose to impede the work." A union card or a letter from a Congressman appeared to be the essential requirements for getting an easy post. "A serious difficulty all along the Canal Zone," one complainer wrote home, "is that many men are sent here to fill positions for which mentally and physically they are absolutely not fitted. They have received and have held their positions because they carry letters from some prominent official in Washington."

More often the incompetents couldn't stick it out. Frequently they didn't even land. On the way down they had picked up enough smoking room stories to promote the conclusion, "Good Lord! This is no place for a white man." They remained on board the transport, paid their own passage home, and forfeited their wages. Men came, stayed for four days or a week, and shoved

106

off. "A union card or a Congressman's letter in the pocket," observed a journalist, "is not a prophylactic against fever or homesickness or the somewhat severe initiary regime which the men on the ground delight to impose upon the tenderfoot suspected of incapacity or nepotism."

Men complained that the Zone was "barren and dull." After the eight hours' work there was nowhere to go, nothing to do. Sorely missed were the most common home staples like fresh milk, ice, apples, eggs. "The three things lacking to make life enjoyable on the Isthmus are all feminine," quipped a shovel operator—"women, cows, and hens"; and he added for good measure, "The Canal Zone is one long whispering gallery. Every-man knows every other man's business better, in most cases, than his own. Men deprived of womankind have to take upon them-selves many feminine functions, and among them that traditional one of gossip."

Fully half the American force had a touch of malaria and were afflicted with the chronic depression that often came with it. Melancholy Chinese fifty years before had strung each other up by their queues to put an end to it all. The Yankees drowned their misery and despair in alcohol. "In Colón alone there are twenty-five saloons and wine rooms for every business house," claimed a W.C.T.U. advocate, "and almost the same proportion in the smaller towns. Temptations to drink, to buy lottery tickets, to take up other vicious habits beset the men just as soon as they land."

Living conditions grew worse instead of better during the early months of 1905. It turned out that the "dietitian" at Culebra Hotel was a former shovel operator who found that he could make better money as a hotel keeper charging his boarders $22.50 a month. He grew rich as his boarders grew thin on a diet of hash and unpalatable stew. And lodgings were worse than the menus. A reputable foreman for a water and sewer pipe project was sent down from the States with the promise of "first-class accommodations," but upon arrival with

107

his family he was assigned three dingy rooms "in the upper floor of a two-story building without any water or sanitary connections," No man was in a better position to provide himself with running water than that foreman, if it had been available, but for three months his wife and children lugged all their water in buckets up the stairs and all their slops down.

From Jamaica came an experienced and well-educated Negro civil engineer. He had been assured of "suitable accommodations." His new home on the Isthmus was a shack with a straw roof, twenty by twelve feet, open to the weather on four sides. It was shared with fourteen other Jamaicans, and all of them were obliged to sleep on the bare floor with a single blanket apiece for mattress and bedding.

With one malcontent leaving Colón for every two recruits that arrived, with a biweekly flood of uncensored letters enumerating the details of wholesale bungling, the American press was not long in catching wind of the fact that all was not well on the Isthmus. For a few weeks reporters, muckrakers, and self-appointed critics stormed south in almost as large numbers as laborers. In the rush to get stories back to their clientele, they found little that was worthy of favorable comment:

" 'Fore God, sir, ah'm tellin' yo de troof!" recorded a correspondent, presumably giving the verbatim reactions of a Negro complainant. "Mr. Taft an dose big people, dey didn't see real things. Dey went to dances and talked with politicians. Dey don't know how de workmen has to live."

The same correspondent made a tour of Colón. "We passed along the front street—the show street—the only street. We went to the Central Market which covers a block, around the four sides of which I found merely pools of stagnant water—'handy for drowning babies,' as a Negro foreman playfully remarked. Every whiff of air blew poison into the public market. The strings of meat in the butcher stalls hung unprotected against flies, dust, and the plentiful body of germs which were breeding luxuriantly in the moist air." He inspected houses which consisted of "a floor, a roof, and four unpainted walls" without kitchen plumbing or conveniences, a "sentry box" in a swamp out back, inaccessible because it was standing in a pond of green slime. "The real latrine was obviously the swamp immediately under the floorboards of the bedroom."

"Mr. Taft spent five days down here," an eminent engineer told him. "In that time he attended three dances and a succession of social functions. But he had no time to look into the conditions of the laboring man. I prayed him to let me show him the real state of things on the Isthmus, but he declined; he professed to know all about it from *official sources.*"

The tangle of red tape caught the eye of one investigator. There was no delegation of authority. Before a train could be moved, the action had to be approved by a chain of foremen and supervisors; before a necessary change in plans for the placement of a door or window in an old building could be made, engineers and architects had to be consulted; "a requisition had to trudge from foreman to general foreman, to assistant superintendent, to division superintendent, to Chief Engineer and be approved by each." While most Colón residents during the drought of 1905 had to purchase their water by the gallon, it was free to employees of the Panama Railroad, but before an employee could get a glass of water he had to go to the proper office and procure a written order for it.

A critic who knew his hardware made a hobby of looking into the confusion of orders for hinges. He guessed that there might be as many as 20,000 or 30,000 new doors, but discovered that 60,000 pairs of T-butts and strap hinges had been purchased prior to April 15, 1905; on that date a requisition was placed for 104,000 more, followed soon after by another order for 84,000 additional pairs. "One pair of hinges is all that is necessary to one door," he reminded his readers, "but provision has been made for about 250,000 doors. This indeed is true devotion to the open door policy."

"Dirt is not flying on the Panama Canal cut," was the consensus. "Instead the American people have only new expectation for the old unfulfilled promises. 'Make the dirt fly!' the phrase used when the digging started, has been an unfortunate expression. It blinded us with the idea that the Canal was really being dug; and at the same time the flying of dirt, haphazard and as concession to popular demand, so blinded Chief Engineer Wallace that he soon could not see how to dig at all."

"We have pitched in after the characteristic American way and hurried a heterogeneous lot of men and materials to the Isthmus," agreed an editor with a little hindsight. He pictured a debacle of confusion and conflict in shipping "without adequate wharfing facilities at either the Atlantic or Pacific ends, without quarters for the men, or storage for supplies, with complicated, duplicated, and erratic methods of accounting. . . . The things ordered were not always right, and when they were, they did not arrive in the right order."

Criticisms from the New York press were severe enough, but the defeatism spread to every section of the country. The Houston *Post* in March, 1905, after surveying the rate of progress, ventured that: "Anyone of this generation might as well give up all hope of ever seeing the Canal completed." The New Orleans *Picayune* chimed in: "Although the commission has been in existence for nearly a year, there is no reason from what is seen in the present situation, to believe that any human being now alive will ever see an actual ship canal through the Panama Isthmus."

Everyone was trying to find a scapegoat during those early months of 1905 and usually the finger was leveled at John Wallace, but there were so many functionaries among whom the responsibility for blunders could be distributed that it was next to impossible to get at the truth. Basically the President was to blame for his failure to foresee that no chief engineer could take orders from six differing Commission bosses in Washington and a very obstinate one in Panama. Roosevelt himself wanted to do some of the directing, though he had delegated executive author-

110

ity to Secretary Taft. On the Isthmus General Davis considered himself the real kingpin, as Governor of the Zone and as spokesman for the Commission. He wasn't yielding an inch to his employee Wallace, except in matters of engineering. Davis was an old man living on his illustrious past. He had a good Army record and was determined not to have it besmirched by any taint of flimflammery; he wasn't going to be hurried into any mistakes. Painfully slow in making up his mind, he'd let documents involving expenditures of millions pile up on his desk while he pondered over the advisability of authorizing a dollar purchase. No one was ever going to accuse him of being a de Lesseps. So in matters of urgent policy, Wallace waited, the engineers waited, and every man down the line waited.

In Washington the administration was worse, for there were six slow-moving Commissioners to weigh matters, and less pressure for an immediate decision. Moreover, they had to take into consideration the politicians who would be voting appropriations. The Senator from Mississippi might object if Oregon got all the orders for lumber. Requisitions for anything had to be parceled out with political discretion.

"Wallace was checked and thwarted in his authority and held responsible for everything that went wrong." But the real blame didn't belong there. Nor was Dr. Gorgas to be blamed. The Chief Engineer was doing his best to pull together a cumbersome organization, and the physician was working tirelessly to introduce a semblance of sanitation. Yet every effort was caught up in red tape. The work was in Panama, but the Commission was in Washington, and every effort to persuade the members that their services were needed nearer the scene of action was fruitless. They rationalized that they could better carry out their "watchdog" responsibilities at the source of supplies. They had seen the extravagant errors of the French, and even at the expense of inaction, those errors were not going to be repeated.

In August, 1904, Wallace had wired a rush order for the pipes needed in Panama City and Colón. The shipment could have

111

arrived within a month. While the Commission pondered in Washington, while the supply department deliberated over an assortment of bids and argued over specifications, Panamanians and work crews continued to drink from cisterns or to fill their buckets from water carts. Wallace wired again, pointing out the urgent need for the pipe. The trenches dug for the system were caving in. The message was ignored. He wired again and was brusquely requested by letter not to spend so much money on cables. The pipes didn't begin to arrive until January, and more months went by before there was enough to conduct the new supply of running water to homes in the two cities.

Dr. Gorgas put in a routine order for porch screening at the hospital. Unnecessary extravagance! claimed the Commission, disregarding the request. He repeated the order, explaining that it was essential to keep out mosquitoes which could convey yellow fever from patients to outsiders. Grudgingly, half the order was filled and he was instructed to economize by boarding up the other half of the verandas.

The Commission was miserly even with screening for the Administration building at Colón until an outbreak of disease forced the issue. Requisitions for heavy equipment—steam shovels, cars, cranes—were routed into pigeonholes. Penny-wise Admiral Walker seemed to consider that his sole mission was the prevention of extravagance. "Gorgas, there is one thing certain," the doctor was informed in answer to a patient plea for needed equipment; "whether we build the canal or not we will leave things so fixed that those fellows up on the hill can't find anything in the shape of graft after us."

So the pigeonholes bulged. Congestion and confusion mounted. Inertia ruled. Ships loaded with supplies waited at anchor for days in Limon Bay because there were not enough longshoremen to unload them, nor space in the bulging warehouses for storage, nor enough freight cars to handle the traffic. Patients waited for competent treatment at Ancon Hospital because young internes had been assigned there rather than experienced doctors;

it would be a good training ground for promising medicos, the Commission reasoned, and their services would cost less. In place of the engineers that were called for, draftsmen arrived; in place of skilled mechanics, men handy with a screw driver. Twenty-five track foremen were specifically requested, and of the twenty-five who arrived, only two had ever driven a railroad spike.

Over the weeks quantities of old machinery were put back into use, the railroad and harbor facilities were improved, and several hundred thousand cubic yards of excavating was done. It all made good news copy and good press photography for the general public, but anyone with a professional knowledge of the real scale on which the work should be progressing was astounded.

"The Commission at present is composed of men who are personally most estimable," the *Independent* tentatively acknowledged in February, 1905, anxious not to tread too hard on any toes. "But whether they are well-qualified for the arduous duties before them is another question. If we are to avoid the disastrous errors of the French company, we must begin by avoiding its errors of administration. The Commission must not be an ornamental one. It must not be an eleemosynary institution for retired statesmen. It must be a responsible, authoritative, effective body of active working men. No man ought to hold a place on the Commission who cannot or will not spend ten months of the year on the Isthmus. If any member of the Commission is unwilling to do that, or is physically unable to do it, he owes it to the Canal enterprise to step down and out, and give his place to someone who can and will do it. . . . If it is impossible to form and to maintain such a Commission, then it should be abolished, or reduced to the rank of a mere auditing board in Washington, and the Chief Engineer of the Canal should be made Czar of the Canal Zone."

That was hitting the nail on the head, and Secretary Taft felt obliged to endorse it with appropriate circumlocution: "It is conceded even by its own members that the present Commission

113

has not developed itself into an executive body as to give hope that it may be used successfully as an instrumentality for carrying on the immense executive burden involved in the construction of the Canal."

Three times Wallace went north to impress Washington officials with the consequence of their procrastination. At the Commission offices he found requisitions that had rested in the files for four months unopened, others rejected without explanation, urgent requisitions going through a slow bidding process among manufacturers scattered across the country. He received promises of reform, and Taft and Roosevelt did take action. Resignations of the old Commission members were accepted, and a new governing body with a less unwieldy executive committee was substituted. The Panama Railroad, one of the major causes of delay, was reorganized under total goverment ownership. A new Governor was appointed. But all the sources of friction were not removed; the chain of command was still awkward. Fundamentally, the whole approach to the canal operation was wrong. First things had been put second. Complicated problems of sanitation and more complicated problems of organization had to be worked out before dirt could be made to fly.

And then suddenly a heavy price was exacted for the topsy-turvy organization and the pinch-penny policy. In November, 1904, yellow fever had become a topic of table conversation at the work camps. Only a few cases were rumored then, but the coffins stacked up at the railroad stations and daily reports of funeral processions to the cemetery were enough to convince anyone that there was reason for alarm. Yellow fever was headlined in the Panama press and given blacker, bolder headlines in the United States press. Mr. and Mrs. Wallace calmly rode through the streets in an effort to allay fears, but the gesture was futile.

The real truth about Panama was reaching the United States in the hundreds of letters sent by laborers. Wives, mothers, and neighbors at home replied with pleas to leave the "sinkhole," to return to God's country—while they could, alive. By scores and hundreds, men dropped their shovels at Culebra and did leave.

In December, the wife of the Chief Engineer's secretary died, and the facts were widely broadcast. If yellow fever could come to the protected homes of Panama aristocracy, questioned the laborers, how much more susceptible were they? The curse was swiftly becoming epidemic. An auditor working in the Administration Building at Panama was struck down. An architect succumbed. During the dry season, when there was the least fear of infection, the cases steadily increased, and with the coming of the rainy season they multiplied. And this was the time that Wallace chose for another trip to Washington—ostensibly to place a large order for machinery. Workmen suspected he had other reasons for leaving Panama. Alarm was turning into hysteria.

Daily trips of the funeral train to Mount Hope Cemetery offered little comfort to those who professed indifference. It was assumed that every cortege represented a yellow fever casualty. Work at Culebra Cut was slacking off. As spring advanced the epidemic increased. The number of cases in May was doubled in June. A panic was on, but the news that precipitated the panic was not the lengthening mortality list. It was the announcement of John Wallace's resignation. He had decided, after all, not to build the Panama Canal. He was not returning from his trip to Washington. The casket he had so farsightedly taken with him to the Isthmus could be used by someone else. M. O. Johnson, the supervising architect he had left behind, was put away in it.

VI

"NOBODY WAS WORKING
BUT THE ANTS AND THE TYPISTS"

To the boys from the West Indies, the place where white people wore a hat was the natural place for carrying a burden. In Panama a native of Jamaica, Barbados, or Martinique strode barefoot along the jungle trail balancing aloft a hundred-pound sack of yams; he carried lumber or a letter the same way, a folded umbrella, a machete, or a shovel. Three recruits fresh from Martinique were assigned a job with a wheelbarrow—an invention they had never seen before. Resourcefully they filled it to overflowing with dirt, then pondered for a moment over the problem of transporting it to the dump a hundred yards away. The solution was easy; the two strongest hefted it onto the other's head, and the bearer proudly staggered off as if wheelbarrows had always been carried that way.

The wheelbarrow scene typified for the new Chief Engineer, John F. Stevens, the state of affairs in the Canal Zone. If there were a hard way of doing a thing, someone seemed to have discovered it. And the Americans had far outdone the Negroes. Among builders the rule of red tape had advanced to an absurd state where a carpenter was not permitted to saw a ten-foot board in half without a written order from a supervisor, though spending an hour sorting a stack of lumber for two five-foot lengths was acceptable practice. Rail transportation was virtually paralyzed because the freight sheds were filled, and the agents spent all their time filing the bales of manifests and bills of lading. A mechanic complained that he couldn't obtain a bolt until he had signed his name in twelve places. Digging at Culebra had become a comedy of errors, with disrupted track, minor wrecks, and men staring at the tangle. "Nobody was working but the ants and the typists," claimed Stevens when he arrived on the Isthmus late in July, 1905.

In the United States the spectacular reputations for nineteenth-century construction had been made on the railroads, on lines spanning the great rivers of the continent, thrusting over and under the Rockies and Sierra, crossing the rugged, waterless wastelands of the West. And so, for a successor to Wallace, Taft and Roosevelt looked once again to the railroads and summoned the man who was recognized as the world's foremost railway civil engineer. Stevens had surveyed and helped build lines in the West all the way from the Mexican border to British Columbia, had done the impossible in laying track along precipitous mountain slopes, bridging canyons, digging two-mile tunnels. He had just resigned a vice-presidency of the Rock Island, and on July 1, 1905, was about to leave Chicago for the Philippine Islands, where he was being sent as the best railroad expert the United States could nominate for the new Territory. He was halted in Chicago, took a day to think over the Canal offer, and then reversed his route.

"I don't know why I'm accepting Panama," he told a reporter, "unless it's because of the size of the job. Of course, it's a compliment. You never get too old to like them."

In engineering reviews and in newspapers Stevens had followed every step of progress on the Canal and was among those who were convinced that the President was responsible for two of the largest boners—rushing headlong into an enormous enterprise without emphasizing the necessity of a long period of preparation, and failing to see the operation as one that concerned the medical profession on very nearly equal terms with the engineering profession. Because Roosevelt was carried away with the vision of flying dirt and because he had neglected to have medicine represented on the Isthmian Canal Commission, the Americans had come almost as near to fiasco as had the French.

"Affairs are in a devil of a mess," the President confided at Oyster Bay where the new Chief Engineer was called for a private briefing. They talked over the reasons for the deplorable bungle: delays in taking adequate sanitation methods, the awkwardness of the old Commission, jealousies and misunderstandings among the other officials, Wallace's one-sided interest in a sea-level canal, lack of aggressive leadership. Stevens held his tongue about blunders that could be attributed to higher authority. What the situation called for now, they agreed, was a man "bent upon smashing a way through all obstacles, a kind of politic 'roughneck' who did not possess too deep a veneration for the vagaries of constituted authority."

"A free hand in all matters, hampered by no one high or low!" the President promised expansively. Nothing, nobody would be allowed to stand in his way—not even the Secretary of War, the Chairman of the Canal Commission, or any member of that body. Stevens was ordered to disregard them, disregard the channels, and report the first signs of trouble directly to him. Then, professing ignorance of the details of the Panama "mess," Roosevelt pointed up his instructions with a little parable: "A certain man suddenly became wealthy and set up a large establishment as a home. When his butler arrived he said to him, 'I don't know in the least what you are to do—but one thing I *do* know, you get busy and buttle like hell!' "

Stevens left Oyster Bay ready to "buttle like hell." He had even extracted from his boss a concession that he wouldn't necessarily have to remain in Panama "until the completion of the canal," but only "until the failure or success of the undertaking was assured according to my own judgment." He knew that he had the

119

unqualified support of the President, knew too that he would soon be in trouble up to his ears if he followed the advice about going over the heads of the Commission and the War Department. However, he would at least not be blocked at every turn by seven superiors, as Wallace had been. A seven-man Commission still existed, but following the shake-up, its executive authority was concentrated in two go-getters with whom Stevens had much in common: Chairman Theodore P. Shonts, another railroader and a hard-hitting businessman, and Judge Charles E. Magoon, the first Commission's legal counsel, now elevated to membership and doubling as Governor of the Zone.

With Chairman Shonts and a scant shipload of labor recruits, Stevens docked at Colón on July 25. There was no cheering throng to greet them, no reception formalities. It was a distressing sight. The wharves were crowded with scared, quiet men waiting to return to the States on the very ship that had brought them. What Roosevelt had recognized as a "devil of a mess," Stevens corroborated: "I found that the President was correct to a superlative degree. It did not take long to realize that discouraging reports current in the United States had not been overdrawn, but rather understated."

The epidemic had passed its peak, but the decline in yellow fever cases was not bringing confidence in Dr. Gorgas' preventive measures. Actually there had been a total of less than 250 victims, and only about 8 deaths—an outbreak hardly worth mentioning compared to the thousands of cases during the French regime. Then the sanitation squads had, perhaps, overdone the educating of the masses; over-dramatized the evidence that a single patient could infect dozens of others. Negroes were generally immune, because of their long exposure to the disease, but any day another onset of "black vomit" could sweep the Isthmus to claim the white man.

Terror was everywhere. If transportation had been available, a majority of the Americans would already have evacuated the Zone. The spirit was gone; even among fiesta-minded Latin

120

Americans it was gone. Fourth of July had been a somber day that year, with a *Te Deum* at the Cathedral instead of parades and street uproar. A solemn speech or two were made, and then water was turned into the mains of Panama City. Fourth of July was "Fresh Water Day," and the celebrating was around faucets and drinking fountains rather than in fireworks.

Theodore Shonts and John Stevens were sensitive enough to read the terror on men's faces, to feel the desperation that gripped the American colony. The situation called for action without delay. Immediately they took a train across the Isthmus to Panama City for a conference with Governor Magoon. Gorgas and his assistant, Dr. John W. Ross, who had also seen long experience in conquering yellow fever at Havana, were summoned. Beginning that night, the medics were to have a major share in determining the needs of Panama.

Without trying to minimize any phase of their predicament, they made as realistic an analysis as a staff of field generals whose armies were boxed in by the enemy. They were indeed boxed in. The Canal was being deserted, present work was wasted effort, an attitude of hopelessness prevailed, food and lodging were atrociously bad; the epidemic was halted, but its effects had not been. The fundamental problem was one of restoring confidence and morale. Health came first. The men needed food supplies and markets, decent living quarters, relief from the drab existence in the form of social rooms and entertainment.

As though their embarrassment had been brought on by negligence of the medical staff, Chairman Shonts pounced upon Gorgas with the charge that his sanitation program was a failure; he had not accomplished what was expected of him. In Havana yellow fever had been licked; it had to be licked in Panama. Beginning at once, every building in Colón and Panama City, from the administrative headquarters down to the lowest hovel, was to be systematically disinfected, and then the process was to be repeated until the fever was stamped out. There was to be no excuse for another outbreak.

Then in words almost as sharp, he ordered the new Chief Engineer to load a freight car with food at Colón the next day, go down the rail line, condemn any building he could find in a suitable location, and distribute food at cost.

Before the meeting was over, both Gorgas and Stevens had a long day's work cut out for them, and a foretaste of more to come.

No one could have conjured up a happier idea than the food car. Stevens found that the men were actually hungry, and the men found that they had a boss who took personal interest in their welfare. With the food went some strong talk, too—talk that had a sting. It wasn't the kind that came from a fine horse-drawn carriage or from the rear platform of the de luxe railroad coach reserved for bigwigs. Dressed like the men, Stevens stood among them, spoke their blunt language, rubbed their elbows. "There are only three diseases on the Isthmus," he charged into them, "yellow fever, malaria, and cold feet. The worst is cold feet. That's what's ailing you."

It was the scolding they needed. Neither the surly nor the timid had any comeback. No one else had possessed the guts or the wisdom to put a finger on the real trouble. And they weren't going to take a challenge like that without proving he was wrong. Word of the new dynamo of a Chief spread from camp to camp before nightfall. That evening they had something to talk about besides defeat, fever, and lousy food. Within twenty-four hours the whole tone of the work camps had altered; within forty-eight hours men were sheepishly stealing off to see the shipping agent, requesting that their names be scratched from the waiting list for transportation back home. Groups everywhere were arguing themselves into sticking it out a little longer. Some good could come out of the chaos yet. Things might begin to happen now.

A Chief as informal and as colorful as John Stevens had to have a nickname, and "Big Smoke" it was from the beginning. When he wasn't chain-smoking cigars, he was chain-chewing them. His stogie was part of him. And for the benefit of those who had forgotten, his engineering cronies revived some of the tales of how Chief Stevens had pipe-smoked peace out of the Indians in the West. They recalled his exploit across two hundred miles of war-torn Apache terrain in Arizona when he was building a railroad there. An urgent message had to be taken east, and even with a prize of five hundred dollars for the job, nobody would volunteer; it wasn't worth the likely cost. So Stevens took it—on foot; and when he returned, declined the five hundred dollars. He didn't do it for the reward. It was a case of "art for art," he claimed.

Then the Zonians were reminded that it was "Chief Big Smoke" who set out from Assiniboine, Montana, with two Indian guides and a pack mule, to try to find a "middle" route for the Great Northern over the Rockies to the Pacific. The mule died on the trail and the Indians deserted, but Stevens went on to discover the famous Marias Pass. Under circumstances almost as rough, he later located another pass through the Cascade Mountains in Washington, and against his objections, it was even named for him—Stevens Pass.

From the start the new Chief Engineer was a hero. Everybody took to him. He was tall, broad-shouldered, and tough, a man's man, uncontaminated by college or West Point erudition. Originally he'd come from Maine, but had gone West before he was twenty. "There is in him something of the canny Maine Yankee, something of the pushing pioneer of the plains," an admirer noted. "He looks squarely at you while he talks with a boy's frankness. There is no condescension, no airs of authority about him." The men sized him up as an important man who didn't have to act important. If anybody was going to build a canal, he could.

From the height overlooking Culebra Cut, Stevens looked down on the job that had been going on for a quarter of a century. It was his first survey tour. He had handled enough railroad cuts not to be awed by this one. It was deeper; that was the principal difference; on a larger scale, it called for the usual mining-excavation and steam-shovel methods with which he was familiar.

123

But such a waste of man power and machine power he had never witnessed. He counted a total of seven derailed work trains. Every steam shovel in sight was idle. The few men who were working, laboriously struggled to get the cars back on the tracks. And this floundering had been going on for weeks—months. The dumps were located too high, and cars could be filled only to half capacity or the locomotives failed to make the grade. Poor track, poorly laid, gave way under even the partial loads. There was no order, no plan.

"We've established a good record this year for no collisions on the main line," explained an official of the Panama Railroad, who had been deflated by the Chief's outspoken slurs and was determined to find one feature that might bring commendation from him.

"A collision has its good points as well as its bad ones," Stevens snapped back. "At least it indicates that something is moving on the railroad."

Immediately Stevens suspended the digging at Culebra and set crews to work installing a new track system. During his first five days he saw so much wasted effort that he halted all Canal excavation. There would be plenty of time for the digging after they were reorganized. Where others had been so eager to make dirt fly, he sounded a new philosophy: "Digging is the least thing of all." First things would come first. All the engineers that Dr. Gorgas could use were released for sanitation work; others were kept busy repairing and constructing quarters. Men who had been clamoring to go home no longer wanted to go; now Stevens dismissed them right and left, sent them back to the States with an agreement to let them know when they were wanted. It had the effect of notifying those who remained that something more than token duty was expected.

Next to Stevens, Dr. Gorgas became the most commanding official in the Zone; even engineers looked to him for orders. He had had a rough time, but his day had come at last. He was the crackpot doctor who was more interested in killing mosquitoes than building a canal and who kept the masons in a tizzy by spraying so much kerosene over stagnant puddles on new concrete that the next layer wouldn't set properly; the crank who was everlastingly upsetting housekeeping by sending men to fumigate and disinfect with obnoxious sulphur fumes; the queer gentleman who went about looking into rain barrels and overturning them, investigating water closets, wasting money on cutting grass, draining pools, tacking up screens.

Gorgas had been subjected to more abuse than any other man on the Isthmus. The giggling of the simple West Indians was exasperating but understandable, since the black folks took it for granted that the crazy American was trying to introduce a new kind of voodoo. Even the heckling of white laborers could be passed off in good spirit; but the open, aggressive derision of educated engineers and executives, and the insults from higher officials in the States were hard to take.

Until four years before, everyone knew that yellow fever was a contagious filth disease, mysteriously passed from one victim to another in foul odors, by contact, or carried on the "night vapors," particularly the "effluvium" of disturbed jungle soil. Most people still clung loyally to the old belief, but Dr. Gorgas was trying to make it fashionable to believe that a mosquito carried the disease. Not just any mosquito. Out of all the seven hundred kinds of mosquitoes which the bug specialists said there were, Gorgas chose one, called *Stegomyia,* and maintained that it was solely responsible. In fact, he had narrowed it down still further, and blamed everything on the female *Stegomyia.* It was too fantastic even for Commission members to believe without a grain of salt. He had made a fetish of it, claiming that he could rid Panama of yellow fever entirely, if they'd give him enough chemicals and screen.

In Washington the requisitions for wire screening and disinfectants had been dismissed as refinements quite in keeping with the extravagances that had doomed the French. What conceivable bearing had thousands of yards of expensive porch screening on

125

building a canal? Or eight tons of insect powder? He wasn't satisfied with the generous budget of $50,000 allowed for medical supplies, and wanted nonmedical equipment that could run into hundreds of thousands. Everlastingly he was plaguing his superiors with what he labeled "paramount necessities," and when he didn't get them, begged, criticized, implored.

The demands and criticisms went directly to Shonts during the few days he was in the Zone. To the harassed Chairman it was nothing short of insubordination. Finally he blew up. He had had enough. The Doctor would have to go. Shonts knew a brilliant young osteopath who wouldn't pester people with obsessions about mosquitoes, and promptly nominated him as a replacement. And that impetuous action touched off the first of many flare-ups between the Chairman and the Chief Engineer. Although Stevens accepted the *Stegomyia* theory somewhat lightly, he was convinced that Gorgas was better qualified than any other man in the American medical profession to contend with yellow fever, and said so in a retort he described as "more forcible than elegant"— words that "perhaps would not bear repeating, and paraphrased would lose most of their picturesque punch." Governor Magoon sided with the Chief Engineer, proclaiming with spirit that "the supreme and necessitous duty of the administration was to get rid of yellow fever, whether a single spadeful of earth was dug in the canal or not." And in the background there was the warm support of the physician-president of the Republic of Panama, Dr. Amador.

On the Gorgas issue the Commission Chairman agreed to disagree and returned to Washington overruled. The biased adversary of *Stegomyia* mosquitoes remained on the job. Under the new regime, Gorgas got his copper screen, his sulphur and his insecticide—300 tons of sulphur; and instead of a meager 8 tons of insect powder, 120 tons, representing the entire output of the United States for a year. He was supplied with 50,000 gallons of kerosene a month, and Stevens saw to it that he had all the help he needed.

126

During the summer and fall of 1905, the war against mosquitoes was the major campaign fought in the Canal Zone. From house to house the battle was waged through Colón and Panama City, and then into the villages in between. Armed with paste pots and paper rolls, the squads of fighters sealed up cracks and knotholes in the loosely constructed shelters. Dutch ovens with a copious supply of sulphur fuel were carted inside and ignited; for four hours each house was guarded against intruders while the fumes did their work. In Panama City the population was 20,000, and not an inhabitant was spared the indignity of having his home fumigated—once, twice, three times. The same was done in Colón and in the villages, until the Zone reeked with the nauseous fumes.

The West Indians never could understand what all the hocuspocus was about, any more than they could comprehend some of the other mysterious doings of the Americans, but they had a respect for the stern arm of the law, were polite, acquiescent, and so good-natured in their derision of the sanitation army that the extermination experts could rarely take offense.

The family of a dozen Negroes moved out and the squad moved in—into "a windowless, six-by-eight room, always a cheap calico curtain dividing the three-foot parlor in front from the five-foot bedroom behind, the former cluttered with a van-load of useless junk, dirty blankets, decrepit furniture, glittering gewgaws . . . every inch of the walls decorated with the pages of illustrated magazines and newspapers." And as soon as the mosquito men were gone, one of their own "doctors" was called in to unbedevil the spell they had cast.

The Governor's residence, Canal headquarters, hotels, laborers' dormitories, churches all received the same treatment, without favor or deference. No edifice was exempt. And the army won its battle. Week by week the number of yellow fever cases declined. A few were reported in September and October, one in November, and that was the last. Victory was complete. After that it was just a question of "holding what had been accomplished," and the health squads could plunge into the war against malaria and *Anopheles*.

Along the entire path of the canal-to-be, brush and weeds within two hundred yards of every house were cut, cleared and burned, and the area scrupulously drained. As tap water became available, the cisterns and rain-barrels were destroyed and the sagging eaves troughs—worst of all breeding places—yanked down. Panama City and Colón both acquired street gutters. Old tin cans, bottles, broken crockery—any discarded utensils that could contain water—were smashed and buried.

To the natives, who valued a rusted tin can as a cooking pot, it was sheer vandalism. But the cry of vandalism was loudest among the nurses at Ancon Hospital. Over a period of twenty-five years nuns had devotedly placed large open pottery rings about the grounds as a protection against destructive parades of umbrella ants, which would devour the foliage of a tree overnight. Inside the rings they had set out hundreds of trees and shrubs, kept them watered, and the pottery rings filled with water—moats in miniature that no umbrella ant would cross. In those moats had bred the swarms of *Stegomyia* mosquitoes which had been largely responsible for giving Ancon its reputation among the French as a death trap. There was no reverence for the endeavor of either priest or good Samaritan if their charity was in conflict with the laws of sanitation. Inspectors sternly reprimanded the Chief Engineer for not reporting a hole in his porch screen the size of a lead pencil. Even the holy water at the Cathedral was diluted with disinfectant.

While critics were still complaining in Boston, Baton Rouge and Battle Creek about the lack of progress on the big ditch, Gorgas and his men were boldly creating a formidable network of little ditches all over the Isthmus for drainage against mosquito propagation—some two hundred miles of rock-filled trenches, another two hundred of subsoil tile, close to three hundred miles of narrow concrete sluiceways, and a thousand miles of open graded gullies. Nearly a hundred square miles of territory over which the pesky mosquito had reigned supreme in defiance of Spanish, British, and French invaders were conquered. That was the preliminary battle for the canal. When it was over, the steam-shovel war could start.

Wrote Dr. Gorgas:

From the best statistics which I could get on the Isthmus, I found that the French lost yearly from yellow fever about one-third of their white force. If we lost in the same ratio, it would give us about thirty-five hundred deaths among our Americans yearly. . . . I believe we would have found a sufficient number of men who were willing to go to the Isthmus, just as did the French. There is always a certain element which is attracted by danger and adventure, and to whom exposure to risk is a sufficient reward for their labor. . . . But if we had lost from disease thirty-five hundred of our Americans every year . . . Congress would not have made the appropriations for continuing the work.

Without a Gorgas and his paste pots, spray guns, sulphur ovens, and endless drainage ditches, there could have been no canal.

Long before the mosquito campaign was over a new spirit had come to the Isthmus. Confidence in the man at the helm brought a pride of participation, enthusiasm, and determination. The fear was gone. Men whistled on the job, sang in the work camps, laughed in the mess halls. They could now get good satisfying United States meals for thirty-five cents. Steamers were equipped with cold storage facilities; there was a cold storage plant at Colón and refrigerator cars on the Panama line. Daily deliveries of frozen meat and ice were made at all the railroad stops across the Isthmus. Where men had long balked at taking their quinine as a precaution against malaria, it now came with a jigger of rum, and there was no grumbling. Club buildings were going up at Cristobal, Gorgona, Empire, and Culebra, and there would soon be recreation rooms with billiards, bowling alleys, cards, and libraries. Baseball teams and a band were organized. And on

129

Taboga Island in the Bay of Panama was a rest camp with all the refinements of a resort hotel.

The refinements were for the men, but not for Stevens. A small palace outside Panama City was designed by the Commission as a fitting residence for the Chief Engineer. He brushed the plans aside and requested instead a cheap bungalow with a corrugated iron roof on the side of Culebra Cut, where he could be near the job. "It has no more style than the Chief's hat," sniffed a Commission spokesman. A special coach—"the brain's car"—outfitted for the Chief and important dignitaries, was ordered put into storage. In overalls and slouch hat Stevens rode the "locals" and the "freights." He talked with the men, chatted with them on the job, tramped with them into the jungles. "You can never tell when he will bob out from under some flat car," a foreman declared with respect. "He drops in for an unexpected meal at the mess where the men are grumbling, and afterward expresses his opinion of the men or the manager in language that is very forcible and not at all polite. He takes a seat incognito in a common car and permits, even encourages, the man who chances to sit by his side to explain to him how the Canal business should be managed, and how all the officials, including the Chief Engineer, are making fools of themselves."

Although Stevens despised desk work, his secretary claimed that "his day's work is so promptly dispatched that he is never a single letter in arrears." Buck passers, responsibility dodgers, and long-winded report writers were his anathema. A carpenter who had been ordered to build sheds at Gorgona found that the designated site was a parking lot filled with old French machinery. Trained under the Wallace regime not to take anything for granted or to assume any unspecified responsibility, he penned a careful letter to Stevens, explaining his predicament. Immediately the letter came back with a scrawl across the bottom: "Wait till I have a free Sunday, and I'll come down and move it for you." A long, unrequested progress report submitted by a timid engineer was immediately returned with the notation: "You are not hired to advise me how your work can be done. You are hired to do it. You may make mistakes, but there is only one mistake you can make that will be fatal with me, and that is to do nothing."

The anecdotes were passed down the tables at the mess halls, and the men were quick to catch on to the fact that the new order had little in common with the old. With his attitude of abruptness and his liberality in delegating responsibility, he had a way of bringing out the best in a man. His talent for sizing up the capabilities of applicants without regard for their previous experience was uncanny. Assigned as gang foremen were a stenographer, a tattooed lion tamer, a former hotel manager, and a dentist. Every one of them made good. A reporter took in the situation and offered the commendation: "He is the one man to grapple the task who has the broad view, the National view, who is making driving, ordered work the inspiration of the day. . . . He is capable of grasping the thing as a whole, knows by instinct what he can neglect, finds fit men to attend to details, and yet makes everyone from Colón to Panama feel that he knows all that is going on. . . . He has made his men feel that there is a great deal of lost time to be made up."

Instead of the former warnings against coming to the Isthmus, men wrote their brothers, sons, and neighbors, urging them to come down and bring two good men with them. By late fall Stevens was ready to recall the laborers dismissed in the summer. Two and a half thousand were put back to work at Culebra. The Chief Engineer had searched everywhere for a work plan of the Cut and found none. He prepared his own with broad levels, like a giant stairway along the sides; steam shovels were eating into the banks with a vengeance, and the dump cars now stayed on the tracks. As many as eighty steam shovels would soon be working there, he prophesied. He had ordered 100, and ordered at the same time 120 new locomotives and 800 flat cars with steam-powered plows for unloading.

Accompanied by an Army major named George W. Goethals, Secretary Taft made another hurried visit to the Zone in November, 1905, and this time decided to be less impressionable. It was the rainy season. Colón was awash in garbage, and the streets of Panama City were a sea of mud—in the process of being paved with bricks brought all the way from Peoria, Illinois. The whole length of the railroad was in a shambles while the line was being double-tracked, bridges strengthened, and old fifty-six-pound rails replaced with seventy-pound iron. Piers at Cristobal and La Boca were torn up and swarming with construction crews. No visiting delegation could have chosen a worse season of the year or a worse moment in construction activity. It appeared that every gang was furiously engaged in trying to destroy what someone else had built, and the rains were helping them. Even Goethals, accustomed to the turmoil of big engineering projects, shrugged this one off as chaotic and hopeless. In all the arduous toil there seemed to be no purpose nor plan.

And the observation was not entirely inappropriate. There was no real over-all plan, and couldn't be, for Stevens still didn't know what kind of canal his employers in Washington wanted him to build.

VII

"IT WAS LOVELY TO SEE
THE ORCHIDS"

To a penurious public, John Stevens' salary of $30,000, plus keep, per diem, and liberal junket allowances, was prodigal extravagance; in 1906 no civil servant could earn that much— unless he were a miracle worker, and Stevens had too much of the common man in him to be counted popularly in that category. Moreover, anyone who could command a salary of $30,000 should have the talent to bring immediate order out of the reported chaos on the Isthmus: he should come up with inspired answers that would silence the political fuming, present a canal plan that no one could criticize.

People didn't understand. The job of engineering the Panama Canal was not one that could be considered in terms of compensation. No salary was commensurate with the responsibilities. The Chief Engineer held the hottest position in the world fraternity of artificers. All eyes were upon him—European eyes, Oriental eyes, American. And they were all critical. His errors would be charged against America. His successes would not be his own; they would be American successes, covetously observed from abroad, jealously claimed at home.

Stevens went to Panama under the illusion that he was to devote his technical talents primarily to the construction of a canal. Problems of health and organization had to be surmounted first.

But as soon as they were mastered, he could turn his full attention to his profession and the creation of the great traffic artery. It took him only a few weeks to learn how wrong he was, to realize that the extraneous duties would go on and on, with ever increasing demands. So relentless were those demands that solution of technical engineering problems was a spare-time operation. For the $30,000 investment the public wanted a superman who didn't exist and couldn't be made to order.

While the business of engineering took a secondary place, Stevens had to serve as lobbyist and social arbiter, magistrate and father confessor, judge and jury in one, propagandist and public relations agent, economist and bookkeeper, author, defendant, and good fellow to boot. But the biggest job of all, and the most trying, was keeping peace with the public back home. Panama had been batted around for so long and with so much fumbling that all the sidewalk superintendents had decided they were as competent authorities on canals as the experts. Any man who had ever sat at a drafting board knew how the Canal should be built, and those who hadn't, possessed an even clearer conception of what was wrong on the Isthmus. Their inspirations flowed into Stevens' headquarters in a daily tidal wave, and he had to answer them all, or run the risk of losing a supporter back home. His workday was fourteen, fifteen, eighteen hours.

"Have you any ideas differing from projects which have been laid before you which you desire to suggest for incorporation in the final project for this canal?" formally queried a member of Roosevelt's Board of Consulting Engineers on a visit to Panama in the fall of 1905.

"I have not," sighed the fatigued Stevens. "I guess I am the only man in the United States who has not."

Particularly he was showered with blueprints for cutting Culebra, the job that had made the deepest impression on public imaginations—"a deluge of plans complete in every way, excepting the quite important one of practical common sense," he quipped. "One genius proposed to wash the entire cut into the oceans by forcing water from a plant in Panama Bay; another, to erect a big compressed air plant at Culebra and blow all the material through pipes into the sea. Still another, equally brilliant, wanted to drive a double-track railway tunnel, at grade, clear through the entire length—nine miles—and haul all the material above out in cars."

Under the Chief Engineer was an army of competent experts —four departments and a great many divisions—but for ultimate decisions of policy they came to him, and usually they brought the details too. He had to stand as authority on tropical housing and sanitation; he was concerned with laundries, bakeries, and bathrooms, with the price of wholesale beef, with refrigerators, recreation, and pay scales for a dozen categories of labor.

From the start he made it clear that he was accessible to all. Any man or his housewife could bring a complaint directly to him. At all costs, he intended to maintain the common touch as his contribution toward building community morale. Weekly he had important meetings of the heads of departments and divisions, but no less important were the sessions with a committee that wanted to start a Sunday school, with the insomniac who couldn't tolerate a snoring roommate, with the steam shovel operator's wife who wanted to know why she wasn't entitled to an extra rocking chair like her neighbor's.

Late at night, when the personal problems slacked off, Stevens found time to place orders for incidentals like eighty-five million board feet of lumber or three million dollars' worth of rolling stock; to make arrangements for the importation of eight thousand West Indian Negroes or seven thousand Spaniards; to give thought to the congestion in the warehouses of the "phantom" Panama Railroad, where freight consigned to places like San Diego, California, and Antofagasta, Chile, had been accumulating for eighteen months; to draw up plans for a rock crushing plant— "probably the largest single one ever erected"; to locate a suitable quarry for the plant twenty miles down the coast and arrange for barge transportation of the stone on the old French canal.

"I know that it is a very weak thing to say that a man is overworked, but I have had five hours' sleep in the last sixty," Stevens confided to the Board of Consulting Engineers. They were the group which was to help decide what kind of canal was to be built—high-level or sea-level. They were eminent engineers assembled from Germany, France, and the Netherlands as well as from the United States, and they had come to Panama to make another interruption in Stevens' overloaded schedule, to tease him with all manner of questions about excavating machinery, labor problems, landslides, and finances.

"I came here practically on thirty-six hours' notice," he replied sharply to the bigwigs, "and on my arrival I found a state of chaos. I have been trying to get an organization that was sufficient to tide over until the type of canal was decided upon. It required a vast amount of work to get the men quartered. I have taken very little time, practically none, for studying the type of canal or the problems involved, first because I have not had time—it was beyond human power to do it—and second, because I considered that the type would be settled for me. . . . I can fix my quarters, and as far as my limited intelligence permits me, I can contract for rolling stock . . . but beyond that I cannot go. . . . You may select an alignment which will interfere with any improvement I might make now. . . . Give us the type of canal just as soon as you can. You must understand that I cannot, and I do not believe that any human being can do much more than mark time until that is done."

The all-out battle of the levels was at last under way. The President had appointed the Board of Consulting Engineers to "serve as advisers in planning the greatest engineering work that the world has ever seen," with the instructions: "I expect you to advise me, not what you think I want to hear, but what you think I ought to hear."

But John Stevens was not going to get the imperative answer to his question for a long time. While the Board meetings dragged on in Panama, Washington, and New York, through October,

November, and December of 1905, through interminable hearings and thirty formal meetings, the Chief Engineer in Panama marked time by keeping his men busy on what would have to be done regardless of the type of canal chosen, and his engineers occupied on an assortment of alternative plans, so that he would be prepared to start more productive endeavors as soon as the great decision was made. He was hampered at every turn. If it were to be a high-level canal, the railroad he was completing would be submerged under Gatun Lake; if it were low-level, the preliminary work for locks would be wasted. To Stevens, the arguing was as futile as it was frustrating. The cut through the high points of the Divide was down only about 140 feet and already "great cracks like those made by an earthquake" had appeared on the steep banks—ominous warnings of the slides that were to come; surveyors who drove a straight line of stakes at night found it curved in the morning. Even for a lock canal, that cut had to be lowered 105 feet more; and a sea-level canal would call for nearly another 100. At that depth the slides would rumble down faster than the bottom could be cleared.

Like most engineers, he had at first felt that a channel without locks was the ideal solution, but his convictions changed as soon as he surveyed the scene. A sea-level ditch would cost millions more and take years longer to construct; he strongly doubted that Congressmen would ever foot the bill and now unhesitatingly said so to anyone who would listen. In fact, he had been so outspoken that rumors were rife about his intention of quitting if Congress did not vote for locks. Reporters kept pestering him with queries on his future plans until he cracked, half in anger: "Now that I have put my hand to the plow, it is not going to be taken off unless somebody pulls it off." Regardless of the type of canal, he intended to stick with the job, as he had promised the President, until success or failure was evident.

But the hand firmly gripping the plow was given a severe wrench on January 4, 1906. It was on that memorable day that the *Independent* came from the presses in New York with a scathing review of affairs in the Canal Zone. "Our Mismanagement in Panama" was the title, and if the account was to be accepted at its face value, John Stevens was indulging in an orgy of bungling that made Wallace's failure and the French scandal look trivial. Nothing was right. Sanitation and housing were abominable, administration was inept, labor relations deplorable. "If Colón were in the Berkshire Hills instead of near the equator, it would still be unhealthy," wrote Poultney Bigelow, distinguished writer, sociologist, and world traveler. "Here, however, I noted such criminal neglect as could not be matched today in any city of Italy or Spain—nor even Turkey. . . . A hundred or more huts did I enter, a hundred or more back-yards and latrines did I inspect, but throughout my pestiferous excursion up and down this filthy city I could find not a single man or woman who had not suffered or was not suffering from fever of some kind, not a single one who did not want to go home."

The article was lethal in its effect, for Bigelow was a foremost authority on tropical colonization and inter-race labor problems. He was angered by what he saw in Colón, for he felt that the United States should be setting an example rather than taking economic advantage of the colored race. Most of his observations were true in part or true as of June, 1905, but grossly exaggerated for January, 1906. He had been piloted around Colón and across the Zone by Tracy Robinson, who had been welcoming engineers to the Isthmus since the days of de Lesseps, but Tracy had a chip on his shoulder now, and Bigelow had been taken in.

The sociologist knew very well that common marriage was the rule among the Caribbean Negroes; there was no excuse for his stretching a point and claiming that the United States Government was importing colored prostitutes. His cynical commentary on graft, jobbery, and inefficient management was based on the past record. "At present," he asserted, "the work at Panama resembles an army of recruits without any commander, or rather with a dozen commanders who spend their time commanding and countermanding. Our Panama patriots are kept busy in find-

ing occupation for young men with political affiliation, who amuse
themselves by playing the doctor, and the engineer, the foreman,
the inspector, the general boss."

That was the one-sided impression the author got from talking
with disgruntled inhabitants of Colón and with displaced officials.
His probing was from behind scenes, and he was so suspicious of
men who might be seeing things through "official glasses" that he
dismissed their testimony altogether.

His most arrogant scorn was reserved for Taft and the Canal
Commission—"those who treat our serious interests in a pleasant,
airy manner, assuring us that nothing can surpass the splendid
work done on the Isthmus of Panama by self-sacrificing politicians—and other engineers"—men who had "generated an atmosphere in which the Ten Commandments walk zigzag."

The revelations were a sellout for the *Independent*. In less than
a week Taft was on the carpet before the Senate Committee on
Interoceanic Canals and Stevens was on his way to Washington
to lend him support.

Poultney Bigelow took a back seat in Canal history, but the
truth he did reveal stung very deeply. Sanitation engineers speeded
up the rehabilitation of Colón; quarters under construction adjacent to an unhealthy swamp were abandoned; and foreign labor
thereafter got something more nearly like the Roosevelt square
deal. Moreover, the Senate Committee hearings were not restricted to the fuss Bigelow had stirred; they gave Stevens a superb opportunity to speak his piece on a lock canal, and he made
the most of it. Before he left Washington he was warmly com-
mended by influential Senators, and he returned to Panama
confident that he had their understanding and backing.

Meantime the International Board of Consulting Engineers
labored and brought forth late in January, 1906, its mountainous
document, a magnum opus calculated to silence forever men like
John Stevens and his advocates of a lock canal. "Resolved," read
the conclusion to hundreds of pages of testimony, "that the Board

adopt and recommend to the President of the United States the plan of a sea level canal."

Stevens was shocked, but he still saw a glimmer of hope. Eight members had signed the report. Attached to it was a minority recommendation, endorsed by five dissenters, contradicting the whole script and calling for a high-level route. It was an ironic stalemate, but it brought Stevens no amusement. He was politely invited to add his comment to the report before it was officially turned in.

Conjecturing that the invitation was little more than a sardonic way of getting him to sound off, he drafted a brief, subdued letter, summarizing his case for a lock canal: "It will provide as safe and a quicker passage for ships, and therefore be of greater capacity. It will provide, beyond question, the best solution of the vital problem of how safely to care for the flood waters of the Chagres and other streams. . . . Its cost of operation, maintenance, and fixed charges will be very much less than any sea-level canal. The time and cost of its construction will be not more than one-half that of a canal of the sea-level type. The element of time might become, in case of war, actual or threatened, one of such importance that measured, not by years but by months, or even days, the entire cost of the canal would seem trivial in comparison. Finally, even at the same cost in time and money for each type, I would favor the adoption of the high-level lock canal plan in preference to that of the proposed sea-level canal. I therefore recommend the adoption of the plan for an 85-foot summit-level lock canal, as set forth in the minority report of the Consulting Board of Engineers."

Stevens wanted to avoid getting caught up in this time-consuming conflict, but there was no way out now. His brusque veto of the Board's majority recommendation gave heart to the Isthmian Canal Commission to disapprove it too, by a vote of five to one. From the Commission the file of documents started on its long bureaucratic journey. Secretary of War Taft sided with Stevens and passed it on to Roosevelt. The President expressed agreement

140

with Taft and forwarded the hot potato to Congress with the notation, "In my opinion, the disadvantages are fewer and the advantages very much greater in the case of a lock canal." That was on February 19. The House dropped the report into the lap of the Committee on Interstate and Foreign Commerce; the Senate, into the lap of the Committee on Interoceanic Canals. Promptly the Canal became a game of political badminton, offering a chance for rooters of transcontinental railroads to lobby against any kind of canal at all, and for Nicaraguan enthusiasts to revive the old idea of locating the cut in the San Juan valley.

The Secretary of War had a bigger campaign on his hands than he had bargained for. John Wallace was back in the limelight cheering for a sea-level canal, and William Barclay Parsons, the engineering hero of the New York subway system, was arguing as loudly for the same, opposing on general principles every suggestion that his long-time competitor John Stevens advanced. In Panama the Chief Engineer followed the debate, still confident that he had the support of the Senate Committee—so confident that he was spending every spare hour he had on plans for getting the construction at Gatun under way. The single phase of the canal structure that would dictate a completion date, he maintained, was the complicated locks at Gatun. In a relatively small area there, it would be necessary to concentrate an enormous amount of activity, and preparations for it were of primary importance.

Days and weeks went by without a decision from Washington. As the work force built up, he was gradually running out of projects that would have to be completed regardless of the kind of canal. Repeatedly he cabled Taft begging for the verdict.

Not until May 17, 1906, did the Committee on Interoceanic Canals report to the Senate. In a vote of six to five they recommended a sea-level canal. To Stevens it was incredible. But before he had time to recover from his distress, he was again summoned to Washington. The last stand would be fought on the Congressional floors, and he was needed.

141

Day and night during the rest of May and into June he argued
with Senators, lobbied openly for the only kind of canal that had
a chance of success, argued with Taft, who was getting cold feet,
swung Roosevelt back into line when he wavered in favor of sea-
level construction, helped Senators draft speeches, prepared maps,
produced statistics, talked back to Congressmen as though he were
a veteran politician himself. As soon as he appeared to be winning an argument, he was rebuked by his enemies for not being
back on his job at the Isthmus. He was branded a glory seeker,
intent on building the kind of canal that would yield him the
quickest credit.

Disregarding the jibes, he calmly pointed out that the sea-level
canal, as planned, would have a width of only 150 feet for nearly
half its length—a narrow, tortuous channel exposed to vicious
crosscurrents from the flood waters of many streams and lined
with jagged rocks; it could be blocked for months by a single
mishap; when two ships were passing it would be necessary for
one to stop and make fast to mooring posts as in the Suez—an
awkward, slow, dangerous procedure.

He told of his conversations with experienced captains and
pilots, who maintained that it would be "extremely hazardous, if
not impracticable" to drive a ship through such a channel; to
provide for steerage, a reasonable speed had to be maintained
and if limited to less than five miles an hour, bank collisions
would be inevitable. The momentum of even a twenty-thousand-
ton ship striking the submerged rocks, he explained, would tear
out every plate in contact. "The consequences of disabling and
possibly sinking a ship in a narrow channel" would be "serious
enough in time of peace; in time of war it might decide the whole
issue at stake for a nation." Certainly the channel could not be
navigated at night, he argued; ships arriving at terminals late in
the day would have to lay up until morning. "The cost of such
delays . . . in a year's aggregate would be capitalized in many
millions of dollars."

Thirty-six to thirty-one was the score when the Senate finally put the question to a vote on June 21. Stevens' arguments had won. By that slim majority they favored a high-level lock canal. A week later the House followed suit, and on June 29 the President's signature put into law the bill calling for a summit level of 85 feet, an enormous lake on the Atlantic side to be created by damming the Chagres River at Gatun, a cut of two hundred feet through the Divide, an intermediate-level lake on the Pacific side, locks at Gatun, Pedro Miguel, and Sosa Hill. It was the momentous decision of the whole Panama saga—a decision that finally came two years, seven months, three weeks, and five days after the coup of 1903.

Stevens took back to Panama a loathing for the ways of politicians from which he would never recover. He wanted to be an engineer, to get a stupendous job rolling. The anxieties of construction were enough to strain a man's endurance, without the frustrations brought on by shortsighted politicians, a nagging press, and an ungrateful public. In Washington he had taken more punishment than he cared to subject himself to again.

But things had not been standing still at the Isthmus during the Chief Engineer's absences. He arrived back there on July 4 to find that equipment he had ordered was now pouring into Colón and Panama—steam shovels, locomotives, cars, unloaders, power drills, stone crushers, quantities of heavy rail, ties, lumber, and hardware of every description. The requisitions had been submitted long before it was known that the equipment was to be used on a lock canal, but so shrewd had Stevens been in his calculations that he could boast with considerable satisfaction: "There was not a single item of the millions of dollars' worth of this plant but what was perfectly adapted to the purposes of its construction."

Within a few days after his return an army of laborers opened attack on the historic little village of Gatun. By vote of the United States Congress for a lock canal, that village and a dozen like it were doomed. They were to be swallowed up in a gigantic dam project. At Gatun, where the coastal swamp met the uplands, the

Chagres was to be tamed with a mountainous earthen barrier. Here were to be built the great locks that would raise ships in three steps eighty-five feet from ocean level into the waters of the biggest artificial lake man had ever created. Natives watched in dismay as hundreds of machete men turned their green jungle hillsides into an ugly waste. The thunder of dynamite echoed across the valley. By water and rail came big machinery to support the assault—towering drills, dredges, steam shovels. To Stevens, Gatun Dam was the "keynote" of the Canal, the one feature on which everything else depended. He surveyed the confused scene with satisfaction late in the summer of 1906 and remarked incongruously, "The Canal will be open for traffic on January 1, 1915."

On the hill east of the dam site a raw construction village slowly took shape, and new towns similar to Gatun sprang up at Pedro Miguel and at La Boca, where the other locks were to be located. From the double-tracked Panama Railroad, spur lines were run to every junction of activity, and surveyors were set to work plotting an entirely new rail line between Colón and Panama City to replace the old one when Gatun Lake flooded it out of existence. The Engineering Department moved to the heart of operations at Culebra, and the rapidly expanding center was dubbed "Brains Hill," Culebra itself "Stevens City." There specifications for locks and dams were being drawn up. At Cristobal, Matachín, Empire, and Paraiso, enormous supply depots and repair shops were functioning efficiently. Almost daily, shipments of heavy equipment arrived at Colón—flat cars by the score, more locomotives, unloaders, spreaders, dipper dredges. Everything came knocked down, and had to be assembled in the shops.

Some fifteen thousand men were on the job and more were needed quickly. Employment agencies in major cities of the United States were doing an adequate service in supplying foremen and skilled labor, but unskilled laborers were not arriving fast enough. Immigrants from the Caribbean islands were getting the idea that they had a monopoly on pick and shovel work, and were setting their own pace. It wasn't the pace that Stevens required. "If there is a cloud across the sky," he complained, "they start out with an umbrella as well as a cigarette, and if that cloud gets pretty large they skud for safety. I should say that if we get thirty-six hours of work per week from them we are doing pretty well."

He talked of importing Cantonese, but the Chinese Government, recalling the fatality rate under de Lesseps, wanted nothing more to do with Panama. Sugar planters of Cuba balked at having their fields raided. An agent sent to Spain was gently conducted to the border. Those tough, hardy Spaniards were the kind of men Big Smoke wanted, so the agent set up an office in Paris, and from there, as Stevens later confessed, "he was able, by some sub rosa negotiations with the steamship lines, to send over about 7,000 peasants from the Biscayan Provinces of Spain." They were put to work in Culebra Cut and soon set an example for industry that the West Indies could emulate.

Moving the soggy spoil of Culebra had been a major problem since the early days of the French. They had shoveled it into cars and shoveled it out by hand. They had tried dump cars and flat cars, but still much of the dirt stuck so fast to the carriers that it had to be shoveled out by hand—a long, tedious, expensive process. The Americans preferred flat cars, and perfected a powerful plow unloader, controlled from one end of a train, that flung rocks and dirt off one side of twenty cars in minutes rather than hours. Mechanical spreaders attached to the sides of locomotives evened the surface. The General Manager of the Panama Railroad devised an ingenious crane for lifting sections of track and ties from one temporary roadbed on the spoil dumps to an adjacent bed. The handling of spoil was completely mechanized. During the months when Washington was arguing over the type of canal, Stevens had given priority to such preparations, and excavation could now be measured in hundreds of thousands of cubic yards a month instead of a few thousand.

In July the Chief Engineer had returned from Washington

as a full-fledged member of the Canal Commission. Automatically this gave him a place on the Executive Committee, and except when Chairman Shonts was in the Zone he was in effect *the* Commission. In September Governor Magoon was transferred from Panama to Havana as Provisional Governor of Cuba—without relief. That left Big Smoke as dictator supreme on the Isthmus. He had tried to convince Roosevelt that Panama had to be a one-man proposition. At last he had his hand on all the controls, and he reveled in it.

Stevens returned from Washington also with the knowledge that Theodore Roosevelt intended to make a visit to the Canal site. It was to be a precedent-shattering trip—the first time that a President of the United States had ever stepped onto foreign shores during his term of office. Glamour and world-wide publicity would travel with him. As host, the Chief Engineer would share the spotlight with the United States Chief Executive. It was the kind of show from which Stevens shrank instinctively. Yet while a thousand engineering and administrative details were vying for his attention, he had to subordinate them all and give first place to preparations for the big history-making splurge.

In all the Zone there was not a hotel or private residence suitable for the entertainment of the President and his party. Tactfully it was proposed that he plan to make the ship his Isthmian headquarters, but Roosevelt would put up with no such compromise. He wanted to stay ashore. To Stevens, that meant building a hotel for him. For almost a year carpenters had been hammering away at the Tivoli, on Ancon Hill overlooking Panama Bay. It was a huge ark of a building, started in September, 1905, as an emergency measure to take care of the visiting celebrities, Congressional committees, and tourists who were everlastingly complaining about the overcrowded Hotel Central in Panama City, its lack of plumbing, its poor service, and its deplorable cuisine. But the emergency project had turned into a nuisance that didn't seem to get built despite the proddings of Stevens and the architects assigned to it. Refinements like plaster, porcelain tubs, and fancy fixtures were hard to come by on the Isthmus, and after months of puttering, the structure was still little more than a skeleton, with the kitchen scarcely started.

The Tivoli was the only logical place for Presidential headquarters, and by late summer its construction became the priority effort in the Zone. Stevens postponed making critical decisions about canal locks and breakwaters to check personally on lighting fixtures and furniture, on lavatories, culinary equipment, and kitchen ranges. He wanted to have the hotel completed by the end of October, against the possibility of the President's arriving early in November. No one in Washington seemed to know exactly when he would be making the trip, who would be in the party, how many rooms would be needed. And the Chief Engineer could get no satisfactory answers to his frantic cables for information. He outlined a proposed three-day schedule, and the approval of that was slow in coming.

Not until the end of October did Stevens begin to get the essential answers. The President would sail on the battleship *Louisiana* about November 8, and would arrive on the fifteenth. The last-minute rush was on. A special landing had to be erected at Cristobal, so that the President could be put ashore in Zone territory rather than in Panamanian Colón. Fixtures for the Presidential bathroom and chairs for the Presidential suite arrived belatedly and had to be given the personal attention of Stevens. Someone remembered that there were no President's flags on the Isthmus. A special cable and a special shipment brought them. The marines had no saluting battery and had to borrow one, along with ammunition, from the Republic of Panama. Matters of street decorations, parades, fire department displays, social protocol, formal invitations occupied all the time of the man who thought he had come to Panama to build a canal.

To cap the climax, on the morning of November 14, a full day before the visitors were expected, the bow of the *Louisiana* broke through a Caribbean rain squall off Colón. While the twenty-one-gun salute was pounding out its welcome, Stevens spent some uncomfortable moments contemplating an entire rescheduling of events. But from the battleship came reassurance that the President would cooperate and remain on board overnight in order not to upset the plans.

For three days the Chief Engineer was exposed to the most grueling routine of his life. It began at 7:30 A.M. the next day. With a reception committee consisting of President Amador, Chairman Shonts, and the manager of the Panama Railroad, he took formal position at the outer end of Dock 11 at Cristobal, ready to greet the President of the United States as he stepped from his launch. The craft was nowhere in sight—an extraordinary circumstance for an executive known for prompt keeping of appointments. But the suspense was brief; behind them, from the opposite end of the pier came a hearty hail, and as Roosevelt advanced toward them he explained that he had been rowed ashore at five-thirty and had been strolling on the waterfront for two hours. No time was wasted on formalities. The President had his eye on some saddle horses at the foot of the pier. He appropriated one of them and in a moment was mounted, leading an impromptu procession in a drenching rain down a muddy street, waving to the crowds, exchanging greetings, en route to the Colón railroad depot.

The three-day program that Stevens had prepared was all but discarded. A grand luncheon befitting the most distinguished guest ever to visit the Zone was readying at the Tivoli, but when the train arrived at Ancon, he decided to visit the hospital instead of going to his quarters; then he insisted on boarding a tug for an excursion around the harbor. It was raining again. The Tivoli luncheon was spurned altogether in favor of dining in one of the employees' mess halls at La Boca. He talked with the laborers, egged them on to voice any complaints they had, embarrassed the cooking staff by striding into the kitchen to ask more questions and collect more complaints. Not until the middle of the afternoon did he see the luxurious Tivoli quarters that had caused Stevens so many weeks of anxiety.

148

Ceremonies in Cathedral Plaza were scheduled to start at three o'clock. Waiting in the Plaza and along Central Avenue were thousands of dripping canal workers and Panamanians. It was still raining, and the soaked crowds looked as wilted as the flags, the bunting, the arches of greenery, and the Chinese lanterns under which they stood. Roosevelt arrived an hour late, escorted by President Amador and a detachment of a hundred police dressed as Rough Riders. He was given a frenzied acclamation, and his brief speech from the Cathedral steps was cheered with the same kind of enthusiasm.

Roosevelt deliberately chose rain-drenched November for his visit, so that he could see the Panama operations under the worst possible conditions. The tropics cooperated. He saw scarcely a sample of sunshine. In lashing torrents he moved from one event to another, sloshing through mucky clay and puddles of sludge wherever he went. Dressed in a white hiking outfit with khaki leggings and a Panama hat, he broke away from the Stevens' entourage to climb aboard a steam shovel at Pedro Miguel and talk with the engineer; at a spoil dump where the ingenious Lidgerwood unloaders were in operation, he became so absorbed in the process that he was all but buried in the mud. He dashed up the steps of the Administration building two at a time to shake hands with every employee in the drafting room. Time and again he strolled behind buildings to inspect water closets—dozens of them, the outhouses Poultney Bigelow had censured Taft for not visiting.

His approval of Stevens and of what he was accomplishing was evident. In a farewell address at Cristobal he went so far as to express regrets that his own boys weren't old enough to work on the Canal. He meant it, for en route back to the States he wrote enthusiastically to his son Kermit, extolling in particular the work at Culebra: "There the huge shovels are hard at it; scooping huge masses of rock and gravel. . . . They are eating steadily into the mountain, cutting it down and down. . . . With intense energy men and machines do their task, the white men supervising matters and handling the machines, while the tens of thousands of black men do the rough manual labor where it is not worthwhile to have machines do it. It is an epic feat."

To Theodore Jr., the boy naturalist, papa Roosevelt, the veteran naturalist, penned: "Panama was a great sight. . . . It is strange and beautiful with its mass of luxuriant tropic jungle, with the treacherous tropic rivers trailing here and there through it; and it was lovely to see the orchids and brilliant butterflies and the strange birds and snakes and lizards. . . . and it is a tremendous sight to see the work on the canal going on. From the chief engineer and the chief sanitary officer to the last arrived—an exceptionally able, energetic lot, some of them grumbling, of course, but on the whole a mighty good lot of men. . . . I was astonished at the progress made."

But Roosevelt was due to receive a surprise more astonishing than the progress he had witnessed. Less than three months after his return to Washington he received an amazing letter from Panama. It was the Chief Engineer's resignation.

Stevens was not a quitter. His original agreement was to stick to the job until he could predict success or failure according to his own judgment. Success was assured. "I fulfilled my promise . . . to the very letter," he maintained. "The hardest problems were solved, the Rubicon was crossed, the Canal was being built, and everything was set for its completion in the time predicted."

Unquestionably he was fed up with serving as political nursemaid, as chaperon to big-shot sightseers, and as mediator for squabbles among his superiors. And at the time of his resignation a monumental squabble loomed. The French company had parceled out the Canal work among some seventeen contractors and forty subcontractors, and Stevens had once advocated following the same system, then changed his mind when he realized that every contract could become an attractive political plum. Enthusiasts in Washington were eager to revive the French plan. "If Congress makes the letting of the work obligatory, the door will be open to the biggest scandal of our day," the Chief Engineer warned. He didn't want to get involved in that racket or any of the other political artifices that appeared in the offing. Big Smoke wanted to be an engineer.

The contract scheme was shortly abandoned, but not the speculation over the Chief's sudden withdrawal. While the press contrived to fabricate a scurrilous hodgepodge of causes for the resignation, the actual reason remained a secret with John Stevens. Twenty years after the event, the man who laid the groundwork for the Panama Canal, the real conqueror of the Isthmus, still kept the public guessing. "The reasons for the resignation were purely personal," he reiterated. "I have never declared these reasons, and probably never will."

He never did.

VIII

"YOU RECEIVED MY ORDERS"

AFTER all the glory Theodore Roosevelt had spread abroad on behalf of John F. Stevens, it was an extreme embarrassment to have the Chief Engineer bolt in the midst of a campaign to persuade the public and political oppressors that things were beginning to take shape on the Isthmus. But Roosevelt held a trump, and he played it at once. "I propose now," he announced "to put the Canal in charge of men who will stay on the job till I get tired of having them there, or till I say they may abandon it. I shall turn it over to the Army."

He had bitterly and publicly denounced Wallace for his ill-timed resignation, but, in view of the tributes he had so recently paid Stevens, the President could not afford to overdramatize another tantrum. In a genial letter he acknowledged the resignation, promised to send a successor shortly, and begged Stevens to continue as head of the work until his relief was broken in. Then anticipating that the transition to military regimentation would come off more smoothly if full authority rested with a civilian for a brief interim, he invited the Chief Engineer to serve also as Commission chairman during his final weeks of tenure.

On the night of February 18, 1907, six days after receiving Stevens' letter, the Canal job was assigned to the United States Army—in the person of Major George Washington Goethals.

The Major was entertaining a Colonel at his home on 1903 S

Street that evening. They had been talking over old times at West Point and reviewing some of Goethals' engineering assignments in the Northwest, his construction projects on the Ohio and Tennessee Rivers, his service in the Spanish-American War, and his present work on the Fortification Board and at the War College. The conversation was suddenly interrupted by a messenger with a note from White House Secretary William Loeb: "The President would like to have you come in and see him tomorrow (Tuesday) morning at half past nine," read the communiqué, "Will you please let me know if you will be able to come?"

The Major had never met the President—had never distinguished himself in any achievement that would call for his being presented to the Chief Executive. He was virtually an unknown. On his record was nothing that had ever merited his being singled out for any particularly newsworthy citation. In line of duty he had visited the Canal, but so had many other Army engineers. Goethals' lack of experience in the limelight left him ill at ease. Hurriedly he excused himself to call Loeb and confirm the appointment.

There was a brief exchange over the phone, and then Goethals returned to his guest. "The President wants me to come straight over," he reported excitedly. "This evening . . . at twenty minutes past ten."

Within an hour Goethals' weight of suspense was exchanged for an enormous burden of responsibility. Characteristically brushing aside introductory formalities, Roosevelt plunged into the subject that was forever foremost in his mind. He revealed the closely-guarded secret of Stevens' resignation and announced who his successor was to be. "It is impossible to think of a successful prosecution of the work at Panama with frequent changes of leadership. An efficient and permanent force can not be maintained under such conditions. I have decided to place the Canal in charge of men who will not resign unless I desire them to do so —to place the task in the hands of Army engineers, thereby securing continuity of service."

The Chief Executive expressed frank regret that the law required him to organize the work under an executive body which had proved to be a constant source of trouble and friction. He dolefully admitted his failure to get the law changed, so he was going to evade it by making the Chief Engineer Chairman of the Commission as well. "Since efforts to work under the law have proved unsuccessful," he concluded, "I am resolved to assume powers which the law does not give, but which it does not forbid me to exercise."

As an Army officer, Major Goethals had no choice of accepting or rejecting his assignment. He was receiving orders from the Army's highest authority. "It is a case of just plain straight duty," he wrote a friend in reply to a congratulatory letter. "I am ordered down—there is no alternative."

Until February 26 the public was kept in the dark about the turn in Isthmian affairs. The news broke with a thud. Wrapped in one package were announcements of the resignations of Stevens and of Shonts as Chairman of the Commission, the rejection of all bids from private contractors, the appointment of new Army engineers to direct different phases of construction, and Goethals' appointment. Not since the end of the war with Spain had the press been given such a field day. In bold headlines even conservative newspapers sprawled the news across their front pages. The Army was taking over. "The next thing we know the railroads will be hiring the entire United States Army," cautioned the Minneapolis *Journal.* Cartoons pictured the infantry leaving their rifles behind and marching on the Isthmus with picks and shovels over their shoulders; mobilized units heading to the front in dump carts instead of caissons; generals commanding a charge on the heights of Culebra.

"Today the whispers, winks and chuckles were much in evidence," editorialized the New York *Times* on February 27. "It was definitely established that the anti-Roosevelt Senate crowd had planned a big probe of tangled Canal affairs for next winter. They will probe for mud with which to plaster the President and

155

Taft. And the President, by turning handsprings in Panama affairs, by permitting confusion to be daily more confounded, is playing into the wily hands."

One editor, puzzling out the reasons for Stevens' withdrawal, claimed to have found the answer in the Holy Scriptures: "Woe unto you when all men shall speak well of you." "Surely if that verse ever fitted any man," he commented, "it was Mr. Stevens. High and low, Panama and Washington, silver men and gold men, all joined in a chorus of praise. . . . He was foreordained to bring order out of chaos; he was the right man in the right place; he was Johnny-on-the-spot, the spot being wherever he was most needed at the moment; he was no quitter."

Instead of making his own prognosis, the editor combed the pages of newspapers and came up with a "tolerably complete summary":

Mr. Stevens resigned because he discovered that the foundations of the Gatun dam were unsafe; because he found that the construction of the canal would injure the transcontinental railroads; because Mrs. Stevens wanted him to come home; because Chinese were or were not going to be employed; because his books became covered with thick green mold; because the Senators found fault with him; because he was not getting enough glory; . . . because the Panama Canal is not a big enough job to occupy his talents; because the President dictated to him; because he dictated to the President; because he did not approve the form of contract which he drew up himself; because he wouldn't work with army officers; because other people got more money; because his health was poor; because he could not play golf on the Isthmus, where fairways are so narrow that a slicing shot is apt to lose a ball in the Atlantic or Pacific hazard; because he was offered another job; because he was crazy. . . . Now we have a regime of army engineers, men who have to go where they are ordered and who cannot resign. . . . We have made a good deal of fun of the Frenchmen. Perhaps we will wish we had not when we observe that we have done less work and spent more money that the de Lesseps Company did in their first three years, notwithstanding that we have ninety-five-ton steam shovels where they had pickaxes and spades.

Senators were angry over the "hocus-pocus"; private contractors who had spent large sums preparing estimates in response to bona fide public advertisements were irate; editors who had recently been brought around to a more conciliatory attitude did an about-face, though the hostility was directed at a vacillating Administration more than at the Army; and Goethals, "breathing the sewer gas of public life for the first time," was utterly confounded by the unexpected malevolence. To make matters worse for him, three days after release of the startling news, he was promoted to a lieutenant colonelcy. Actually it was a coincidence; it happened to be the date when he was due for an increase in rank according to regular seniority routine of the Corps of Engineers, but to everyone else it looked like a spot promotion granted to the President's favorite of the moment.

In Panama the change to the new order was accepted as the worst scourge since the yellow fever epidemic. The Panama *Star and Herald,* with tactful understatement, referred to the imminent military regime as a "disappointment" and hesitated to make any "unpleasant predictions," but the editors did suggest:

> It will be as well to prepare ourselves for certain changes in method which will no doubt follow the proposed departure. It is unlikely that the rank and file of the canal workers will be made to go about in uniform and other military accouterments. But we mustn't be surprised if the men are enlisted instead of employed hereafter; if they are required to answer roll-call every morning before turning out to work (or drill); if they will be obliged to salute their superior officers while in the Cut (or at the front).

The men on the job at Panama looked upon the coming of a colonel and the new order he would bring with grim apprehension. Big Smoke Stevens was a humanitarian. Give every man as much responsibility and as much leeway as he could take, was his idea. He didn't care how a job was done so long as it was done efficiently and in good spirit. His blunt talk often had a sporting challenge in it. There was room for byplay, give-and-take, an in-

157

formal relationship. He liked his men and they loved him. They would do anything for him. Over and over again he had gone to bat for them, and they had repaid him collectively in the steadily increasing excavation reports, and now the boss was leaving them to the mercies of an Army colonel. There would be no more banter, no more fun.

As the word of Stevens' resignation spread through Culebra Cut, one by one the steam shovels stopped and the trains came to a halt. Men stood about in knots mournfully rehearsing the scant facts as if they were talking of death. "Culebra's Cut to the Heart," sadly punned an old-timer; "we are cut through and through." Delegations were sent to the Chief Engineer's office to find out if there weren't some mistake. There was none. They pleaded with him, tried to reason with him. "Don't talk, dig," he threw back at them.

Before nightfall four thousand men had fixed their names to a pathetic petition: "Please withdraw your resignation and remain in charge of our work. We will show our appreciation and loyalty by working for you even harder than we have up to this time." Within a few days there were ten thousand signatures on similar appeals—representing practically all of the American employees. And when it was apparent that the petitions were of no avail, committees started taking up a collection for farewell gifts. Everyone wanted to contribute. The hundreds of dollars went into a gold watch, a diamond ring, and a silver table set, on the tray for which was symbolically engraved a design of the completed canal.

The Chief Engineer who arrived at Cristobal on March 12, 1907, was a fine officer, straight from the Army mold—literal, unbending, devoted to the rule of command. He took orders and gave orders with equal facility. Compared to Stevens, he was colorless, uncomfortably serene, slow to anger, stuffy, and patient enough to contend with any quantity of red tape. He wasn't hampered by a sense of humor or by any sense of shading in his interpretation of duty. There was only one way for a thing to be

158

done—according to orders. Orders were everything. Within that ideology, he was fair, just, and reasonable, and he never set forth any kind of limitation that he wasn't ready to follow himself assiduously. He was a model West Pointer.

For important personages arriving in the Zone, banquets and palm-decorated receptions had been established as the traditional welcome, but for Colonel Goethals all that could be whipped up was a Saturday night smoker at the Corozal Club. The slight was the more obvious because he had brought with him a squad of celebrated engineers and a flock of probing Congressmen for whom a decent welcome was in order too. Out of deference for the beloved retiring Chief Engineer, the usual protocol was set aside and the dignitaries had to be content with an affair that had the markings of a trumped-up rally—which the hero of the hour, John F. Stevens, declined to attend. And even this meager reception wasn't arranged until Goethals had been on the job for two days.

The toastmaster was on the side of those ten thousand men who had signed the petitions. To him the Army was expendable, and the introductory cracks at the military were calculated to please the audience rather than the guest of honor. The West Pointers squirmed while the men roared and cheered. Even the Congressmen enjoyed it. No chillier reception for an Army officer could have been planned. Every time Stevens' name was mentioned, prolonged bursts of applause came from the audience. When Goethals was referred to, there was frigid silence. One of the Congressmen in a spirited address inadvertently implied that the Colonel would merely be carrying on the work that Stevens had organized and started. The clapping drowned out the rest of his speech.

Goethals was indignant—more irritated with the general aspersions cast at the Army than at the personal affronts—but the audience was kind when he rose toward the end of the program to speak for himself. Everyone had had his fun and it was only fair to give the newcomer his chance for a rebuttal. To the surprise of all, he had come to the smoker in mufti and the tenor of his talk had other larger surprises. First off, he credited Stevens with an organization which he intended to keep. That brought genuine applause, as did his announcement that he expected salutes from no one, and that he planned to keep open office to complaints of any kind, as had his predecessor, without appointments.

"While we are on this subject of militarism," he explained disarmingly, "I will say that I expect to be the chief; the division of engineers and the heads of departments are going to be the colonels; the foremen are going to be the captains, and the men who do the labor are going to be the privates. You have your colonels with you, and they will remain. There will be no more militarism in the future than there has been in the past.

"I am no longer a commander in the United States Army. I now consider that I am commanding the Army of Panama, and that the enemy we are going to combat is the Culebra Cut and the locks and dams at both ends of the canal, and any man here on the work who does his duty will never have any cause to complain of militarism."

The plain words brought an abrupt end to the stored-up antagonism. No Colonel could be a substitute for Big Smoke Stevens, but the situation looked more hopeful than the men had dared suppose. With the elimination of any threat of mustering, saluting, and martial law, they'd give the new Chief Engineer a break. In relief, they applauded him roundly.

The interregnum lasted just two more weeks. It was comfortable for neither Goethals nor Stevens. Day after day Big Smoke went over the terrain with the Colonel, explaining, demonstrating, making suggestions for the future, as if he were giving up his awkward brain child with reluctance. Goethals had expected to see more of the chaos he had witnessed on his visit with Taft, but the chaos seemed to have vanished. Every hour, as he went over the details, he was more deeply struck with the impressive achievements.

The location of the Panama Canal was determined largely by the Chagres, a wily, serpentine river that had cut a deep valley more than halfway across the Isthmus. Subject to violent rampages, the river could rise forty feet in an hour.

Between 1880 and 1904 French companies had labored sporadically to dig, first a sea-level canal across the Isthmus, then a lock canal. When the Americans took over in 1904, abandoned French machinery was strewn from Colón to Panama City. Weeds and brush were even growing in the spoil on these dump cars.

—Panama Canal Official Photo

Abandoned French excavators settled into the jungle swamp.

During the first months of work in the Canal Zone, the American effort came almost as near fiasco as did the French. Dumps were too high, the transportation system snarled, sanitation measures ineffective.

—Courtesy United Fruit Co.

—Courtesy United Fruit Co.

Reminded that the French failure was due primarily to extravagance, the Isthmian Canal Commission adopted a policy of parsimony, and tried to make do with the antiquated French equipment. Here an up-ended excavator serves as signal tower on the one-track rail line.

—*Panama Canal Official Phot*

The American Chief Engineer who brought order out of the chaos, between July 1905 and April 1907, was John F. Stevens who persuaded Congress that the Canal should be a high-level lock type. He was the basic architect of the Panama Canal. This relaxed pose fails to demonstrate how intensely he despised desk work.

—*Courtesy United Fruit C*

Colonel William C. Gorgas (center), medical hero of the Panama epic, convinced his superiors that mosquitoes were the worst enemy on the Isthmus. His victory over yellow fever saved thousands of lives. In 1906 he was guest of a delegation of health authorities on an Isthmian tour sponsored by the United Fruit Company.

Cumbersome churn drills prepared holes for dynamite charges.

New labor villages sprang up along the line of the Canal, all built in a new style of architecture labeled "Commission."

An early blast displaces 29,640 cubic yards of rock.

A dressing-down is delivered personally by Theodore Roosevelt on his historic visit to the Canal in November, 1906. The trip to Panama was the first outside the continental limits ever made by a United States President in office.

"The Czar of the Canal Zone," Colonel George W. Goethals, succeeded Stevens as Chief Engineer in April 1907.

This scene on November 21, 1908 provoked one of the major crises in Canal history. Rock fill for a Gatun Dam retaining wall settled several feet, as engineers had anticipated. A green journalist reported that the Dam had collapsed, and headlines carried the falsehood around the world.

Not a single motor truck was used in the Canal-building operation. All heavy equipment was on rails. Steam shovels on rails loaded cars running on an adjacent rail line—though the warped tracks sometimes gave the impression of not being the shortest distance between two points.

—*Panama Canal Official Photos*

Living quarters for American "gold" employees were not as luxurious as pictures circulated by recruiting agents in the States portrayed them. These scenes, tidied up for the photographer, were representative: I.C.C. Hotel or boarding house (upper); Bachelor quarters (middle); Y.M.C.A. Club House reading room (lower).

—*Panama Canal Official Photo*

"Gold" employees were served meals in relatively comfortable dining rooms; "Silver" laborers were served cafeteria style, and dined in the vertical. All meal service was under the jurisdiction of the Isthmian Canal Commission.

The most celebrated among chronic Canal visitors was William Howard Taft. Leading an entourage of engineers including Colonel Goethals, he inspects the Miraflores Locks in November 1910.

—*Panama Canal Official Photo*

Artist Joseph Pennell declared that these chamber cranes in Pedro Miguel Locks were the most monumental and the most picturesque feature of the Canal construction equipment. The Rube Goldberg apparatus was designed to deliver to the lock walls 320 cubic yards of concrete per hour.

In place of the giant cranes used for conveying cement to the Pacific locks, a fantastic aerial cableway was used at Gatun. The system was compared to a celestial cobweb over which noisy, gigantean spiders raced. In August 1911 the center wall monolith was taking shape behind the towering forms.

—*Panama Canal Official Photo*

From the top of Contractor's Hill, Culebra Cut through the Continental Divide began to have the look of a finished channel by the summer of 1911.

Cucaracha Slide proved to be the worst nightmare the Canal engineers encountered. In millions of cubic yards, mud and disintegrating rock poured down the mountain slopes faster than they could be hauled out. The slide swept aside and buried tracks, trains, steamshovels, and everything in its path.

—*Panama Canal Official Photo*

The most dramatic moment in the decade of Canal-digging came on May 20, 1913 when two steam shovels met on bottom grade deep in the Continental Divide. Every steam whistle in the Cut contributed a hoot of jubilation.

—Panama Canal Official Photo

Steam shovel operations were discontinued on September 10, 1913, after the engineers had decided that the remaining excavation could best be done by dredging. However, blastings at the foot of Cucaracha Slide failed to budge this block.

Tourists swarmed to the Canal in thousands, and during the dry season (December to April) collectively constituted an irritating obstruction to progress.

—Panama Canal Official Photo

Although the *Ancon* (above) is credited with making the first official ocean to ocean voyage at the opening of the Canal on August 15, 1914, actually the French craneboat *Alexander La Valley* (below) was the first steam vessel to make the passage, on January 7, 1914. The *Cristobal,* sister ship of the *Ancon,* also made a test run on August 3, and during the spring and summer of 1914 commercial lightering service between Balboa and Cristobal was available.

Passing from the Atlantic to the Pacific, the Canal transit begins with the triple lift at Gatun Locks into Gatun Lake (above).

Following the circuitous twenty-mile passage through the channels of Gatun Lake, the transit continues for nine miles through the Continental Divide—Culebra Cut, now officially named Gaillard Cut for the engineer Major D. D. Gaillard who sacrificed his life in directing its construction.

—*Panama Canal Official Photos*

Headed toward the Pacific, a ship is lowered from the level of Gatun Lake at Pedro Miguel Locks (above) into a small intermediate lake, then two more steps at Miraflores Locks (below). From the harbor entrance at Colón to the end of the breakwater in the Bay of Panama, the total distance is fifty miles—instead of more than ten thousand miles around the Horn.

"The magnitude of the work grows on me," he wrote to his son after five days of inspecting. "It seems to get bigger all the time, but Mr. Stevens has perfected such an organization so far as the R.R. part of the proposition is concerned, that there is nothing left for us to do but just have the organization continue in the good work it has done and is doing. As I go over the line and see what he has accomplished, and the organization that he has perfected, I cannot see why he has resigned. . . . Mr. Stevens has done an amount of work for which he will never get any credit, or, if he gets any, will not get enough. . . . I am very agreeably surprised at the conditions as I find them. Mr. Stevens has done work along the lines that our training hasn't taken us, and the lock and dam propositions I do not fear nor dread. The hard part of the work is not going to be the Engineering end."

Goethals had brought to Panama a highly critical attitude and a little sense of superiority; he was the doctor called in to treat the patient who had fared badly in the hands of fumbling quacks, and to his embarrassment discovered that his ministrations weren't as essential as he had imagined. His only criticism was of progress on the locks and dams—his special field—and Stevens was fully cognizant of the deficiences there. Congress had delayed so long that he had been allowed only a few months in which to get started.

The Colonel was increasingly puzzled as to why Stevens was throwing up the job. "I think he has broken down with the responsibilities and an evident desire to look after too many of the details himself," he guessed. But inconsistently he confessed a few days later: "I presume I am burdening myself with many details that Mr. Stevens trusted to his private secretary."

Between the two Chief Engineers there was a minimum of fraternal expression. Goethals was the guest of Dr. Gorgas rather than of Big Smoke. "The latter didn't seem inclined to take us to his house," the Colonel regretted. In fact, the only common ground for sympathy they seemed to find was in a mutual contempt for the visitations of Congressmen. Besides the lawmakers

161

who arrived on the same ship with Goethals, they were shortly afflicted with another committee who were on a West Indies junket. They had made an unfortunate call at Caracas and been exposed to yellow fever there. Dr. Gorgas refused to grant them permission to land at Colón until after the expiration of the six-day quarantine limit. On board they fussed, fumed, and finally exploded. The doctor had no right to keep them confined. They went over his head and demanded an interview with Stevens. "Laws are made to be obeyed, even by Congressmen," tossed off the free-speaking Zone boss, who still held the reins.

When they were eventually allowed to land, they had nothing but vilification for engineers, doctors, and the whole canal project. Stevens had insisted on their remaining aboard, they claimed, to keep them in ignorance of the intolerable conditions on the Isthmus. "They were ugly and anything but pleasant traveling companions," Goethals commented, pointing particularly at one honored Representative who "ought to have been spanked, for he behaved like a spoiled boy and made very insulting remarks about the Canal and its officials. . . . They were so ungracious and ungentlemanly that I told Mr. Stevens I could not go to Colón with them." The veteran engineer grinned indulgently. He had suffered so much of the same that he rather pitied his inexperienced successor.

On March 27 Stevens called together the new Commission—men who by executive direction had to reside on the Isthmus. It was the only meeting over which he was to have the honor of presiding. The agenda was long, but the item over which the chairman seemed most concerned was one last favor for his men. He wanted an Isthmian Canal Commission Band with paid members, a full-time director, and a librarian. Stevens got his band and then relinquished his chair to George Washington Goethals.

Officially, Big Smoke remained in command until midnight on March 31, but for more than a week his principal occupation was accepting tributes. There was a dinner at the United States

Legation in his honor; the *Star and Herald* devoted a page to his acclaim; Secretary Taft arrived on March 30 with still another group of Congressmen and they joined in paying homage, insisting that he alone take them on the grand tour of inspection. The University Club, where he was not entitled to membership because he was not a college graduate, had made him an honorary vice president; on April 3 they gave him a magnificent farewell splurge.

In the three years of United States occupancy, with the comings and goings of Presidents, Cabinet members, Senators, and foreign dignitaries, the Zone had witnessed memorable splendor on many occasions, but never anything that equaled the send-off for Stevens on the night of April 7. Pier 11 was the only area large enough to hold the throng that wanted to attend—or to hold all the flags, bunting, palms, and lights with which people wanted to decorate the setting.

To the thumping strains of "The Conquering Hero Comes" as played by the I.C.C. Band, Stevens walked down a long aisle toward the brilliantly decorated stand. It was as though the people were honoring a man who had already built the Panama Canal—and they were fully aware that it was he who had made it possible. No oratory could quite meet the spirit that pervaded the gathering. Several spokesmen tried and failed. There was too much feeling to put into words. At the end Stevens solemnly received the gold watch, the diamond ring, the handsome silver service, and two bound volumes containing the signatures of ten thousand men who didn't want him to go. Choking, he turned, left the stand, and walked to the tug waiting at the pier. "Captain, I am ready," he said to the tugmaster in a breaking voice. The *Gatun* sounded a blast and chugged out into the bay toward the S. S. *Panama,* which would take him back to the States.

Even that wasn't the end of the ceremonies, for the next morning—Sunday—every man who had been able to crowd aboard the special trains from Panama City, from Culebra, from Empire and Gatun, was on the Colón docks to wave Big Smoke off. Many of them had spent the night in Colón after the to-do on Pier 11. Thousands upon thousands were there, darkies from the West Indies, Italians, Spaniards, Chinese, Panamanians, as well as the Americans. And as the *Panama* stood out into the Caribbean, a few of those who could carry a tune joined the band in a sad rendition of "Auld Lang Syne."

Colonel Goethals did not attend the Pier 11 demonstration, but he learned enough about it to realize how large a vacancy he had to fill. In his maiden speech he had promised that there would be no more militarism in the future than there had been in the past. It was an extravagant pledge from one who had spent his life in uniform, taught at West Point, served as a member of the War College Staff, done all his professional engineering under the aegis of the Army. To the Colonel the new order wasn't militaristic, but to workers it was thoroughly regimented.

"See the Colonel," "Ask the Colonel," became the new bywords. It was a benevolent dictatorship in the hands of an officer of uncommon wisdom and charity. "No President of the United States, not even Lincoln in war times, exerted the authority he daily employed in the zenith of his power," claimed one analyst. The supreme authority that Stevens held for three weeks was held by George Goethals for seven years. In all that time he never wore a uniform to emphasize his power, but there was no doubt that the full weight of the War Department was behind him.

> See Colonel Goethals, tell Colonel Goethals,
>   It's the only right and proper thing to do.
> Just write a letter, or even better
>   Arrange a little Sunday interview.

That was the theme song among the populace.

He followed Stevens' precedent of keeping his office door ajar for anyone who wanted the benefit of his counsel, and on Sunday mornings it was wide open. Sunday was the day set aside for his patriarchal court in the interests of some forty thousand workers speaking forty-five different languages. It was the only day when complainants wouldn't have to take time off from work. Salesmen who had a half-million-dollar crane to promote, Congressmen who wanted to cut the Canal budget by a few million, were encouraged to see the Colonel on weekdays. The forlorn, the homesick, the disgruntled came to see him on Sunday. Wives dropped in for judgment on marital woes, social committee chairmen to arrange a date for a dance in the Tivoli ballroom, an irritated steam shoveler to bemoan his discharge.

"And why were you discharged?" inquired the unsmiling dictator.

"Because I can't play baseball," he replied.

As a morale builder, the Colonel was pushing intramural baseball. The drillers had challenged the steam shovelers to a game, and the steam shovelers lacked a pitcher. A competent shovel operator with a good arm and a good eye had applied for a job at the crucial moment. He had been hired and the man who couldn't pitch fired.

This was a tough one that involved clear injustice to the steam shoveler, but it also was a test of the Colonel's loyalty to the diamond.

"They want shovelers on the Pacific end," he ruled after a moment's cogitation, without so much as a twinkle in his cold blue eyes. "Go over there in the morning and go to work."

The Colonel fixed it up by phone.

A builder steamed into his office with the intention of explaining that he couldn't possibly carry out instructions for completing a pump house in the allotted time. "Now I got that letter of yours, Colonel——" he began, and paused there, sensing something unresponsive in the steely gaze of the Chief Engineer.

"I beg your pardon," interrupted the Colonel suavely, "but you must be mistaken. I have written you no letter."

"Oh, yes, Colonel, it was about that work down at Miraflores."

"Oh, I see. You spoke a little inaccurately. You meant you received my orders, not a letter. You have the orders, so that

165

matter is settled. Was there anything else you wished to talk with me about?"

The builder suddenly decided there wasn't.

An order given by Goethals to any civilian in the Army of Panama was as peremptory as any he had ever issued in Cuba or on the riverbanks of the Tennessee. An order was not debatable. In all matters, the Colonel represented the legislative and the judicial as well as the executive branches of government.

Goethals had inherited a wave of disgruntlement among steam shovelers over pay scales. With a fierce jealousy they felt that they were entitled to higher wages than locomotive engineers and threatened Stevens with a strike.

Big Smoke, with characteristic bluntness, had dismissed a delegation of them with the conclusion: "Well, fellows, you know my reputation for standing by my men. You all know damn well that strikes do not get you anywhere. Now, get the hell out of this office and back to work on those shovels."

They went back to work. But when the same appeal was presented to Goethals, his militaristic orders did not have the same effect. They struck. The Colonel sent them back to the States in ignominy. For a time there was a serious slowdown at Culebra. But he took the slowdown in stride and soon had a new squad of recruits who were ready to take orders.

Every weekday morning was devoted to inspecting some part of the canal workings. He was forever snooping in unexpected places at unexpected times. "Look out for the Old Man!" was the signal passed from engineer to engineer, from foreman to foreman, by a prearranged whistle or a casual wave when they saw him coming. And the train engineers were particularly cooperative in spreading the word; the coast was clear if the "hogger" sitting in the cab window merely raised an arm in greeting, but if he sat there poker-faced, intently looking ahead, with a hand cupped to his chin, it meant that the Colonel was aboard—"Look out for the Old Man!"

In his special motorized railroad limousine, running on flanged wheels, a colored flagman sitting beside the chaffeur, he rode north and south, ordering a halt whenever a whim directed. The sighting of that car, dubbed the "Yellow Peril," was the signal for redoubled effort. "The thing looked like the nightmare off-spring of a passenger engine and a taxi," according to one description. "Because it was painted the regulation bilious yellow of the P.R.R. day coach, its nickname was obvious. You could scare a shirker out of a wet season's growth by shouting, 'Here comes the Yellow Peril!' "

Every Isthmus worker soon developed a dreadful respect for the itinerant boss who rode the yellow car. No one could be sure of establishing immunity to his interrogation. One hour he was cross-examining a prominent engineer from St. Louis; the next, a quivering Negro from Barbados. On the dot of eight o'clock he appeared at a district health office to check on the punctuality of employees in that department. A clerk and two West Indians were at their desks, but the chair of the health officer was empty. The Colonel sat down and waited. He waited for half an hour.

"Why are you nearly half an hour late reporting for duty?" he charged, when the delinquent finally appeared.

"I was out inspecting my district, sir," replied the health officer, visibly ill at ease.

"Where?"

"The garbage dumps over in Guachapali, sir."

The Colonel knew all about the filthy slime of the Guachapali dumps and knew something of the condition of one's clothes and shoes after wading in it. Slowly he looked over the spotless attire of the health officer, from head to foot, front and rear; then turned and walked out of the office, leaving the immaculate late sleeper to guess the purpose of his call.

Goethals, who had criticized his predecessor in office for taking on so many details, took on many more himself, until he described his job as something that was "not at all big, but only a mass of irritating details." To his authority he added censorship. It was no longer advisable for a visiting journalist to send off a

167

magazine article until the Colonel or one of his staff had approved it. He started the weekly *Canal Record* for "the publication of accurate information, based upon official records, concerning all branches of the work." It included reports of social life, amusements, sports, and letters from employees "subject only to the restrictions that such communications must be couched in respectful language." Goethals' name was not on the masthead, but no one doubted who the editorial arbiter was.

He was not a penny pincher like old General Davis, but economy was his daily preachment—economy consistent with efficiency. On an old French map he noted the name of a big construction camp, Caimito Mulato, that wasn't on his map. Was there such a place? Hadn't it been investigated? Couldn't some of the buildings be renovated instead of building a new camp? Explorers fought their way into the jungle behind a gang of machete men, and there they found the forgotten Caimito Mulato—an entire village built by the French, completely buried by the dense jungle growth. The Compagnie Universelle had never used it, and the Americans had overlooked it. So close was the tangle of vines that there was scarcely room to swing an ax. But when it was finally cleared away, the Colonel surveyed a town of thirty-two buildings, all in fair condition—nine sets of married quarters, twenty-two barracks and mess halls, and a machine shop outfitted with a boiler and engine, lathes, shapers, and drill presses. "It had needed but twenty-five years for the talons of the jungle to bury a village large enough to shelter a thousand men." In the interests of economy, Goethals soon had the machinery salvaged and the buildings occupied.

The frugality extended even to empty cement bags. Why shouldn't a perfectly good cement bag worth eight-and-a-half cents be returned to the manufacturer for a refund and used again, instead of being destroyed? Tied up in bales of a hundred, the canvas sacks went back to the States. But they weighed more than they should. There must still be a salvageable amount of cement stuck to the linings in them. He engaged a special gang of Jamaicans who did nothing but shake empty bags. "The sweepings resulting therefrom amount to fifty or more barrels a day," he reported.

Fringe benefits that Stevens had promoted were carried on by the new Chief Engineer—free entertainments, Y.M.C.A. clubhouses, commissaries with a line of goods almost as varied as those advertised in a Sears, Roebuck catalogue. More and more the Colonel came to realize that he was merely carrying out the plans that Big Smoke originated. As one observer with historical insight concluded: "In spite of the short time that Stevens was Chief Engineer, he was able to rescue the Canal from chaos and defeat; to arrive at the great decision for a high-level, lock-type canal plan . . . and secure its adoption; to solve the problem of the Culebra Cut; and to form an efficient organization for constructing the Canal. The testimony of those who witnessed his work on the Canal and the perspective of many years of marine operations established John F. Stevens as the greatest constructive builder of the Panama Canal."

Stevens had taken the rap for the last major trials and errors that had to be made to arrive at a workable plan. Goethals, the specialist in locks and dams, had only to perfect the organization and set things rolling.

"It's all over but the shouting, gentlemen," exclaimed a visiting journalist, "—barring a few years of work."

IX

"THINKS GATUN DAM SAFE"

EVEN before Stevens surrendered his command to Goethals, carpers in the States, looking for something new on the Isthmus to discredit, had discovered Gatun. Enemies of the Panama waterway and press agents for a Nicaragua project took grim delight in turning out an endless grist of statements to convince the public that any massive barrier, any concrete structure built on the porous rock and slippery mud at Gatun, would soon collapse under the pressure of water from an artificial lake covering 164 square miles. Nobody in the history of engineering had ever dared try to create so huge a lake, and no man-made embankment could hold back that much water, particularly an embankment founded on the sludge of the Chagres River.

Chafed by the "lurid statements" coming from Senators who knew nothing about engineering and from their constituents who knew less, Stevens finally let fly a public rebuke: "All these statements are absolutely and unqualifiedly false. . . . Nothing in any investigation made during the last year and a half has tended to show but that the foundations of the Gatun locks will be as solid as the eternal hills, and any statements to the contrary are either the products of diseased imagination or wilful lies."

Goethals was now the inheritor of all this clamor. Temporarily, the engineers as well as the cantankerous critics had swung over to the conviction that it wasn't Culebra Cut, contagious fever, or corruption that would determine whether or not ships would be sailing through the Panama Canal on January 1, 1915; the principal deterrent was Gatun. Public attention was focused on the magnitude of Gatun Dam, Gatun locks, Gatun Lake.

By the end of June, 1907, well over half a thousand acres around the dam site had been cleared. It was an ugly denuded waste of uneven land, across which the Chagres snaked. Jungle stubble was everywhere—tree stumps hacked untidily by native machetes, never close enough to the ground to strain the backs of the indolent choppers. And standing out like pockmarks were hundreds of black ash heaps where the tangle of greenery had been burned, or half-burned. The slopes were gouged and gullied by streams on rampage after the cloudbursts, but nobody cared, for all that surface was destined to be carted away, buried in more dirt, or inundated.

Across the soggy waste stretched miles of pilot rail lines and more miles of spur track. With no more apparent aim than disfiguring the landscape, steam shovels scooped into little hills here and piled up levees there; a dredge in the Chagres sucked out mud in one place and vomited it forth in another; dynamite crews periodically sent up enormous geysers of rock and water; pile drivers were barely keeping ahead of carpenters in throwing an unsteady trestle across the Chagres. In isolated spots towering drills were patiently pounding and grinding. Men in gangs of twenty, forty and a hundred labored with hand tools or swarmed about their monster machines.

The square mile of disrupted land was alive with armies tearing away old hills and making new ones, cutting embankments, leveling, reshaping contours—"shovel gangs, track gangs, surfacing gangs, dynamite gangs, gangs doing everything imaginable with shovel, pick and crowbar, gangs down on the floor of the canal, gangs far up the steep walls of cut rock, gangs stretching away in every direction till those far off looked like upright bands of the leaf-cutting ants of Panamanian jungles; gangs nearly all, whatever their nationality, in the blue shirts and khaki trousers of the

Zone commissary, giving a peculiar color scheme to all the scene."

And the babel of the world's languages fitted into the confusion. Poles weren't to be pared off with Portuguese, Chinese with Czechs, nor Italians with Irish. There had to be a common bond in speech and birth. Nationality lines were drawn as carefully as color lines in recruiting a gang. In the interests of concord, it was wise to keep the Basques separate from the Castilians, the French Negroes at a respectable distance from English Negroes, Italians far removed from the Greeks, "Spigoties"—native Panamanians—well segregated from all the others. By themselves Martiniques would wallow contentedly in mud up to their thighs for hours, but give them a soft job of unloading railroad ties or shoveling gravel along with Antiguans, Scandanavians or Spigoties, and their snarling and quarreling soon turned into a free-for-all.

There was such a vast army of men that the life of a single individual seemed to have lost its significance. Like the quantities of expendable equipment, men too were expendable. It was only a short distance to the hospital, where the medics, a priest, and the undertaker were waiting. No one stopped to grieve for long when a body was dug out from under a landslide; workman number 42947 was checked off the list, the proper officials were notified, and arrangements were made for a quick interment at public expense.

"In an explosion of dynamite near Gatun on Sunday," ran a typically dispassionate notice, "four men were killed and nine were injured. . . . A locomotive in coupling onto a flat car loaded with 550 cases of dynamite jarred some of the explosives off the car. The cause of the explosion is unknown. The dead are: R. M. Preddie, Jamaican negro, timekeeper, check no. 37401, and negro laborers—Simeon Gordon, Barbadian, check no. 37456; Son Trotman, Barbadian, check no. 37467; and one unknown whose legs were found but are unidentified."

To the blue shirts, the work at Gatun was meaningless. It was

173

a man-created cataclysm far too vast to comprehend. Gatun Dam was to be the most colossal earthen dam ever built, and Gatun locks the world's most massive concrete structure. Even the American straw bosses had no conception of the whole. They took their orders from foremen who themselves were a little hazy on exactly how their particular project fitted into the grand scheme.

The works spread out over such an immense area and in such a confusion of parts that few on the scene could visualize how everything could possibly be fitted together. The locks with their approaches covered an area nearly a mile long. The spillway for the dam alone was talked of in terms of another Niagara. A long hill of broken rocks over a hundred feet broad at the base, thirty at the top, and sixty feet high was already reaching across the valley, a stupendous dam in itself, but that wasn't Gatun Dam proper. A third of a mile downstream was a similar elongated hill, and that wasn't the Dam either. Those two hills were merely retaining walls or "toes." The real dam would be erected between them and supported by them; every cubic foot of space from lower to the upper wall was to be filled with clay and sand—three million cubic yards of fill—until it formed a small mountain 135 feet high and a mile and a half long. That was to be the Gatun Dam that criticasters in New York and New Orleans were sure the thrust of the Chagres would topple.

Freed of cumbrous engineering lingo, the plan was to block the river valley with this mile-and-a-half-long embankment reaching from the hill range on the east to the hill range on the west. The locks would hug the natural slope to the east, and the spillway for the dam would be approximately in the center, where a sprawling hogback was providentially located. Spillway Hill, it was called, and Spillway Hill would anchor the middle of the dam as well as take care of the Niagara that would flow over it.

Actually the critics had something on their side; whether they knew it or not, all the ticklish engineering problems hadn't yet

been worked out. In addition to the Chagres with its unpredictable floods, the dam had to cross three other channels: two
broad diversion ditches which the French had built to keep the
water out of their canal, and the French canal itself. Moreover,
nature had conspired in every way to make it difficult to construct
a dam at Gatun. Far back in geological time, the area had been
on the edge of the Atlantic, but Chagres floods had brought
down mud, silt, and clay to push the shore line back seven miles
and to clog the valley with unstable layers of wash 50 to 150 feet
deep. Building on it was like building on jelly. Any superimposed
weight would squeeze the subsoil so that it would continue to
settle for years; it was sheer folly to consider planting the concrete
lock floors or side walls ten stories high on the jelly. The topsoil
had to be dug out—all the way down to bedrock—except under
the rock toes; according to the engineers' calculations, the toes
of their own weight would gradually settle and force out what
was underneath them. That settling process would raise havoc
with rail lines laid on the surface, but repairing the tracks would
be easier than doing the extra excavation at depths below sea
level.

"An open cut 70 feet below sea-level is difficult to make and
even more difficult to maintain," complained the usually un-
complaining William Sibert, who was put in charge at Gatun.
Sibert was another West Pointer with a lot of river and dam
experience in the United States, but nothing that resembled the
job handed over to him on the Isthmus. Down in those open cuts,
he discovered that the surface of the bedrock was tilted and
irregular in texture, solid enough to hold any weight he intended
to put on it, but because of the slides and the seepage a veritable
hell in which to work.

What could be done with men, machines, and material was
reasonably predictable, but there was nothing predictable about
the river. One of those sudden rises of thirty or forty feet could
sweep away a year's painful labor and a million dollars' worth of
equipment in an hour. Every shower back in the hills sent a

freshet downstream; a widespread downpour turned the whole valley into a rampaging sluice; and since Atlantic tides were felt all the way inland to Bohio, eight miles above Gatun, an amateur hydrologist had made the amazing discovery that at times "the upstream flow was greater than the downstream." The general course was northerly, yet the river was so serpentine that in places it actually doubled back to flow south. The river crossed the channel plotted for the Canal twenty-three times, and made a last sweeping loop at Gatun before heading northwest to the sea. It was as ornery a river as any engineer ever tried to tame, yet if it could be mastered, the waters would be impounded in a magnificent inland lake, eighty-five feet above sea level—a bridge of water on which the mightiest ocean liners could ride majestically from the Atlantic to the Pacific.

Then, as if Sibert weren't afflicted with enough trouble in overcoming the resistance of the waters, he was beset with the task of overcoming the resistance of some six hundred natives in the ancient village of Gatun. They liked their town as it was and as it had been even before the gold-hungry Spaniards used it as a port of call in the 1500's. They refused to move, refused to be frightened away by stories of a gigantic dam that was to cover the settlement, refused to be lured away by promises of much better quarters in the uplands. They hadn't forgotten de Lesseps. His men, too, had told tales about a water passage that was going to be pushed across the Isthmus. Old-timers were wise enough to know that the Americans would never do any better than the French.

Cash was paid for the land and a substitute village provided a mile back on the edge of the jungle. A few of the younger generation complied with evacuation orders, taking the move in good humor, seated in rocking chairs on front stoops as the wagons hauled their huts to high ground. They helped to persuade others, but among the elders there were tears, explosions of anger, and threats of violence before they were persuaded to go. Not until steam shovels were tearing up front yards, until carloads of rock fill were bursting in the sides of shanties, did the last of the stragglers yield.

Destruction and construction were equally prevalent at Gatun during the turbulent years of 1907 and 1908. While the top of Spillway Hill was being blasted off, the great bulk of a cement-mixing plant was rising below; while lock sites were under excavation, railway trestles were being strung across the valley; to change the course of the Chagres, the old channels east of Spillway Hill were filled and the channel to the west deepened. As fast as rock was blasted out of lock sites it was loaded on dump cars, hauled up the inclines, and dumped from the trestles to build up the toes—a slow process that would go on for years. Completing the toes between the locks and Spillway Hill was the first objective, and in thousands of carloads the fill came from Mindi and Bas Obispo as well as from Gatun. By the fall of 1908 one section of wall had reached the height of sixty feet.

Meanwhile, every conceivable kind of test and measurement was made by Sibert and his corps of engineers before proceeding with any phase of the vast project. Experimental drillings were made above the dam and below the dam. In forty-five spots drills were driven to test the foundation rock for the lock footings, the holes averaging a hundred feet in depth—penetrations totaling almost a mile. Then as a double precaution five test pits, six by eight feet, were dug by hand seventy feet down, virtual graves for the men who had to dig them, for slides and cave-ins were a daily occurrence. On Spillway Hill more drillings were made and a pit twenty feet square was excavated. At administration quarters, reports of what was being encountered in those shafts were fully as important as the excavation reports in thousands of cubic yards coming from Culebra Cut. Words like "impervious clay" and "hard brown conglomerate" were worth millions of dollars and months of work.

On the banks of the Chagres, as a final conclusive test, a model of the dam was constructed in a great wooden tank. The rock "toes" were built to scale, fill was pumped in, and intricate

177

instruments calculated the seepage. It proved that the estimates of the engineers were correct; the structure was feasible. But, to make sure, it was all torn out and the experiment repeated.

From all the drillings, the pit and the model experiments, Sibert was satisfied and Goethals was satisfied that the whole plan was completely practicable. But one day a journalist elbowed his way through the workmen to peer down into an experimental shaft. Far below he sighted water. It gave him a wonderful idea. He hurried back to his typewriter to concoct a masterpiece explaining how the United States Army was building Gatun Dam on an underground lake. The dispatch was on the wire before Goethals had a chance to censor it, and it was in every American newspaper the next day—accepted as gospel truth, so disturbing to the public and to Congressmen that Roosevelt immediately had to assemble a team of experts and pack them off to Panama to learn what was being put over on him. Goethals' denials of the fiction merely whetted appetites. Sibert waited.

One by one the experts climbed down to the bottom of eighty-foot shafts to inspect the rock surface, and one by one they came up with the same answer that Sibert and his associates had given. The foundation rock was completely safe. Congressmen came, too, to question the whole idea of a high-level canal that depended on any dam. Still fresh in the minds of some of the oldsters was the catastrophe of 1889 caused by the collapse of what had been the largest earthen dam in the United States— South Fork Dam. The breaking of that barrier had released twenty million tons of water on Johnstown, Pennsylvania, and accounted for a death toll of 2,200. They were suspicious of earthen dams intended to hold back vast areas of water.

"The pressure of water against the sides of a container increases only in relation to the height of the column, without respect to the area of the surface," an engineer recited.

"But," countered the Congressmen, "you say that you are going to create a lake of more than 160 square miles. I don't see how this dam, or any other dam, could hold back such a tremendous volume of water."

"Ah, shut up!" suggested one of his legislative colleagues. "How do you suppose the dikes of Holland hold back the Atlantic Ocean?"

What one reporter in search of a headline had started, no engineer at the Isthmus—regardless of his academic degrees and his reputation—could stop. Opposition to the creation of Gatun Lake grew more bitter by the day. The public, two thousand miles from Panama, was convinced that the underlying ground was entirely unsuitable either "to carry the heavy superincumbent load of the structures, or to resist the tendency of the impounded waters to break through by extensive seepage."

The editor of a scientific magazine came to the rescue with an explanation aimed at putting matters into perspective: "The particular storm center around which has raged the fiercest of all the technical controversies of the Panama Canal is to be found at the Gatun dam and locks; and of all the questions debated in this connection, perhaps the most important is that of the character of the rock underlying the site of the locks. . . . During the sinking of borings to ascertain the character of the foundations a small quantity of water appeared in some of the holes. It was insignificant in amount, rose only a small distance in the holes and was found to be restricted to a few limited areas. Yet on the strength of this fact, the rumor has started that the whole of the dam was founded on a subterranean lake. . . . A special committee of engineers individually entered each of the test pits, the deepest of which was extended to a depth of 87.4 feet, and disproved the rumor. . . . The high professional standing of the board of engineers, the thorough character of the sub-surface examination, the highly favorable character of the findings, may be taken by the American public to have settled the vexing question once and for all. With this out of the way, the last of the serious uncertainties as to the ultimate and satisfactory completion of the great work may be considered to have been removed."

Suggesting that the uncertainties had all been eliminated was immoderate optimism, but the article did help. In spite of the wisdom of Congressmen, the fantasies of reporters, and the carping of amateur critics, form gradually emerged from the slough that was Gatun. The pattern began to make sense; one thing connected with another; tracks that had appeared to wander aimlessly into a chaos had an evident destination. The spirit was drive, drive, drive. Pressure for getting things done on schedule and done right was felt all the way down the chain of command. Major Sibert was in charge, but his boss, the Colonel, was everlastingly intruding.

"Your schedule calls for those forms to be finished by the end of next week," Goethals reminded a foreman on his rounds. "You are not very far along."

"I know, Colonel. But we are doing our best."

"I don't expect you to do your best," Goethals coolly reprimanded. "I expect you to complete your work on time."

The new town of Gatun, which Stevens had started on the hill above the lock site during the period when Congress was relentlessly arguing high-level versus low-level canals, was expanding into a development that looked like the rail center of an industrial metropolis. Scores of cars were constantly moving in and out of the depot, with others fretting on the sidings or being shunted down the yards. East of the tracks was the town, with a new structure or two for the Colonel to inspect every time he passed through. There were over a hundred buildings—two-deckers and three-deckers for the administration offices, bachelor quarters, married quarters, a handsome home for Major Sibert, a half-dozen dormitories, a huge hospital, a school, a hotel, messes for feeding two thousand men at a sitting. Main Street was a plank road sixteen feet wide—a boardwalk more than a mile long.

A firehouse was added, a public market with sixteen stalls, a commodious warehouse two hundred feet long and fifty wide, a post office, and a clubhouse costing $25,000, with a ballroom, bowling alleys, billiard room, and refreshment stand. Here and there efforts at landscaping were made, with the Gatun Hotel setting the example; to honor the proprietary Quartermasters Division, twenty-foot initials "Q.M.D." appeared on the front grounds in gaudy tropical flowers and foliage. Gardeners proudly groomed lawns edged with crotons, hibiscus, and poinsettia. Altogether, the residential section of Gatun looked more like a summer resort than a labor camp. Nothing like it had ever been built outside the Isthmus. From it evolved a new style of tropical architecture—the "Commission." Whether it was a school, a commissary, or an engineer's residence, the style was distinctly "Commission"—a square corrugated metal umbrella, with broad screened porches and a minimum of walled space.

Residential Gatun had little in common with the helter-skelter of industrial Gatun. The old French canal to the Atlantic had been re-excavated to make the town a port as well as a railroad center, and everything radiated from the docks on the waterfront. The warehouses and power plant were there, the huge cement-mixing factory was close by, and so were the towers to support a tangle of overhead cables on which would ride an endless procession of buckets for conveying concrete to the locks as soon as their construction was started. Docks were being extended to accommodate the steady run of barges that would come from a subsidiary rock-crushing plant at Porto Bello twenty miles down the coast, and from the sand-washing plant at Nombre de Dios ten miles farther.

Transporting the materials for the massive locks was going to be a major undertaking in itself. Already the engineers for the locks and spillway had estimated that 3750 barges of crushed rock would be needed, each barge carrying 600 cubic yards. The sand required would fill another 1875 barges. Then an imaginative mathematician had projected the figures on a map to give his clientele a more graphic idea of the size of the job: "If all of those barges were made into one tow, allowing one tug for four barges, the tow would be almost 1500 miles long. It would reach three-fifths of the distance from Colón to New York."

Another engineer trying to impress the public with the complications of some of the technical problems worked up figures on the stresses that had to be taken into account in building the floors for the locks. They were to be of reinforced concrete thirteen feet thick—the floor for a single lock weighing 100,000 tons. But the base wasn't being made that thick or that heavy just to support the volume of water that a lock would contain. The problem was to offset upward pressure from possible underground seepage when the lock was empty. And the weight of 100,000 tons wasn't enough; the floor had to be anchored down with steel rails driven fifteen feet into bedrock and spaced six feet apart over the entire area. Each rail would provide additional resistance of 178,000 pounds.

Such figures, indeed, were convincing evidence that every conceivable precaution was being taken by the engineers to build an enduring canal. No nonexplosive force could ever dislodge a lock, the technicians claimed. Keeping the American public indoctrinated with popular translations of what was being accomplished on the Isthmus was now a recognized part of Goethals' task. Good public relations could save him uncomfortable days of contending with false information. In news releases he explained how well the rock toes on the east side of Gatun Dam were coming along, picturing how the fill was dumped from cars on high wooden trestles, and when the trestle was completely embedded in stone, it was abandoned and the track laid directly on the wall. But he overlooked one item in which he was sure the public would not be interested; he neglected to explain the details of how the toes kept settling as the top-heavy loads found stable footing at the bottom. In little shuddering quakes a hundred feet of surface would suddenly sink, throwing tracks out of line and sometimes the trains off the tracks. The constant shifting of surface was exasperating to the train gangs, but exactly what the engineers had expected would happen—too confusing a subject to try to explain to the average newspaper reader.

Yet there was nothing confusing about it to another overeager journalist looking for a better Panama story than the official handouts from headquarters. To him it looked like disaster. Early on the morning of November 21, 1908, he wandered over to the Gatun Dam, poking around for a colorful yarn. During the night a slip had occurred directly over the old French canal—a deep one, the first he had seen. He didn't know that they were a daily event. Making some rough calculations, he rushed back to his copy desk with more enthusiasm than had the reporter who saw an underground lake at the bottom of an experimental pit. His story and amplifications of it hit the front pages of United States papers three days later.

COLLAPSE OF GATUN DAM, screamed a headline. CHAGRES RIVER PLUNGES THROUGH GAP IN ISTHMIAN WALL. *Engineers Face Problem.*

Nothing could be more ludicrous. To the engineers, the dam proper was the sand and clay fill between the two long retaining walls, and that work hadn't yet been started. The valley west of Spillway Hill was still an open cut through which the river was running. Water was very high because of recent rains, but there was nothing abnormal about it. Gatun Lake did not yet exist. There was no head of water to plunge through a gap.

The cautious Boston *Transcript* gave a more refined account:

Sensational reports are in circulation to the effect that what is known as the south toe of the Gatun dam of the Panama Canal has sunk . . . For the past twenty days it has been raining continuously throughout the Republic. The Chagres River is flooded and all the railroad tracks are under water. The floor of the pumping station is submerged to a depth of more than five feet and the lock sites are also flooded.

183

The London *Times* sedately announced:

A portion of the Gatun dam, forty feet in length is inundated. The sites of several locks are under water and work on the Panama Canal generally is greatly impeded.

"Predict Failure at Panama" came the reaction from Paris. *Figaro* and Bunau-Varilla got into the act by pointing out that the whole trouble was "the substitution of dams at Rio Grande and Gatun for dams at Miraflores and Bohio, where the foundations were demonstrated by French engineers to be solid."

Proponents of the Nicaragua Canal suggested abandoning Panama altogether: "The whole matter better be dropped and the money spent charged up to profit and loss."

HEAVY RAINS DAMAGE CANAL. One Section of the Gatun Dam Is Said to Have Sunk 60 Feet, headlined the *Chronicle* in faraway San Francisco.

The New York *Times* played it safe at first. The editors called Goethals and waited for a reply.

When the first wires began pouring in from New York and Washington, Goethals hadn't even heard of the particular settling of November 21. It was such a commonplace occurrence that Sibert had not bothered to report it. Goethals investigated and cabled back to the *Times* that the settling was routine and of no consequence: "Reported injury consists of slip in rock piles intended to form south toe of Gatun Dam, and has no effect on body structure. . . . Slips of this kind not new. Present slip is no consequence and of character to be anticipated in such work."

THINKS GATUN DAM SAFE, warily plugged a *Times* headline. But it was only the beginning for the big New York daily, which had long been rooting for a canal in Nicaragua. That story was soon followed by a page-one sensation: MAY DIG SEA-LEVEL CANAL AT ISTHMUS. Will Increase Cost. More Time Will Be Consumed if the Plans Are Changed. Goethals Wants Millions. Then the payoff came

184

on December 20, a full month after the shift of fill over the old French canal. MUST THE PANAMA CANAL BE BEGUN ANEW? the *Times* inquired in startling headlines sprawled all the way across the top of a feature page. EXPERT OPINION AGREES WITH RECENT CRITICS IN VIEWING THE GATUN DAM AS A FATAL BLUNDER—ARMY ENGINEERS SATISFIED WITH THE WORK. The article revealed:

A gigantic and tremendously costly engineering blunder has been made in the construction of the Panama Canal. It is the Gatun dam and its locks that are now being fiercely assailed. . . . Only a few days ago an engineer of high standing and recognized ability went so far as to make the flat assertion that if the present plans are persisted in, the cost will reach the stupendous sum of $550,000,000 instead of the $145,000,000 originally estimated, and that even with that vast expenditure the canal will be an utter and disastrous failure. . . . It is discouraging to note that all experts consulted by the *Times* agree that the Gatun dam is a great mistake. . . . While the dam itself might be constructed so that it could be made to hold water, the surrounding hills are so pervious that it will be impossible to impound the flow of the Chagres.

The absurd concoction of one whippersnapper reporter had upset world confidence in Goethals, his engineers, and the whole plan for a lock canal. For this exigency neither a high-powered committee of investigators nor delegations of Congressmen were enough; Taft had to accompany them. It appeared that there was a general migration from Washington to Colón.

John Stevens, solicitous for the work he had started, tried to calm down the furor by attacking the "outbreak of yellow journalism in regard to the Gatun dam." "The choice of its location has been wisely made and the work properly planned," he reassured in a public statement. "It is in competent hands and is being executed with a rapidity that surprises even the Colonel's friends. The thing to do is to extend to Colonel Goethals and his assistants all the encouragement and moral help possible, and the

185

engineering world will have every reason to be proud of the result."

The most respected spokesman for the construction profession, the *Engineering News,* went to bat with this authoritative statement:

> The structure at Gatun is as sound and safe as any engineering work could possibly be. . . . The dam is so absolutely safe that at least half its width is wholly useless. . . . The settling of the waste rock dumped in the mud of the old French canal channel along the south toe of the dam has been magnified into a disaster of ominous portent to the whole work. Stories concerning it have been published in ten thousand newspapers, while hardly one has published the real truth—that the settlement of the rock was expected to occur and saved a needless expense of dredging out the layer of soft mud before dumping the rock.

Visiting experts poked and prodded; visiting Congressmen fumed, asked more unintelligent questions, and eventually reached the same conclusions as had the *Engineering News;* but for months few of the United States taxpayers who were footing the bill for the Panama Canal had any hope that it would ever be a success. Everything depended on Gatun Dam, and it could collapse again at any moment.

A reporter for the *Canal Record* had his tongue in his cheek when he wrote a month later for the Colonel's official news organ: "The building of the Gatun Dam was begun on December 24, when the 20-inch suction dredge, No. 82 was set to work pumping sandy clay from a point 2,000 feet north of the dam site into the channel of the old French canal between the two toes."

People back home were still thinking of Gatun in terms of river and reservoir dams they knew—projects that could be completed in a season or two. Their failure to comprehend the proportions of the Panama job was responsible for all the naïveté. No word description issued from Colón could begin to convey the magnitude of the Gatun barrier. Thousands of men and the biggest construction machinery in existence were going to take five years just to complete the rough work for it. The river bed on the west side of the valley couldn't be closed until a gigantic concrete spillway was built to take care of the Chagres flow, and that couldn't be done until more acres of Spillway Hill were excavated, until the power plant, the cement-mixing plant, and aerial cableways were in operation, until the quarries at Porto Bello were furnishing crushed rock and the barge transportation system for shipping the rock was organized.

Not until April 22, 1910, nearly a year and a half after the waters of the Chagres were reported to have plunged through "a gap in the Isthmian wall," did Gatum Lake actually come into existence. Late in the afternoon on that date Sibert passed the word that conditions were right to attempt filling the last gap in the valley through which the treacherous Chagres flowed to the sea. The river was high, seven feet above low water mark, but the rainy season was starting and it was now or never. The east section of the dam was well along; for the west section, two rock toes thirty feet high had been extended out from both banks of the river bed, leaving only narrow channels for the discharge of the Chagres. The idea was to fill the gaps in these channels with stone dumped from trestles faster than the force of the river could wash it out. Hundreds upon hundreds of cars loaded with rock were on the sidings at Gatun ready for the assault, with hundreds more on the tracks leading far back into Culebra Cut. Trains of twenty dump cars were on the trestles over both the north and south toes. The signal was given and the battle was on. The first cars plummeted their loads into the rushing current below, sending up geysers that soaked the men on the tracks above. Quickly the trains moved on, making way for the next. The tussle continued around the clock for four days.

The wall slowly rose, and so did the river. The surge of current grew stronger with every passing hour. Half-ton rocks were swept downstream like matchsticks. It was a nip-and-tuck struggle.

187

On April 23 a total of 760 carloads went into the south toe alone. The water level had to be raised fourteen feet before it would flow over the spillway. The crisis came the next day. Water was rising faster than the barrier. The pressure on the south toe was enormous. Even rocks of several tons were now being washed downstream. For any emergency someone was bound to remember the mountains of discarded French equipment and think of a use for it. There were hundreds of miles of useless rusted train rails—just the thing for an entanglement to hold the rocks. In carloads they were brought and hurled below on the upstream side. "They'll either close the river or tear out the trestle," conjectured Sibert.

For a time the rails did the trick. The unloading was speeded up so that there was almost a continuous rain of rock on the tangle of rails. Then suddenly, with a screech louder than the thunder of spilling rock, the south trestle gave way and moved downstream a few inches. The whole bridge with a train on it was threatened. Disregarding the peril, men unflinchingly climbed down the sides to add braces to the structure. Miraculously, it held. More trainloads of rock rolled onto the trestle and emptied their cargoes. The flow of the Chagres stopped.

But the following day came the first of many slides. The whole north retaining wall "moved leisurely downstream and spread itself out on the bottom of the river. Piles that had thirty- and forty-foot penetration moved downstream vertically." On the site was left twisted and broken track with ties still holding to the rails, piles leaning at crazy angles, and scarcely a trace of the magnificent stone barrier. "It looked as if the Chagres River were the victor," moaned Major Sibert. But the upper retaining wall inexplicably held. The rising water started slides along the banks, and at one point a lip of earth only three feet wide was all that kept the Chagres from resuming her former course. Thirty thousand cubic yards of rock were frantically dumped into the area, and two dredges were put to work in a precarious spot above the barrier to pump out an island of sand and clay that would give body to the dam.

Before the end of the month the conquest was complete. The lake had risen to fourteen feet, and the overflow was roaring over the spillway. Men could now return to the task of rebuilding the north toe, and in the years ahead the slow process of pumping hydraulic fill into the area between the toes would go on monotonously. Sibert had subjugated the Chagres. Let the yellow journals at home print as many scare headlines as they wanted; he knew that Gatun Dam was going to hold.

After the hysteria of November, 1908, when Secretary Taft was obliged to accompany jittery Congressmen to the scene of the reported Gatun disaster, he returned to New Orleans mad as a hornet. "There is nothing so discouraging as a fire in the rear . . . when you are on that isthmus," he expounded. "The men who are carrying on this great work . . . 2000 miles from base . . . cannot understand and cannot have the sense of appreciation of the importance of what a gentleman says on the floor of the House or the floor of the Senate, when he is only talking for buncombe. . . . I say that that kind of fire in the rear is calculated to break down the nervous system of those persons on the Isthmus working day and night, tooth and toenail to build the greatest enterprise of two centuries."

As Sibert had blocked the flow of the Chagres, so Taft, at least temporarily, had helped to block the flow of Congressional buncombe.

X

"CULEBRA CUT WAS A HELL'S GORGE"

PROGRESS in Culebra Cut was measured in cubic yards—cubic yards of excavation for the day, the week, the month, the year. Behind clanging locomotives, trains of sixteen or twenty dirt cars screamed out of the Cut every three minutes, until it seemed as though they were lugging away more soil than could exist in all of Central America. Yet the disgorging had little appreciable effect on the landscape. A profile of the Cut at Paraiso in January was hardly distinguishable from a profile of the same spot in July. Statistics in cubic yards were the only impressive evidence of accomplishment. The engineers knew—or thought they knew—how many cubic yards had to be taken out of the Cut, and by subtracting the yardage removed in a month or year, they could convey some vague conception of what had been done and what there was still to do.

Actually the figures were not always convincing. There was too much disagreement among the authorities on the content of Culebra. French promoters had been very reckless in advertising the dimensions of their Isthmian labors; and the Americans demonstrated little more caution. In 1906 a special committee for the International Board of Consulting Engineers delved into the matter and settled upon 500,000 cubic yards as the "probable total" that would have to be excavated.

"Incredible, fantastic error!" cried the dissenting minority on that Board, who were more familiar with problems of moving Panama spoil. They went on record with an estimate of more than a hundred times that amount—53,800,000 cubic yards. And the dispute went on from there. In 1908 the Canal Commission itself officially raised the measurement to 78,000,000. Slides had to be taken into account, as well as an increase in the bottom width of the Canal from two hundred to three hundred feet. By 1910 the estimate had jumped to 84,000,000; three years later to 100,000,000.

These diggings from Culebra—the black dirt, the red clay, the yellow, brown, and blue rock—were all lumped under the heading of "spoil." It was freighted out in thousands and millions of cubic yards, sometimes even faster than the surveyors upped their estimates of how much more there was to come. In the States the computations of monthly spoil were as boring and meaningless as an audit of the national budget; but at the Isthmus they were watched as eagerly as the baseball scores of the American League. Goethals made a kind of game out of it. The object of the sport was to beat the record of the French, the record of the previous week, the record of the previous month. One train gang was pitted against another, one canal division against another; steam shovel crew at Whitehouse worked against steam shovel crew at Empire. The results were followed with excitement, zealous rivalry, suspicion of dishonesty among accountants, and not infrequent intergang blows. But tabulations of figures, as published in the weekly *Canal Record*, stood; e.g.: shovel number 215—35,853 cubic yards, shovel number 225—36,560, shovel number 212—36,986. Over the years the monthly tallies showed the combined results of the competition: January, 1906—120,990; December, 1906—307,689; June, 1907—624,586; December, 1907—1,025,485; March, 1909—1,434,597.

The assault on Culebra began on January 10, 1880, when Ferdinand de Lesseps, a sprightly seventy-five and bubbling over with youthful exuberance, stepped down from a Panama Railroad train at Empire, and trailed by his wife and three children, the Bishop of Panama, an international commission of nine members, the railroad president, and a delegation of Latin American dignitaries, led a little procession to the crest of a hill where enough dynamite had been planted in a ledge to make a spectacular eruption. Petite Mademoiselle Ferdinande had the assignment of pressing the button that would set off the explosion.

"The Bishop's blessing had been pronounced," described an eyewitness, "and the champagne, duly iced, was waiting to cool the swelter of that tropic sun, as soon as the explosion went off. There the crowd stood, breathless, ears stopped, eyes blinking, half in terror lest this artificial earthquake might involve general destruction. But there was no explosion! It wouldn't go. A humorous sense of relief stole upon the crowd. With one accord everybody exclaimed, 'Good Gracious!' and hurried away, lest, after all, the dynamite should see fit to explode." It was fiasco number one.

But the *Bulletin du Canal Interocéanique*, with more of a flare for drama than for fact, pronounced the operation "perfectly successful," hailed the event as "the beginning of an immense series of labors that should have for their termination the opening of the interoceanic canal. . . . Rocks were much less resistant than we had anticipated, which is a good augury of the rapidity with which the great trench will be made."

This auspicious ceremony was enough to keep impatient advocates of a quick route across the Isthmus content for over a year. Work on the Canal was again officially started February 1, 1881, and soon afterward it was proclaimed that some ten thousand recruits from Colombia and the West Indies would definitely begin the Culebra diggings in October, 1881, but neither men nor equipment materialized. And by the time a few squads of laborers did show up, so many months had elapsed since the original inaugural that a new celebration had to be arranged. The date was January 20, 1882. "Among the invited guests," advised the Panama newspaper, "may be mentioned the Right Reverend Bishop, the President of the State, the Chief of the general staff of the division, his staff officers, the commanding officers of the two English frigates now lying in the harbor, representatives of the local press, businessmen, financiers, and politicians of our city, the officers of the garrison, the employees of the Panama Railroad Company and those of the Canal in a body, and finally the band of the pioneer battalion and a picket of troops. The crowd was so considerable that at the last moment it became necessary to attach another car in order to accommodate everybody."

Again the dignitaries dismounted at Empire. The Bishop once more placed his benediction on the undertaking. The ignition button was pressed, and this time the whole Isthmus quaked as thunder boomed across the hills and tons of rock were flung into space. Posing on the edge of the still smoking pit, an engineer solemnly explained to his audience that they were standing exactly ninety meters above the axis of the Canal, that "the cut would be opened by successive terraces where tracks could be laid for removing the excavated material . . . that the works properly speaking were opened from that moment on; the cut, in truth, had been commenced on that very day. . . . From this moment beyond a doubt the Canal is assured."

All that evening champagne toasts were poured in succession to most of the ranking officials of Colombia and France, to de Lesseps, to "Universal Progress, of whom the agents of the company are the standard bearers," "to Republican France, the beacon of liberty whose rays light the world." The program was topped off with an "illumination," a banquet, and dancing until dawn in a great ballroom "elegantly decorated, spacious and cool." Off to Paris went the triumphant cable: "First work on great cut of maritime channel formally inaugurated at Empire today. . . . City of Panama celebrating event with grand fete."

In the next twenty-two years, the French took 24,588,520 cubic yards out of Culebra Cut. The high points of the hills, the ridges, and the peaks were brought low. Between 1882 and 1886 a rough plateau, 307 feet high, was lowered twelve feet, leading a cynic to conclude that it would take only ninety-eight years to do the remaining excavation to the floor of a sea-level canal. But Gold Hill, which had stood at an altitude of 534 feet, was cut down to less than 200 above sea level.

During those years the world was introduced to a new vocabulary of Isthmian geography. Rumor circulated that *l'or* was the principal component of the highest elevation and men dug into it frantically for the precious metal that wasn't there, but the name "Gold Hill" stuck. So many contractors and sub-contractors went broke clawing into the slides of an eminence to the south that "Contractors Hill" became a permanent spot on the map. North from Gold Hill through the gap were railroad stops, villages, and construction centers like Empire, Las Cascadas, Bas Obispo, and Matachín; and to the south Paraiso and Pedro Miguel—place names that became as real to French investors as little historic towns in their own provinces. And all the Cut through the Divide retained the name Culebra—"the snake"—and to the last it retained the worst in reptilian character.

The years 1887 and 1888 were the big ones for the French at Culebra. The work was sectioned and allotted to five big construction companies. Electric lights were installed, and thousands of men worked day and night in the Cut. There were twenty-three steam-powered dirt elevators, fifty-four locomotives, and eight hundred dump cars, and the excavation was progressing with such rapidity that it was estimated there were only 6,500,000 more cubic yards to take out of the gap.

But on January 7, 1889, all work stopped at Culebra. The French company was in bankruptcy. Five years later operations were resumed and carried on for a decade, but victory at Culebra was never again in sight for the imaginative French. The machinery was broken and obsolete, and the spirit was broken too. One slide alone—the Cucaracha—had them beaten, for the

Cockroach crept into the Cut faster than it could be shoveled out. And it was just as well the French did give up, for the ditch they planned across the great Divide was so narrow that few of the big liners and battleships soon to slide down the ways would ever have been able to squeeze through.

The peak excavation record set by the French in Culebra for a single month was 282,528 cubic yards while some eighteen thousand men were employed. That was in 1888. By 1904, when the Americans were ready to take over, they were down to 33,000. Puttering around with the antiquated bucket elevators, little dump cars, and Belgian engines, John Wallace's men weren't able to do any better. Over an eight-month period they averaged only 30,434. In fact, the old French record wasn't broken until the Americans had been on the scene for a year and a half. But the day of the marvelous United States steam shovel was at hand, a tool that could heave five cubic yards— eight tons of "run-of-the-Cut" earth and rock—at a single bite. Given a break in the weather and luck with slides and accidents, a million and a quarter a month was standard expectation by 1909.

When political big shots turned up, there had to be a show of respect, but generally the Americans shied away from French-style celebrations. On October 23, 1909, a blow was in order, yet no one tossed a firecracker or raised a toast. That day Culebra was half finished. The statisticians had worked overtime to figure it out. HALFWAY MARK AT CULEBRA ran the headline in the *Canal Record*.

Culebra Cut was half completed on October 23, when 39,002,299 cubic yards had been excavated, and a like amount of digging remains to be done. . . . The section of the Canal work referred to as Culebra Cut is nine miles long, extending from Bas Obispo to Pedro Miguel Locks. It will have a width of 300 feet at the bottom, which will be at 40 feet above sea level, the normal level of the water being fixed at 85 feet above the sea. . . . At present the work is being prose-

196

cuted at a rate that should insure the completion of all excavation in the Cut within four years. At the summit of the Cut near Empire, the lowest point at which a steam shovel is working is 94 feet above the bottom, at Las Cascadas 37 feet, and at Bas Obispo one cut has been made for drainage purposes below the level of the bottom, at 33 feet above sea level. On the south slope of the summit the lowest excavation at Gold Hill is 78 feet above the bottom, at Cucaracha 30 feet above bottom, and at Pedro Miguel part of the excavation is down to the bottom.

Reading that somber announcement was as near to celebrating the big event as the boss of Culebra, Major David D. Gaillard, and his Irish assistant L. K. Rourke allowed his men to come. Gaillard was a taskmaster and a worrier who worked himself even harder than he worked his men, virtually unknown in engineering circles except for his construction of the Washington Aqueduct. He was establishing his reputation in Panama, and Rourke had already established it there in planning and installing with Stevens the original layout for mass excavation. The lion's share of the Canal was theirs—a stretch of over thirty miles reaching from Gatun to Pedro Miguel. Gatun Lake would cover most of the northern section, and aside from a little channel-dredging, it did not present much of a problem, but any two men who could conquer the nine miles of Culebra Cut from Bas Obispo to Pedro Miguel were writing their own tickets to fame.

Panama publicists had succeeded temporarily in concentrating public attention on Gatun. It came easy because it was something new. People had been hearing about Culebra and the failures there for a generation. Gatun offered spectacle, glamour, and a new cause for criticism, but Culebra wasn't forgotten. It was the greatest man-made canyon of all time and in 1909, at the "Half-way Mark," a sight even more awe-inspiring than Gatun, because of its vast proportions. Nothing like it existed in North America south of the Grand Canyon in Arizona, claimed the tourists:

The spectacle exceeded all anticipations, for nowhere else on earth was there to be found a display of human activity on so large a scale and with so marvelous a setting. It was this combination which added the final touch of the extraordinary to the picture. To stand at the southern end of the Cut, between the towering, majestic hills of the Great Divide, was an experience which few who had ever had it could easily forget. On either side were the green, forbidding, perpendicular walls of rock, and in the steadily widening and deepening chasm between, a swarming mass of men and rushing railway trains, monster-like machines, all working with ceaseless activity, all animated seemingly by human intelligence, without confusion or conflict anywhere. Throughout the Cut the scene varied only in the setting. The rock walls gave place here and there to the ragged sloping banks of rock and earth left by the great slides, covering many acres and reaching far back into the hills, but the ceaseless human activity prevailed everywhere. Everybody knew what he was to do and was doing it. . . . It was an organization reduced to a science—the endless-chain system of activity in perfect operation.

Other visitors were dumbfounded as much by the sounds as the sights:

From the crest on a working day you looked down upon a mighty rift in the earth's crust, at the base of which pigmy engines and ant-like forms were rushing to and fro without seeming plan or reason. Through the musky atmosphere strange sounds rose up and smote the ear of the onlooker with resounding clamor. He heard the strident clink, clink of the drills eating their way into the rock; the shrill whistles of the locomotives giving warnings of some small blast; . . . the constant and uninterrupted rumble that told of the dirt trains ever plying over the crowded tracks; the heavy crash that accompanied the dumping of a six-ton boulder onto a flat car; the clanking of chains and the creaking of machinery as the arms of the steam shovels swung around looking for another load; the cries of men, and the booming of blasts. Collectively the sounds were harsh, deafening, brutal, such as we might fancy would arise from hell were the lid of that place of fire and torment to be lifted. . . . He who did not see the Culebra Cut during the mighty work of excavation missed one of the great spectacles of the ages—a sight that at no other time or place was, or will be, given to man to see.

And before tropical vegetation had blanketed the exposed substrata of Gold Hill and Contractors Hill, the riotous colors made the deepest impression on still other visitors—"the barbaric wealth of hues which blaze forth from these precipitous walls. Reds predominate—red of as deep a crimson as though Mother Earth's bosom thus cruelly slashed and scarred was giving up its very life's blood; red shading into orange, tropical, hot, riotous, pulsing like the life of the old Isthmus that is being carved away to make place for the new; red, pale, pinkish, shading down almost to rose color as delicate as the hue of a maiden's cheek, typifying perhaps the first blush of the bride in the wedding of the Atlantic and the Pacific. Yellow too from the brightest orange to the palest ochre, and blue from the shade of indigo—purple as royal as Ferdinand and Isabella ever wore, or the paler shades of the tropic sky are there."

Nobody bothered to record officially the temperatures in this gaudy gulch, clouded with dust and crowded with the rackets of hell. At Empire, high on the crest above, where the cool breeze from the oceans could be caught whenever there was one, the maximum dropped to a humane 105° or 104° in the winter months, but, in the sun, official summer temperatures of 123°, 127°, 132° were common for the middle of the day, and it was a long way from Empire down to the sweltering oven on the floor of the Canal, where the brilliant walls trapped the heat and the only stir of air was what the machines created. Despite the disruption that showers brought, men looked forward to the rainy season.

Tourists didn't exaggerate what they saw from the brim of the canyon; they didn't have to. The "ant-like forms" crawling about far below numbered 7350 on June 1, 1908, and the rolls steadily increased after that; the "pigmy engines" they saw included 60 steam shovels on the same date, 156 locomotives,

199

241 rock drills in operation, and 2370 spoil cars of a dozen shapes and sizes, ranging from fifty-ton steel flats and eighteen-yard Western dumps to I.C.C. gondolas and over twelve hundred Lidgerwood flats.

John Stevens had conceived of Culebra largely as a "transportation job," and the most intricate rail system ever devised for a narrow nine-mile stretch it was. Over 130 miles of track were laid there, and along the narrow right of way roared twenty trains an hour through a congestion of steam shovels, cranes, drills and work crews.

Every steam shovel rested on its own spur track and parallel to it was a private siding where dump trains in monotonous procession shuttled in to pick up their loads of spoil. Empties came in on an upgrade toward the summit and moved out on the downgrade. Lirio, near Culebra, was the highpoint of the line, the demarcation between the north and south slopes. Trains from the Pacific end filled on the north slope; those from the Atlantic filled on the south. Their circuit was endless.

An engineer halted his string of eighteen empties alongside a steam shovel on one of the terraces of the Cut. A monster maw gently spilled eight tons of yellow rock onto a car. One by one the empties were filled as the engineer jogged forward. In less than an hour he was off on the twenty-four mile run to Gatun, to the huge Tabernilla dump fourteen miles away, or to Mamei, ten miles. At the central tower he was directed to Tabernilla, where a Lidgerwood unloader could empty his train quicker than it was loaded. But he didn't waste time waiting. The locomotive was uncoupled; the engineer picked up another string of cars already unloaded and he headed back to the yards at Whitehouse to have his train checked for damaged cars—"bad orders"—and was off to the Cut again to repeat the circuit.

Culebra was never silent at any hour. The Panama siesta lasted from eleven to one and during those two hours the steam shovels stopped their coughing; not a smoke-spewing locomotive was in sight. But that was when the dynamite crews moved in to shower the canyon with loose rocks and send echoes of thunder up and down the nine miles of deserted chasm. Again at five-twenty, as soon as the regular workday was over, the blasting was resumed. Sunday was a holy day when the Fourth Commandment took precedence over the commandments of the Canal Commission, but there was always overtime work for gangs who had failed to meet the weekday commandments of Colonel Goethals.

Even at night, when the mists settled into the Cut and muffled all sound, out of the depths came the eerie wheezing of fourscore steam shovels which attendants kept fired up twenty-four hours a day, week in and week out. Along toward midnight supply trains rumbled through, leaving off a few tons of coal in the bunkers of every steam shovel, ready for the next day's effort. Then at dawn the dynamite crews were back at it again with their shuddering explosions and shattering bombardments.

Danger was always present in Culebra Cut—danger from falling rock, rushing trains, mechanical failure, and human failure, but mostly from explosives. For every two cubic yards of rock that came out of the Cut, a pound of dynamite went in. Six million pounds was a modest annual quota. Tons of it were daily exploded in the war against the Isthmus. It was handled with respect by porters and drillers, but frequently with not enough respect. The toll for a half-year in 1908 was typical. Two porters were killed on May 27 at the Culebra storehouse. *The men had been sent to the storehouse to get some caps,* read the official explanation, *and the Spaniard, becoming impatient with the Negro's slowness in opening the box, started to knock the cover off with a machete.*

On August 19 there were a dozen casualties: *In placing the charge it became clogged and while tamping a little harder than usual to get it in position, the blast exploded.* A steam shovel operator and four of his crew were killed on October 6, and eight others grievously wounded: *Steam shovel 210 was making a cut*

201

*through some material recently blasted and a shovel tooth struck
the cap of an unexploded charge of dynamite.*

*Nineteen men are dead, about forty are more or less injured,
and a few are missing,* read the casual report of a premature
explosion at Bas Obispo on December 12.

*It will be difficult if not impossible to determine exactly the names
of all the laborers who were killed, as some of them are so disfigured
that identification is impossible. The accident occurred at 11:10
o'clock when the men were leaving for their noonday meal. Fifty-two
holes had been loaded. The cause of the explosion can only be conjectured. It was intended to set off a blast of 53 holes containing
44,000 pounds of 45 per cent dynamite after 5 o'clock. The charges
had been tamped in and fuzes set in all but one of the holes. One gang
was tamping the last hole. . . . It was a clear day and there was no
lightning to which the explosion could be ascribed. . . . The holes extended a distance of about two hundred yards along the Cut going
down 50 feet through solid rock. . . . The explosion threw a mass of
rock which is estimated at 55,000 to 60,000 cubic yards onto the
lower levels, completely filling in the lowest three cuts, and piling the
rock 20 to 30 feet high over the lowest channel. It is believed that
several laborers were walking through the lower levels when the explosion occurred.*

Two weeks passed before the last of the dead were disinterred,
and the list of fatalities had risen to twenty-six.

Half a dozen spectators witnessed the eighty-foot ascension of
Miguel, who happened to be sitting on a ledge the day another
explosion went off prematurely at Matachín. Every bone in his
legs and arms was broken, a few ribs were fractured, and his
spine was dislocated, but he was patched up and lived to tell
the story with consummate pride: "Caramba! I seet on ze aidge
of ze cut, smoke my pipe, watch ze work when—Boom! I fly up
in air, up, up! I stop. It seem I stop long time. I see ozzair sings
fly up past me. I start down—I breathe smoke, sand. Bang! I hit

ground. When I wake I in bed at hospital. Can't move. Same as dead!"

A few casualties from dynamite accidents, however, never were allowed to delay excavation schedules. For every man carted away on a stretcher there were two others ready to take his place. The chronic obstruction to progress as Culebra was the slide. Men could be indoctrinated with safety-first instruction; but no precautions, no ingenuity of science, could cope with the unstable earth that was everlastingly coming down the steep slopes of the Cut. All the way across the Divide, nature had mixed a hetero-geneous combination of sedimentary rocks, igneous intrusions, lava flows, and clays. Once the layers were disturbed, any ad-hesion they possessed was lost. The blue-green volcanic sediment, the red and black clays quickly crumbled. Wet clay flowed down any sloping surface, and as soon as the lateral support was re-moved from rock beds, "breaks" occurred and a slide was in the making.

Rarely was there a thundering letdown from the banks. The slumps were more insidious. Vast slides advanced a few inches or a few feet a day. During the rains the movement was accelerated, but dry-season slides were common too—slides "composed wholly of material so dry that when loaded on the trains, the cars were almost hidden by clouds of dust." Gaillard complained of a slip that claimed the exclusive services of one steam shovel for months. The clay oozed down at the rate of exactly two and a half feet a day. Tracks were laid parallel to its base and a shovel was in-stalled where it could move back and forth on the rails. "That shovel," claimed Gaillard, "made one hundred and three cuts across the toe of this slide with the position of the loading track unchanged."

Slides came in two forms—the "natural" and the "break." The natural was a slow-motion avalanche of loose surface dislodged from a compact layer beneath, and easing down an embankment in thousands or hundreds of thousands of cubic yards. The break moved more like a glacier—a broad column of rock and clay

203

that had lost its underpinning and felt its way downward for a new point of support. The deeper the Cut was dug, the greater became the downward pressure of the high banks. So prodigious was the weight that something had to give. The floor of the Canal buckled and bulged under the strain. This "humping" was unpredictable, and often hardly perceptible over long periods; or in minutes an enormous upheaval could appear without a rumble of forewarning. While observing operations from the Canal floor, Gaillard was once astonished to see a steam shovel at his side suddenly appear to settle six feet or more, but on looking about, he discovered that it wasn't the shovel that was losing its footing; he had been raised his full height by the uncanny lifting of a hump.

The havoc created by the slides was all but calamitous. A shovel operator knocking off work at five o'clock could never count on finding his equipment intact the next morning. In the rainy season traffic was disrupted almost daily. With crushing force slides would inch down to bury tracks and cars, to topple cranes and shovels; they blocked drainage systems and built up floods, wrecked equipment, necessitated the moving of scores of buildings back from the brim of the canal. The excavation estimate allowed by the Commission in 1908 for possible slides was 3,862,000 cubic yards, but even that enormous figure was unrealistic. Before Culebra was finished, slides had accounted for more than a quarter of the total excavation in the Cut.

As with Gatun, the United States public had the answers for conquering Culebra, and Gaillard's suggestion box was always full. The most popular proposal was tried—plastering the sides of the Cut with concrete. But the concrete slid down too, and had to be carted away. The experiment helped to prove that the slides were "basic," not superficial. There were no sure ways of preventing them. It was a case of letting the debris continue to come down until an angle of repose was reached, and the angle varied with every slide. The breaks were attacked from the top to relieve the downward pressure, and the Canal was broadened by the width of the slide. There was no alternative to shoveling out the bed of the Cut again and again as the mountainous masses flowed in.

Scorching steam and clouds of blue smoke rose from a break below Culebra Station after it had been attacked by successive blasts of dynamite. To jittery West Indians it was a horrifying demonstration. They begged for assignments elsewhere. As the heated area spread out over the bank for five hundred feet and sent out springs of boiling water, it looked as though the whole flank of the Cut was about to erupt. Planting more dynamite in the hot rock was suicidal. "Nothing but heat generated by friction of rock moving on rock under mighty pressure," was the first explanation. Gaillard was summoned. He placed his hand over one of the vents and was rewarded with a scorching. He pulled a Manila envelope from his pocket and held that over a crack. Although it did not ignite, in three seconds it disintegrated into flakes of carbon. The pine cover from a dynamite box was charred in three minutes. Gaillard called his geologist.

"Oxidation of pyrite" was the ready explanation of the scientists. But while the rocks continued to belch steam, smoke, and sulphur fumes for weeks, the blue shirts were convinced that they had cut into the side of a sleeping volcano. The heating posed a new problem for the dynamite crews too. Holes drilled for dynamite thereafter had to be tested for temperature before explosives were tapped into drillings in the breaks.

Cucaracha slide, a half-mile south of Gold Hill, was a natural. It first began to move in 1884—a whole mountain side skidding down on a layer of greasy clay as fast as space in the canal channel was opened to accommodate it. The French were utterly baffled. But the sliding ceased as soon as the blasting and digging ceased, so they referred the enigma to special engineers for "study" and abandoned the Cockroach. It was abandoned for twenty years and remained motionless as long as steam shovels kept their distance. The Americans moved under the slide in 1905 and confidently started clearing out the accumulation of two decades. Cucaracha immediately started on a countermove. In the next two years it dumped into the canal site half a million cubic yards—the equivalent of what that special committee of celebrated engineers in 1906 had estimated for the entire excavation of Culebra Cut. And that was not the end. It kept coming— a moving mass of forty-seven acres. Sometimes it crept across the bed of the canal as much as fourteen feet a day. Anything in its path was swept away, buried, and mangled. It not only filled the Canal but rose on the opposite side to a height of thirty feet. Repeatedly weeks of work were obliterated, and work was cut out for months to come. Benches a hundred feet wide were cut into the front of the slide to stop the flow before it reached the channel below, but they were only a temporary protection. As long as men were in the process of digging the Canal, they were digging periodically at Cucaracha.

In an auxiliary undertaking almost as costly as Dr. Gorgas' drainage system, miles of diversion ditches—small canals in themselves—were constructed on the high land back from the lip of the Cut, to carry off water from streams that would otherwise inundate the floor of the Canal proper. The ditches ran for miles parallel to the Cut and in the rainy season became raging man-made rivers. But landslips occasionally intercepted even the diversion ditches and at an importune moment carried the flood into the depths below, washing out track and trains, burying shovels in a slough of mud. On October 1, 1909, three and a half inches of rain fell in one hour at Empire, causing minor slides and washouts along the full length of the Cut, flooding the sump pumps at Bas Obispo, and holding up work for two days while the rail system was untangled.

Six weeks later came another deluge of over three inches, on top of steady rain for days. Reported the *Canal Record:*

At eight o'clock on the night of November 16, in consequence of continuous and heavy rains, the slides at Culebra near the old station of the Panama railroad, broke 300 feet back from the edge of the Cut and about 110,000 cubic yards of material, loosened by the water, moved toward the prism of the Canal. It pushed steam shovel 214 ahead of it. . . . The old main line of the Panama railroad was carried away, and three of the five main lines for construction trains in the Cut were either broken or covered up. . . . Most of the steam shovels are covered with water. Only two main tracks have been left open by the slide at Culebra village.

That slide was the most ornery of all the breaks. There a mile of bank with an estimated two million cubic yards of earth was slowly moving into the excavation, carrying with it a dozen homes, a hotel, a Commission Club house, and the post office. Telltale cracks in the earth had appeared on the surface for several hundred yards back from the edge. Half the town was sitting on a break that was settling into the Canal. "There is absolutely no danger whatever of any loss of life due to the continued use of these buildings as living quarters," came the reassurance from headquarters. "If the ground continues to slide, the movement must necessarily be so slow that there will be ample time to prevent any serious property loss."

It was not very consoling. People living in those dwellings were suspicious—and the suspicion was well founded, for eventually it was a choice of demolishing the buildings where they stood or carting their wreckage out of the Canal below. They were all razed—twenty nine of them—and the steam shovels also had another two million cubic yards of spoil to move out of the Canal.

"The Culebra Cut was a hell's gorge with the heat and the earth glaciers we were fighting," voiced a crane man who participated in the agonies. "A nine-mile canyon through the backbone of the mountains. . . . The rains and the sun beat down on us in that gorge. Blacks from the West Indies stoked our roaring machines, and shouting Spaniards struggled and strained in gangs about the machines and along the tracks. . . . Men broke down, men went crazy, men took to drink."

Eventually even the hardy Gaillard broke under the strain, but in honor of the man who led ten thousand men into battle there, the Cut took on the name of Gaillard.

XI

"MIRAFLORES AND PEDRO MIGUEL
WERE SLEEPING PEACEFULLY"

WHILE alarmists were lamenting the inevitable disaster of Gatun and worrying about the cataclysmic slides of Culebra, they were complacently ignoring far more tangible cause for dismay at the Pacific end of the Canal. Under construction there was the major weakness of the whole Canal plan, a very expensive error, but no one seemed to mind; people just weren't interested in an elevation called Sosa Hill between Panama City and La Boca, near the mouth of the Rio Grande.

The Canal would never be any better than a single flaw in it, but that flaw was being incorporated against the objections of a few soft-spoken engineers who knew what they were talking about and couldn't make themselves heard. At Sosa Hill were the makings of colorful scandal, yet newsmongers were so preoccupied with Gatun and Culebra that they overlooked the opportunity to expose the most vulnerable feature of the Panama Canal.

When Congress belatedly approved a high-level plan in June 1906, the law called for a lake of intermediate elevation on the Pacific side in addition to the sprawling Gatun "water bridge." That meant building a dam and one-flight lock at Pedro Miguel to bottle Gatun Lake at the south end of Culebra Cut, and a much larger dam with a two-flight lock at the mouth of the Rio

Grande. Between the two Pacific lock systems, Sosa Lake would spread out over some seven square miles. As Spillway Hill formed a natural anchor for Gatun Dam, so Sosa Hill would anchor the locks at the Pacific entrance, but the location of that hill was most unfortunate, for it meant that the works would virtually jut out into the ocean and the docks would have to be on the Lake, requiring a lockage every time a vessel used the port facilities, whether or not it made a canal transit.

John F. Stevens had warmly opposed the arrangement. The entrance would be a sitting duck inviting sea bombardment from enemy ships, and the fresh water lake, so near a port city, would be a grave health hazard. "If the Canal is not to be made neutral," he ad libbed at a Senate committee hearing, "I would prefer putting my artificial works at Miraflores and Pedro Miguel. . . . the entire lockage system at the south of Pedro Miguel and Miraflores—these together—with this idea in view: that the locks at that point will be from eight and one half to nine miles—say eight miles—in a straight line from the nearest point where a ship can lie, providing she reduced the fortifications in the outer harbor. . . . She would have to throw a shell eight or nine miles before she could strike anything that she could damage. . . . A ship would have pretty hard work to do any damage at that distance. Then my idea at the south end of not creating that lake was . . . not to make an artificial fresh-water lake right at the doors of Panama on account of mosquitoes and fever breeding."

Stevens had already persuaded the Secretary of War of the validity of his arguments, and in transmitting the report of the Board of Consulting Engineers to the President, Taft echoed the Chief Engineer's opinions: "The great objection to the locks at Sosa Hill is the possibility of their destruction by the fire from an enemy's ships. If . . . those locks may be located against and behind Sosa Hill in such a way as to use the hill as a protection against such fire, then economy would lead to retention of this lake. The lake would be useful to commerce as a means for relieving any possible congestion in the Canal should the traffic be very great, and would give, in case of need, a place for concentrating or sheltering the fleet. If, however, Sosa Hill will not afford a site for such protection, then it seems to me wiser to place the locks at Miraflores."

The logical location for all the Pacific locks was at Aquadulce Hill near Miraflores, built, as at Gatun, in two flights of triple-lift locks. There the Rio Grande valley provided a natural site for a dam and ample space for anchorage of vessels awaiting passage in either direction, but in 1906 there wasn't time to make the necessary surveys or to draw up final plans. Moreover, if such radical alteration had been pressed while Congress was disputing the virtues of sea-level versus high-level, it would have been interpreted as general indecision and the battle for a lock canal would have been jeopardized.

The law was a law after it was passed. Engineers continued to raise objections to the Sosa Hill dam, but no one in Washington or in the Zone was ready to risk another Congressional scuffle for the sake of planting the Pacific locks where they ought to be.

Colonel Goethals went ahead with preliminary construction at the mouth of the Rio Grande, where Stevens had reluctantly started it. After going over the La Boca area with particular care, the Board of Consulting Engineers could see no reason why any difficulties should be encountered. Their borings had showed "so-called mud" in some swampy parts eight to ten feet deep, but so firm that it could be walked on. No need to go to the expense of digging the stuff out; just dump the handy rock waste from Culebra into it: "If compressed in place, the material will be impervious." When they discovered that the rock base was hard trap, they didn't even bother to sink test pits, as had been done so laboriously at Gatun. "There is no question whatever as to the stability of the foundations at this place," they vouched, "and it seems highly probable that the rock will be so firm that it will not be necessary to build a masonry floor for the locks except at and near the location of the gates."

The Chief Engineer at that point was taking orders from a

higher command. He was not in a position to question or dispute the wisdom of an international board of distinguished engineers. If they were correct, the plan for the Pacific end looked like the simplest construction along the whole line of the Canal.

The first job was laying the rock "toes." Steam shovels at La Boca and Pedro Miguel joined the Colonel's cubic-yard competition league, and the scores compared favorably with those of Gatun and Culebra. Three old French dredges started scooping up the bottom of the bay for a navigable channel to the lock sites. The seven square miles that Sosa Lake was to inundate were cleared. Nearly half a mile of expensive high trestle was constructed along the line of the toes, and all the spoil that could be spared from Culebra was plummeted into the "so-called mud."

From the laboring man's point of view, La Boca was good duty. It didn't have the prestige of Gatun or the Cut, for the Pacific end of the Canal never seemed to get the publicity plugs of other sections, and inquiring Congressmen were so exhausted after exploring the sinking dam on the Atlantic side and the dramatic slides in the mountains that Sosa received only a cursory look. However, the temperatures and rainfall were more moderate along the Pacific, the inviting temptations of Panama City more accessible, and the "Yellow Peril" less annoying; the advantages easily offset the lack of prestige.

But La Boca was short-lived. The crisis came in 1907. Piles under the trestles began to settle; the vast amount of Culebra rock dumped into the mud upset Sosa terrain until weird hummocks were appearing adjacent to the toes of the dam. A train plunged over the side of the weakened trestle. In one night the rock fill settled eight feet, and when a locomotive eased over it the next morning, it sank six feet more. It was the worst setback that had occurred on the Isthmus, for it obviously meant that a terrible engineering blunder had been made at a point almost as crucial as Gatun. Yet the La Boca operation had claimed so little public attention that no serious hint of it ever reached the United States newspapers.

Goethals halted the work on Sosa Dam, hurriedly put his engineers to work drawing up alternative lock plans, and then, in the best military tradition, tossed the error back at his superior, the Secretary of War. In a courteous letter he blandly reminded Taft of the findings of his Board of Consulting Engineers, quoted from their documents, and reported the results. "To construct the dams in accordance with their views, trestles were built along the toes of the Sosa-Corozal dam, the trestles failed after the dumping of the material from them began, and the material overlying the rock moved laterally carrying the superimposed mass with it, the dumps flattening out. . . . The ground on either side of and in some distance from the dump was forced up forming mounds of mud, the crests of which gradually approached the level of the top of the dump proper. After an equilibrium was established between the dump and the adjacent mounds, the hump or wave would again move out when the track was shifted toward it, accompanied by a sudden vertical settling of the track of six to ten feet when loaded trains were applied. . . . An investigation by boring and testing pits was made to determine the character of the material underlying the rock. It was found to be for the greater part an unctuous blue clay without grit, possessing but little supporting power, instead of stiff clay as indicated on existing profiles."

The Chief Engineer explained that the soft mud went down as much as seventy feet, rather than "eight or ten"; that it would all have to be removed and replaced with impervious material imported from a considerable distance at an additional cost of $7,259,800, whereas the entire budget for the dams had been set at little more than half that. Since the expenditure appeared to be "excessive," he outlined several alternatives and recommended a plan providing for a single lock at Pedro Miguel and two at Miraflores with a mile-square lake in between, and a three-mile channel, five hundred feet wide, running from Miraflores to the sea. "The location of the locks," he reiterated, "secures them against all possibility of distant bombardment and affords them greater

213

security against gunboat or torpedo boat attack." Ease of transit for vessels was virtually left out of consideration.

Since Congress was not in session, the President cheerfully approved the change by return mail—on December 20, 1907. It was a major alteration in the authorized plan for the Canal, but was passed off as lightly as a temporary relocation in the rail lines leading to Tabernilla dumps. By minimizing the significance another full-scale Congressional investigation and visitation of consulting engineers was avoided, but the change in location of the locks still wasn't right. As Stevens had proposed in 1906, and as William Sibert had later insistently urged, the locks belonged at Miraflores in a triple flight, with space for anchorage above the lifts, but in the interests of haste and political expediency, Colonel Goethals had his way, the fundamental weakness in design was incorporated, and a possible bottleneck at the Pacific end became a permanent fixture.

Even in the Zone the news of the vital shift in plans was played down. On Christmas Day of 1907 under NOTES OF PROGRESS in the *Canal Record,* appeared the inconspicuous caption, *No Dams or Locks at La Boca,* and the incidental note that Sosa Dam was to be abandoned and a substitute built farther inland across the Rio Grande valley. The editors elucidated:

The locks themselves will essentially constitute the dam. The locks lie directly across the valley and almost eliminate the question of dams. . . . Under this plan there will be no Sosa Lake.

Actually the news should have been almost as significant as a sudden announcement that Gatun Dam wasn't going to be built after all; they were moving to Bohio. But Sosa fortunately was a kind of unobtrusive stepchild.

Everlastingly suffering the admonishment of Congressmen who thought too much money was being spent at the Isthmus, Goethals pounced on the drastic change of program for the Pacific locks as an excuse for a general shake-up in Canal organization for the

sake of economy. He had no affection for the civilian organization inherited from Stevens, and particularly he had no affection
for the man in charge of locks and dams, William Sibert, who was
constantly intruding with ideas at odds with his own. This was
the Colonel's big opportunity to exercise the chain of command
discipline he had learned at West Point. In orders as crisp and im-
personal as those emanating from a field general's office, La Boca
Division of Lock Construction was abolished and the Pacific
Division created under the supervision of an old engineer friend,
Sidney B. Williamson. The head of Labor, Quarters and Sub-
sistence, long unpopular with United States labor organizations,
as well as with his clients in the Zone, was tossed out, along with
his department, and a more armylike Quartermaster Department
formed. The Department of Lock and Dam Construction was
scratched, Excavation and Dredging went, and then the Department of Motive Power and Machinery, Municipal Engineering
and Building Construction. To the chagrin of Dr. Gorgas, the
Sanitary Department was reshaped. Major Sibert was much too
distinguished an engineer to be dropped, so he was placed in
charge of the Atlantic Division where he would have less opportunity to contest what was being planned for the opposite end of
the Canal.

The important divisions were now Atlantic under Sibert, Central under Gaillard, Pacific under Sidney B. Williamson. Major
H. F. Hodges who had served as general purchasing agent in
Washington received his promotion to Colonel, and arrived at
Canal Headquarters as Assistant Chief Engineer in charge of
design. The organizational shake-up went right down the line,
and from topside in Washington came the corollary executive
order: "The Head of each Department shall make a report upon
the work and operation of his Department to the Chairman of
the Commission as often as may be required. The Chairman of
the Commission shall make a report to the Secretary of War. . . .
The Secretary of War shall report to the President at least an-
nually." All this, explained Taft from Washington, "is not an

amendment or a change ... but merely a comprehensive revision."

Operations at the Pacific locks, which were responsible for the summary "revision," began to acquire some of the prestige they deserved. The cast-off French dredges and excavators were replaced with modern equipment. More seventy-ton and ninety-ton steam shovels were allocated there. During 1908 the site of Miraflores Lake was cleared with dispatch, and diversion channels were created for the Rio Grande. Pedro Miguel got a brand-new commissary, sixty by a hundred feet, as fine as the one at Culebra. Living quarters, shops, storage sheds, a power house sprang up at Miraflores. At Ancon Hill a special quarry and rock crushing plant for the Pacific works was opened, and at Chamé, twenty miles west of La Boca, a peninsula of sand was appropriated to supply the million cubic yards needed for the concrete work.

Miraflores and Pedro Miguel received more frequent press notices. A feature story in the spring of 1909 read:

Within a square mile, at Pedro Miguel, five steam shovels are excavating, preparation is being made for the laying of concrete in the locks, and the building of a dam is in progress. . . . Compared to the great barrier that is being built across the Chagres valley at Gatun, the Pedro Miguel dam is small, but is being constructed as carefully as Gatun Dam itself. . . . At Miraflores two dams are to be constructed. . . . The work has reached the stage where each part shows its relation to the other parts, and the outline of the completed whole appears.

The neglected Pacific end of the Canal was even accorded a touch of dignity in 1909 when the Peruvian Minister to Panama modestly suggested that it was appropriate for him "to agitate the question of changing the name of the Canal entrance from the meaningless La Boca [the Mouth] to Balboa, in honor of the discoverer of the Pacific Ocean. . . . As the Atlantic entrance of the Canal is named 'Cristóbal Colón' for the great navigator and discoverer of our continent, so should the Pacific entrance be named after the intrepid Balboa, its discoverer."

The proposal went through channels directly to the President, who chose to express "no view in regard to the change," but the very next day Circular Number 245 was posted in the Zone:

By direction of the President, it is ordered that the Pacific entrance to the Canal, heretofore known as "La Boca" shall hereafter be named "Balboa," in honor of the discoverer of the Pacific Ocean.

GEO. W. GOETHALS, *Chairman and Chief Engineer.*

And "Balboa" it was thereafter.

Gatun had its aerial bucket brigade—a far-flung network of cables strung at dizzy heights carrying scoops of cement in all directions, and looking for all the world like celestial cobwebs on which outsized spiders raced back and forth for prey. Culebra had a utopian track-and-train layout that would have gladdened the heart of any boy Brobdingnagian in search of toyland. But after the major excavation was completed, the channels and lock chambers cut, Miraflores and Pedro Miguel had a display of Rube Goldberg apparatus that could easily outdo their competitors in mechanical fantasy.

From Cleveland, Ohio, came contraptions in the form of cantilever cranes which looked like mechanized adaptations of cropped Eiffel towers balancing steel suspension bridges aloft. The "berm" cranes and "chamber" cranes were designed especially for the Pacific locks, incredible monstrosities of girders and machinery so enormous they could span the width of the locks and tower above their mountainous walls.

Sidney Williamson decided upon a system for cement laying entirely different from Sibert's method on the Atlantic side, and it was the show of Panama—"the most monumental piece of work on the Canal, and the most pictorial," declared artist Joseph Pennell, who had a superior eye for proportion. "These great cranes travel to and fro, and as I drew the nearest I found

217

the lines changing, but thought there was something wrong with me. So huge were they, and so silently and solemnly did they move, that I could not believe they were moving." Williamson had eight of them to play with.

The berm crane was little more than a glorified cement mixer, traveling on five-foot-gauge tracks, fifty feet apart, along the berm or bank of the canal. Its center tower was a steel skeleton, forty by fifty feet square, topped by an engine house and control room for the elaborate electric motors. Directly under the house was an enormous bin for crushed stone and sand, under that the mixing drum, and alongside both, running through a series of three working platforms, an automatic elevator for conveying cement bags to the top bin.

On either side of the engine house, stretching out for a total span of 350 feet, were the cantilever arms, supporting traveling trolleys for huge buckets, and enclosed cabs for control engineers. Dump trains, operating on trestles far below the arms of the crane, deposited hills of sand and crushed rock to feed the monster.

The electrician high in the control room touched a button and signaled the cab, and the gargantuan robot went to work. On squealing cables the buckets dropped from the arms to scoop up two and a half cubic yards of sand or rock at a grab, rose to the trolley, were carried along the tracks to the center, where they were tripped over the bins, then raced back for another load. With hideous noises of grinding and churning, tons of rock and sand swirled around in the bin. Sweating laborers on the upper platform ripped cement bags open as fast as they popped up on the inclined elevator, and feverishly emptied them into the mill.

Everything else in the tower was automatic. Crushed rock, sand, and cement in correct proportion funneled automatically into the mixer below the bin; gauges automatically measured the exact amount of water, and the mixer automatically spewed forth wet concrete into buckets containing exactly two cubic feet. Then a pivoted shelf swung the buckets automatically onto wait-

218

ing cars of a narrow-gauge railway, and they were ready for transit to the chamber crane.

The chamber cranes were slightly higher than the berms, and similarly constructed except for the absence of bins, elevators, and mixing apparatus. The legs of the tower straddled a double-track trestle on which the buckets from the berm were delivered. There the cement containers were hooked onto cables hanging from a duplicate trolley system and were whisked up, along the arms, and down to their destination behind the forms for the massive walls. "The four chamber cranes," boasted Williamson, who understood the mechanism better than his entranced audiences, "are designed to pick up the buckets, deliver them to the lock walls, dump their concrete and return the empties to the cars at a combined average rate of 320 cubic yards of concrete an hour." Awed by the magnitude, the confusion of sound and motion, no one ever challenged his statement.

The cranes were such a marvel of ingenuity that it was soon discovered they could be used for hoisting to a high spot anything from a dozen laborers to a few lengths of rail, and proved so adaptable on the loftier walls of Miraflores that cantilever arms were converted into lifting booms for additional height. And when smart tourists ventured to make irreverent remarks about the extravagance of machinery for a simple process of mixing and moving a glob of concrete, the guides were ready with an answer: "Oh, the cranes are just pinch-hitting here; their real purpose is to serve as booms and runways for unloading ships at Balboa docks after the Canal is done."

By 1910 the Panama Canal had become one of the world's leading tourist attractions, and construction on the Pacific locks was as wonderful as anything at Gatun and Culebra. Excursion specials were making the round trip regularly between Colón and Balboa, with a stopover at luxurious Tivoli, where no less than six hundred transients could be festively dined at a sitting. In addition to the fortnightly sailings of the old Panama Railroad Steamship Company between Cristobal and New Jersey, United

Fruit was running ships weekly to the Zone from New Orleans and New York; the French Line brought in continentals via Guadeloupe and Martinique; Hamburg-American steamers arrived every Saturday for a two-day call; Royal Mail had fortnightly service from both New York and Southampton.

The most voluble rooter for Canal tourism was Roosevelt. When he couldn't persuade people to take the trip, he tried to shame them into going. "I really think," he declared sadly in a speech at Omaha on September 2, 1910, "that outside nations have a greater idea than our own people of the work. I wish our people realized what is being done on the Isthmus. If a man of intelligence who had never left this country asked me whether I would advise him to make a short trip to Europe or a trip to the Panama Canal, I would, without hesitation, advise him to go to the Panama Canal. He would see in operation the completing of one of the great feats of modern times . . . which can only be paralleled in our past history by some of the services rendered in certain wars."

Many did take his advice. Tourists swarmed into Colón and Panama City and made a nuisance of themselves along the line of the Canal. It was easy now to visualize the lay of the great waterway. Where water and fresh diggings failed to delineate the route, the miles of trestles helped to mark it. In fact the extravagant use of elevated railways for temporary construction service—most of them soon to be buried and abandoned in the fill dumped from their heights—was one of the first sights that caught the eye of a visitor late in 1910. Trestles crossed the dam at Gatun, paralleled the Canal course for miles where they were supplying fill for the relocated railway line, ascended to the dumps, stretched out into the Bay of Panama the two and a half miles to Naos Island and into Limon Bay where a three-mile breakwater was under construction. The Colón trestle was double-tracked, already extending out almost a mile from the shore and half-buried in huge rocks. That trestle was the first symbol of

Panama construction seen by passengers from the deck of a transport moving into Colón, and the symbol stuck.

Anyone wanting to get a view of the operations in 1910 had to take it piecemeal. For a preliminary view, boarding the excursion train across the Isthmus was the best plan—first class fare $6.00 one way, or for $1.00 extra there was the parlor car "America" with reclining rattan chairs, camp stools on the observation platform, a porter, and paper drinking cups instead of the usual public glass. It was wise, too, advised the ticket agent, to hire a guide—$7.50 a day. "Gongs will be sounded at Colón and Panama, indicating starting time for trains: five taps, five minutes before the train starts; one tap, one minute; and two taps for starting."

But to make a proper survey, one needed to poke around on foot by himself. The guides had a tendency to steer their clients away from the danger zones and the interesting places where rubbernecks were in the way, and the train route was just far enough from the Canal to miss many of the sights. Moreover the line was in the process of being relocated, so that service was badly disrupted.

Gatun alone was worth a day's stopover. The heights of the town offered a superb view of Limon Bay and the three-mile Canal channel leading straight inland, both cluttered with dredges and miscellaneous utility barges. The massive upper lock was completed in the rough, another was half done, and the excavation for the third was nearing completion. The big attraction was the aerial cableway swinging half-ton buckets of dripping cement through space to the middle lock as if they were cotton wads. A precarious walk across the Dam was worthwhile, too. The east side was some sixty feet above sea level, the west side thirty-two feet up, and acres of cement were still being poured on Spillway Hill.

Here, however, guideless tourists were at a disadvantage. Over and over again, after taking the mile-and-a-half hike across the growing mountain of fill, they returned to the locks, quite unaware of what they had seen, to inquire how to reach the famous Gatun Dam that had once collapsed. And one scatterbrained clubwoman from Philadelphia, gazing out over the expanse of Gatun Lake at its fifteen-foot level, never suspecting that it was to be seventy feet higher, exclaimed appreciatively to an engineer: "How lucky you were to find this huge body of water right in the middle of the Isthmus!"

That body of water, indeed, was already impressive—four miles wide in places—but only a puddle compared to what it was to be. It was washing into the lower roadways of towns like Ahorca Lagarto, Frijoles, and Bohio, and they were hurriedly being evacuated. To imaginative tourists, the markings of old settlements were all abandoned French cemeteries.

"Oh, look! There is another of them!" wailed a sentimental American female, within the hearing of a calloused Canal reporter. "See the square headstones, deserted, forgotten, far from any town. Poor Frenchmen, how very pathetic."

"Pathetic! Shucks! Those ain't headstones," corrected a blue shirt, "they're house posts!"

These doomed or deserted villages were scattered along the shores of the Lake for twenty-three miles between Gatun and Gamboa, and that was also the section that was farthest advanced. The ship channel across the Lake was clear enough to float a ship through as soon as the water level was raised. At Gamboa the thrills of Culebra Cut started. That was where the Chagres swept in from the mountains and where a temporary earthen dike was slowly being erected to keep Gatun Lake from backing into the Cut while excavation was in progress.

From Gamboa south one could see almost anywhere the havoc raised by the slides. Along the nine miles the banks had broken away in twenty-two different places, and all the major slides were active in 1910—Cucaracha, Gold Hill, Contractors Hill, a big break at Bas Obispo, seven and a half acres of mud and rock at Las Cascadas. The track repair gangs were having a rough time keeping the rail lines clear. Blue shirts and bosses alike seemed to be working under feverish pressure, but despite the setbacks, three-quarters of the total Culebra excavation was reported to be done, and at one point the digging was down almost to the final level.

For the independent sightseer, Empire was a convenient place to step back from the edge of the canyon and look over a typical Canal village with a population of some five thousand. Here a temporary suspension bridge crossed the Canal site; roads led back into the hills on either side, and a north-south road connected with Culebra and Las Cascadas. It was a four-corners town, divided into four distinct divisions: American, native, European, and Negro. "Commission" was the distinctive architectural style for the American quarter; everything else was a hodgepodge. The palatial "Commission" home of Colonel Gaillard looked down on a weird assortment of other structures, ranging from pleasant Chinese homes with an Oriental roof line to grass-thatched Negro huts. Empire had a spacious Y.M.C.A. clubhouse, a huge commissary where the women gathered daily to exchange the latest gossip from the States, the headquarters offices relinquished by the French, and a sprawling shop where all the broken-down steam shovels from the Cut were brought for repair; but no feature of Empire was more enthralling to the outsider than the bridge. From it could be caught a stupendous view of the Cut below, and across it came a steady stream of Negroes and Indians from the interior with loads of produce, carried on their heads, or strapped on the backs of donkeys, yams, papayas, bananas, brilliant flowers, all for the markets of the town. Empire had local color as well as commission rule.

Culebra Cut ended at Pedro Miguel. Its two-chamber lift was ahead of all the other lock construction in 1910—major excavation long completed, center and side walls two-thirds up, and more than half the total concrete work done. By comparison, Miraflores, so long delayed by indecision, was far behind in the race—not more than 8 per cent complete according to official

223

statistics, but the monster cranes of the Pacific division still provided the climax for a trans-Isthmian tour.

Beyond Miraflores there was little of spectacular interest. Shovels were digging the channel to the Pacific; Balboa was a harbor city in the process of being rebuilt; a fleet of four dredges was busy in the Bay of Panama, and then there was the long breakwater with more miles of trestle. Getting back to the Tivoli at Ancon after a tour of the Canal was like a sudden return to the luxury of a home resort.

The most famous tourist of 1910 was another President of the United States—William Howard Taft. He came late in November to look over the ground with greater circumspection than the average visitor, to attend a banquet spread by a fellow President, the chief executive of the Republic of Panama, to give the workers another fight talk, and a boost to the Zone Red Cross and Y.M.C.A.

"This is the fifth visit I have made to the Isthmus since the United States acquired title to the Canal," he recounted. "The first I made in April, 1904, when substantially no work had been done except a little experimental excavation in Culebra Cut. . . . Then Gatun and Miraflores and Pedro Miguel were sleeping peacefully, with no knowledge of the world-wide reputation that they were subsequently to acquire. The hills that the relocated Panama Railroad has cut through, the valleys that have been crossed by its immense fills, were in the center of an undisturbed forest and jungle. Colón was reeking with filth and disease. The city of Panama was picturesque, but its condition unsanitary.

"Since that time there has been developed a wonderful organization by which the greatest modern work is being carried to a successful completion. . . . The first thing that strikes me is the fact that work is being done apparently on every foot of the fifty miles of the Canal. . . . The Gatun Dam and Locks with the Lake now eighteen feet deep, . . . the Culebra Cut and the locks at Pedro Miguel on the Pacific side, give a definite picture of what the canal is to be. . . . The work is so far advanced that the

224

time has come for the discussion of plans for the management and maintenance of the Canal; for economical disposition of the vast plant, and the proper means of policing and defending this greatest constructive work of many centuries. . . . Americans are justified in an intense pride that so great a work is the creation of their own people. . . . I congratulate all who hear me."

He was content to avoid any allusion to the fumbling at Sosa Hill or the compromise of Miraflores.

XII

"THE REAL GOOD THAT WOMEN
ARE DOING HERE"

Socially the Canal Zone was as class conscious as a well-regulated military camp or Boston's Back Bay. Majors remained happily aloof from the working man; Yankee blue-bloods had nothing to do with the O'Connors, Carduccis, and Chings. Away from the steam shovel pits, the dredges, the chamber cranes, and Culebra Cut, the social strata were fixed and inviolable. Never in peacetime history had the United States of America fostered an enterprise involving so much snobbery and authoritarianism.

Zone residents retained the benefits of the U. S. Constitution, but locally they had no vote, no elections, no elected officers. A Commissioner of Civil Administration supervised schools, churches, police, fire wardens and the judiciary, but the Colonel could override him if he chose. And quite aside from the undemocratic government was the highly cliquish society, with a system of recognized cleavages from top to bottom.

First there were two hemispheres, "gold" and "silver." Since the exchange of the Isthmus was traditionally in silver, native employees were paid in silver; the American elite—whether day laborers or engineers—were paid in gold. Bimetallism served as the convenient symbol for race delineation. Negroes and swarthy Europeans were silver; whites were gold. The delicate question of who was entitled to enter a toilet, a mess, a railroad car or a

227

commissary was ingeniously solved by posting the two signs: "Gold," "Silver." The distinctions were everywhere—a clear-cut caste system. In fact, the system was so thoroughly implanted that veterans habitually transposed the conception and explained to newcomers: "White employees are those who are commonly known as gold employees."

The social maze within the gold classification was too complicated for a neophyte to comprehend, for there were distinctions of military rank, Commission title, relative compensation, seniority, type and location of job, and integration was not the rule. People could let common interests and bonds of home locality break down the barriers, but it was at the risk of social displacement. On the Isthmus one's rank in society depended entirely on the wage scale, and that was public information. Salaries of foremen, for instance, ran from $75 to $275 a month, engineers $225 to $600, draftsmen $100 to $250, teachers $60 to $110 and any housewife familiar with longevity bonuses could compute who outranked whom, and check on whether a social climber was getting out of line.

The badge of progress up the social ladder was variety of living room furniture. Families of employees receiving less than $400 a month were assigned quarters with one kitchen range, one double bed, two pillows, two kitchen chairs, six dining chairs, one chiffonier, two center tables, a mosquito bar, a refrigerator, one double mattress, a kitchen table and a dining table, a sideboard, one dresser, one bedroom mat, three wicker rockers— no more nor any less.

To employees receiving over $400 went three additional dining chairs, a second chiffonier, a towel rack, a parlor desk, two parlor chairs, a porch swing, a serving table, an extra dresser, another bedroom mat, one parlor wicker rocker, one Morris chair, and a porch double seat.

Folks boasting of a Morris chair and a porch swing did not hobnob with neighbors whose porch furniture was limited to three wicker rockers. Moreover, the breadwinner earning a salary of $415 a month rated a separate bungalow with a front yard, whereas an unfortunate engineer getting only $395 might have to put up with a flat in a four-family tenement.

From a resident familiar with every phase of Canal life, including the seamy and the sociable, came the fulmination: "Caste lines are as sharply drawn as in India, which should not be unexpected in an enterprise largely in charge of graduates of our chief training-school for caste. The Brahmins are the gold employees, white American citizens with all the advantages and privileges thereto appertaining. But—and herein we out-Hindu the Hindus—the Brahmim caste itself is divided and subdivided into infinitesimal gradations. Every rank and shade of man has a different salary, and exactly in accordance with that salary is he housed, furnished, and treated down to the last item—number of electric lights, candle power, style of bed, size of bookcase.

"His Brahmin highness, the colonel, has a palace, relatively, and all that goes with it. The high priests, the members of the Isthmian Canal Commission, have less regal palaces. Heads of the big departments have merely palatial residences. Bosses live in well-furnished dwellings, conductors are assigned a furnished house—or quarter of a house. Policemen, artisans, and the common garden variety of bachelors have a good place to sleep. But it is doubtful, to be sure, whether one fourth of the Zoners of any class ever lived as well before or since. The shovelman's wife who gives five-o'clock teas and keeps two servants will find life different when the canal is opened and she moves back to the smoky little factory cottage and learns again to do her own washing."

The Canal working force was in a constant state of fluctuation. While five hundred quitting Jamaicans were boarding a third-class steamer at one Cristobal pier bound home for Kingston, a thousand more Negroes from St. Lucia, Martinique, or Grenada were disembarking at another. With good reason, the United States Census takers were unable to make their figures tally with Commission rolls. But between 1909 and 1912, those rolls swelled from 35,000 to 40,000—with never more than 6000 Americans among them.

Few of the living refinements were lavished on the racial hodgepodge of West Indians, Spaniards, Italians, Greeks, Portuguese, Scandanavians, Irish, Turks, Slavs, Russians, and Chinese. Silver labor lived in great airy sheds, dined in stuffy mess halls and kitchens, did their drinking "in the perpendicular" at dingy bars where tables and chairs were illegal, and found their entertainment in the back alleys of Colón and Panama. An Italian, a Spaniard, or a Barbadian would no more think of seeking admittance at the Hotel Tivoli than of appropriating a rocker on Colonel Goethals' front porch. Besides, he couldn't afford it on wages of ten, thirteen, sixteen, and twenty cents an hour for common laborers, scaled to a high of forty-four for "artisans."

In the Zone social register appeared names from the gold roll only, and marriage was a necessary hurdle for such recognition. Bachelors, who composed the great majority of the Canal employees, were quick to learn that they paid a high price for their freedom. Instead of living in neat flats or attractive bungalows, they took up residence in cheerless dormitories, where they could accidentally draw from one to three roommates, all clashing in interests, nocturnal habits, and moral standards. Rooms were cubicles partitioned several feet short of the ceiling, for the sake of proper ventilation, without regard for further privacy. The modulations of midnight poker games, minor altercations, and inveterate snorers echoed through the entire building for the benefit of all.

Any official inspector who ever visited the dormitories in daytime quiet had nothing but extravagant praise for the tidy accommodations. However, a different story came from the occupants. "A bachelor is a bachelor on the Zone," observed a novice assigned to House 47 at Empire, "and though he may be clerk to his highness 'the Colonel' himself, he may find himself carelessly tossed into a rough-neck neighborhood. House 47 was distinctly an abode of rough-necks. . . . That fact became particularly evident soon after supper, when the seven phonographs were striking up their seven kinds of ragtime on seven sides of us; and it was the small hours before the poker games, carried on in much the same spirit as Comanche warfare, broke up. Then, too, many a rough-neck is far from silent after he has fallen asleep; and about the time complete quiet seems to be settling down it was four-thirty; and a jarring chorus of alarm clocks wrought new upheaval."

A Paraiso insomniac became so exercised over the lack of consideration of his fellow roomers that he proposed "the absolute prohibition of the practise of bringing liquor into quarters" and "establishment of a curfew hour not later than 10 p.m.—something analogous to taps in military service. . . . When the action of various roisterers periodically make their quarters an assembly of brawlers, whom a respectable saloon keeper would not tolerate, it is evident that the service given to the Isthmian Canal Commission is not, nor can it be, as efficient as it should be."

That blast touched off a series of other concussions—descriptions of bachelor quarters "where six or eight of the occupants were 'laid out' and empty bottles lay scattered over the floor"; accounts of rude disturbances, of "profanity, loud talking, vulgar language, and running about quarters naked. . . . The fellow who will persist in annoying his fellow lodgers and trampling on their God-given rights should be expelled from the service and the Zone."

The complaints revealed the intimate details of a fraternity-house decorum, but it was burly locomotive engineer "Andy" Bearup who had the final say: "I have been a resident of Paraiso for eight months, and put myself on record as not having seen a drunken or disorderly person in said station in all that time. The noise complained of is only the natural exhilaration which is bound to present itself where entire satisfaction and good will exists."

The principal offenders were the floaters and those known as "T-T's"—tropical tramps, good fellows all. They were disarming, kept out of serious trouble, indulged in just enough work to avoid censure, and had a way with the boss. They continued to keep the bachelor quarters in a state of disquietude as long as the Canal was a-building, while their more moderate associates took refuge in marriage at the first opportunity.

"By its provision for the comfort of unmarried employees, the Isthmian Commission has justified the allegation that it systematically encourages matrimony among the men," was the satirical conclusion of a free lancer who looked over the unmarried houses more critically than either the welfare workers or the chaplains. "Bachelor quarters house from twelve to sixty men, and are wholly made up of sleeping rooms. The broad screened verandas constitute the only living room and social hall. If that does not serve the young bachelor's purpose he has the Y.M.C.A. which is quite as public. In fact, unless he is one of the few favored with a room to himself, he must wander off, like a misanthrope, into the heart of the jungle to meditate in solitude. As hard outdoor work does not make for misanthropy, most of them wander off to the church and get married."

Sometimes the lucky girl was a Commission secretary or nurse, frequently a "tourist" who had learned that the Isthmus was the happiest hunting ground in North America, more often she was a home-town sweetheart from Massachussets or Missouri, where the employee headed with a secret mission on his first forty-two day furlough. Uncle Sam had never before provided more ideal matrimonial inducement. At the Zone waited free rent, free electricity, free janitor service, free distilled water, free cooking fuel, free furniture—even a free honeymoon on idyllic Taboga Island for those who knew how to work it. Only the most reluctant of males returned from holidays in the States without a bride on his arm.

Colonel Goethals was accustomed to conducting Army camps of celibates, but for his mission in Panama he was ready to experiment with a different order. He needed to build up an organization that would stay with him until the Canal was completed, and he discovered that married men were less mobile than bachelors. The influx of women created a great many more problems, but they at least helped to solve the problem of transient labor. Although he was not in a position to issue an order on the subject, he left no room for doubt regarding his ideas, and by the end of the summer of 1908 he was faced with a bigger crisis than he had anticipated. At La Boca 26 newlyweds wanted rooms he couldn't supply; at Gatun, 30; at Empire, 34; at Gorgona, 53. In three months were accumulated a total of 309 more applications than could be taken care of. Solemnly he apologized: "The construction of the desired quarters, including furniture, light, water, and sewer system extensions, sidewalks, etc., would entail an expenditure of fully $900,000. In view of the additional applications which are constantly being received, it is not believed advisable to incur this large expense without ascertaining fully the attitude of Congress."

A few of the bachelor houses were converted into married quarters; carpenters were put to work restoring more of the abandoned French homes; Congress came through with an increased housing appropriation—and every ship brought a new delegation of wives and fluttering fiancées. Gradually they began to change the tone of the brawling little towns along the Panama Railroad.

The one institution on the Isthmus that made gold housekeeping possible was the Commissary. In the early days of American control, prices in native stores had skyrocketed. The Commissary was the answer, and it developed into an enormous chain department store where anything from lettuce and shoelaces to bodices and bedspreads could be purchased more cheaply than in the States.

At four-thirty every morning a train of a dozen cars pulled out of Cristobal with stock replenishments for branch stores along the line, cold-storage goods, ice, laundry, bread. Twenty-four cents a pound was a good price for the best sirloin roast or porterhouse steak at the Commissary. A forequarter of lamb cost ten cents a pound, a half-gallon keg of oysters seventy cents, limes thirty-six cents a hundred, bananas five cents a dozen.

An eighty-page catalogue of dry goods and hardware was distributed monthly, and housewives could thumb through it to determine the urgency of a special trip to town: "Pants, wash, Battleship brand, stock no. 37,521, pair $1.25; Parasols, stock no. 38,722, each $1.25; Lace, Valenciennes, stock no. 38,751, yard 2½ cents; Freezers, ice cream, White Mountain, 8 qt. size, stock no. 38,867, each $3.35; Cruets, vinegar, glass, stock no. 38,973, each 13 cents; Finger bowls, glass, stock no. 38,977, each 10 cents."

If it wasn't convenient to call at the Commissary in person, orders could be placed by mail; deliveries were made without charge. And no cash payments were necessary; coupons were good for everything. But it was a government business, and occasionally bureaucracy got in the way:

New employee to Commissary clerk: I want some lemons.
Commissary clerk: We don't keep such things.
Employee: They are on your grocery list.
Clerk: You get them from cold storage.
Employee (after walking five blocks to cold storage and return): They say I must get an order from you.
Clerk: We don't give orders except between the hours of 9 and 4.
Employee: I have to work in those hours, but will send you the order for the lemons.
(Employee makes order and attaches coupons in payment. A week later gets the following letter from cashier at Commissary):
Dear Sir: Owing to the fact that coupons are not good when detached from the book, I have had to confiscate same.

As a general rule there was a 20 per cent markup on all prices over wholesale stock in Chicago or New York, but even then the Commissary managers could boast that consumer costs on the Isthmus averaged two and one-third cents cheaper per item. Every demand of the public seemed to be anticipated. In addition to the Cristobal warehouses, there were a government coffee roasting plant, cold storage, laundry, printing office, ice plant, and a bakery that turned out different kinds of pies, at ten cents each, for every day in the week. Monday was apple pie day, Tuesday mince, Wednesday peach, Thursday plum, Friday apricot, Saturday greengage, Sunday fig. And if one lost track of the day of the week, the cake served for supper was a good reminder, e.g. ribbon on Wednesdays, brownies on Saturdays, jelly squares on Mondays.

United States fruits were delivered in season, and one May the Commissary was particularly embarrassed when the early crop of strawberries, transported all the way from New Orleans, wilted on the way. "It has been decided not to attempt any further shipments until the Norfolk crop is on the market," the Chief apologized. The good news came a week later: "Three hundred and twenty quarts of strawberries will arrive on the *Panama* May 20, and every five days thereafter until the close of the season a fresh supply will arrive. The berries will not be served in the messes but will be delivered only to families on special order."

The payoff for Commissary dependence came when the Pattersons dined at the Petersons'. Set before them were all the market specials they would have had if they'd stayed home: Squabs (twenty-five cents a pound), onions (four-and-one-half cents), those ten-cent Commissary finger bowls, and the inevitable strawberry shortcake.

Into this jungle fringe, long dominated by men and just beginning to be reclaimed to civilization by the introduction of Bucyrus steam shovels, cantilever cranes, strawberries, and American women, charged Miss Helen Varick Boswell, tireless advocate of the General Federation of Women's Clubs, in September, 1907. "We hear a lot about the Fatherhood of God and the brotherhood of man," she dogmatized; "let us prove that there is a sisterhood of women." She wanted to establish women's clubs at Ancon, Culebra, Gorgona, Empire, and Colón, "with branches or separate organizations in the neighboring settlements." "The club should be for social and educational purposes, to promote social feeling among the women, to enable them as an organization to take a part in municipal matters, governing of schools, and matters where a woman's wisdom may be considered to go far."

Miss Boswell took a quick look into half a dozen homes and eloquently expatiated on "the real good that women are doing here," on the profound influence of "the sight of domestic life and happy homes on the young men." "The influence of their development of social spirit is scarcely to be overestimated," she exclaimed.

She was right. Panama was never again wholly a man's world. Even the surliest capitulated to Miss Boswell and her General Federation. She ordered all the red, white, and blue streamers that had been procured for Roosevelt's visit to be displayed on the verandas of the Hotel Tivoli, and assembled her enthusiastic disciples in the most celebrated chambers of the Zone—the President's suite. There they learned the full scope of their projected endeavor—the home, education, philanthropy, music, literature. "It is a historic occasion," she orated, "which has brought together such a gathering of women from one end to the other of the Zone." Within a few weeks women's clubs were sprouting all over the Isthmus and growing with the rank luxuriance of any seedling in the tropics.

The multifarious interests of the clubs were soon felt in every quarter. They promoted riding, driving, and launch excursions; took up home horticulture and town beautification as a cause; engaged Spanish teachers and talked of making every member bilingual; scheduled whist parties, euchre parties, and dance parties. There were lectures on "Native Fruits and How to Prepare Them," "White Slave Traffic," "Lacemaking and Mending," "Settlement Work in New York," "Japan—Its People, Its Music, Its Art and Literature." At Las Cascadas a dancing class was started, at Cristobal a class in Shakespeare, at Ancon a highly specialized class in "Sketching by Moonlight." In every community weekly teas and weekly sewing circles became a fixture on the calendar. Wherever a stage could be rigged up, women turned to dramatic art and went on the Isthmian road with performances like *Lickskillet Deestrick Skule.* Come October, there were Hallowe'en parties; come November, there were turkey parties; December brought Christmas trees from the States, presents for every child, native or white—Santa Clauses, carols, and pageants. No excuse for a seasonal festivity was overlooked. Even the Battle of Lexington was celebrated in colonial garb at Culebra.

If anyone intimated that the commemorations were being overdone, a solid exponent of Federation philosophy was always ready to shore up the society with the axiom: "There is a greatly felt need for social diversion in this community, and the club is making every effort to meet the situation. . . . One of the most gratifying features of the movement is the interest that the men are taking in it. Not only the unmarried men, who greatly appreciate the increased opportunities for social intercourse, but the married men as well, give every encouragement to their wives to take an active part in the work."

Actually, the men weren't doing too badly by themselves without the additional prompting from the girls. On arrival they had first gravitated into state get-togethers. Ohio had a strong club, as did Georgia; then the boys from Texas had come along and outclassed them all with a gorgeous banquet, "elaborately decorated with palms, bunting, and the United States, Panama and Texas flags. The tables were in the form of a 'T' and decorated with rare potted plants. The cakes and ices were served in red, white and blue stars, and over the Toastmaster's head was suspended a large white star." They dined on such delicacies as consommé aux macédoine, French peas, ham with champagne sauce, Pontet Canet, roast chicken à la mazerine, stewed mushrooms, and shrimps en mayonnaise, topped off with Imperial cheese, fresh peach ice cream, and Lone Star cakes.

It was a losing game to keep up with the Texans, so after a few poor attempts to match their display, most of the men from other states turned to the fraternal orders they had brought with them. There were more than a dozen—Knights of Pythias, Foresters, Eagles, Odd Fellows, Masons, Elks, Woodmen of the World, Haymakers, Knights of Columbus, eight tribes of the Improved Order of Red Men; and for the unaffiliated, a local brotherhood known as The Independent Order of Panamanian Kangaroos.

Of them all, the I.O.R.M. had an éclat that caught the imagination of the workingclass, starting with the first public announcement: "On Saturday evening, October 5, of the Common Era, on the fifth sleep of the Travelling Moon, there was chosen by the chief of this tribe a new set of chiefs, principally young men who have the interest of the order at heart and will devote their leisure time to the improvement of it. Therefore, we shall be pleased to entertain any visiting brothers on any Saturday's sleep they care to call at Fraternal Hall." A young clerk was the new sachem, a carpenter the senior sagamore, and a foreman carpenter the collector of wampum.

With the wampum collected they went on to noble triumphs, such as the Washington's Birthday parade "at the hunting grounds of Cristobal, C.Z., 22nd Sun, Snow Moon, Great Sun of Discovery 437; Common era, February 22, 1908." For that great occasion a special flag-decked train left Panama at 6:00 A.M., picking up the various tribes on the route north; and later in the morning, with the Daughters of Pocahontas, they paraded through the streets of Colón and Cristobal in a half-mile procession of bands, floats, and Indians on the warpath including Aztecs, Incas, Caribs, Chiriquis, and San Blas. It was an all-day affair with a "corn and venison" beach barbecue, track meet, tug of war, and a dance until midnight, "when the members and their guests boarded the special train at one o'clock and returned to their own hunting grounds."

Competing with the array of fraternal orders was a score of other organizations, ranging from the United Spanish War Veterans and the Army and Navy Union to the University Club and the Pan-hellenic Society—a conglomerate of all the college fraternities in Baird's Manual. There was the exclusive Tivoli Club of 150 members, which arranged a formal dance at the Tivoli twice a month; the Camera Club; Strangers' Club; Gu-Bahay, restricted to Filipinos; the Ancon Amusement and Improvement Association, devoted to "any and every kind of amusement not forbidden by law"; the Stewards Club; the Isthmian Canal Pioneers Association, to which only the old-timers could gain admission; and at least one social group per village all the way across Panama. Any gold employee who didn't belong to two or three organizations was either a snob or a recluse.

Then the superorganization to which everyone was expected to belong was the Y.M.C.A. That was the one official institution supported and abetted by the Canal Commission as well as the United States Congress. Membership cost ten dollars a year, but the fees came far from meeting the expense of all the clubhouses erected by the government or the barbershops and Bible classes, lunch counters and libraries, bowling alleys and billiard tables, phonographs and physical education programs. The home Y.M.C.A. merely furnished the professional supervision.

In view of the federal sponsorship, directors kept tallies of their accomplishments almost as complete as the Colonel's cubic yardage in excavation, and in a single month they would report that there had been 5422 bowling games rolled, 1292 books withdrawn from the library, 6925 letters written at the public tables. The men were almost as avid students of Spanish as were the women in their clubs, and the "Y" curriculum also included classes in subjects like electricity, mechanical drawing, business law, and English.

Baseball was the major Canal sport, and plumbers challenged clerks or shovel operators challenged dynamite crews frequently enough that Y.M.C.A. directors did not have to stir up any

239

artificial enthusiasm. In the larger towns there was a game every night during the dry season, double-headers on week ends; and sport-page news from the States was of little consequence compared to the standings of the Isthmian Baseball League.

A "Y" athletic director, however, was as busy as a one-man coach in a university, with boxing, wrestling, basketball, fencing, tumbling, track meets, tennis—occasionally even branching out into cricket and football. A group or an individual was forever issuing challenges of physical prowess: the Marines at Camp Elliott put up a hundred-dollar purse and dared any group of eight to take them on in a tug of war; David Barry, who had made a plunge into the Chagres from the top of the old French bridge, challenged "any man on the Isthmus for high diving for any sum of money." An athletic director was called upon to referee a walking match from ocean to ocean, high water at Cristobal to high water at Panama. But the challenger himself backed out the last minute, leaving the field to two entries. They were on their mark at eleven-fifteen one dark night, and the next afternoon at four forty-five the race was declared a dead heat, time seventeen hours and thirty minutes. "In estimating the time," noted the referee, "it should be remembered that practically the entire distance was walked on railroad ties." Whatever was in fashion back home on college campuses in the line of dares and endurance found a quick reception on Colonel Goethals' big campus in Panama.

How his Canal ever was dug in competition with all the distractions he allowed remains one of the great mysteries of the century, for this organized extracurricular activity was only the beginning. A steady stream of concert and entertainment artists, eager to do their bit for the deprived and underprivileged of the Zone, poured into Colón. Spacious park bandstands were a landmark in the larger towns of the Isthmus, and the Commission band, fully subsidized by the Government, went the rounds frequently enough to keep Canal employees whistling the latest in popular music. To make the whistling livelier, the brass ensemble of any ship putting in at Colón or Panama was given a few shore engagements. Amateur glee clubs, minstrel shows, lyceums, stereoptican lectures, and vaudeville companies performed to packed audiences, and even the big top arrived in town: "Shipp's Great American Circus, which had come to the Isthmus by the way of New Orleans, opened at Colón on December 28, with its old-fashioned circus performance, remaining there three days. It opens in Panama on the evening of January 1, continuing for two or three performances, and then to Gorgona for one or two."

The biggest holiday of the year, of course, was Fourth of July. At Cristobal the celebration started with a "ragamuffin parade" at 6:30 A.M. and wound up with a public dance lasting until midnight. In between were aquatic races, two band concerts, "a national salute of twenty-one guns fired from the United States war vessels in the harbor," hose races among volunteer fire companies, obstacle races, tugs of war, track meets, greased-pole contests "with a prize of a $5. gold piece at the top of the pole," and evening pyrotechnics the like of which only a major United States city could afford: "The fireworks display will commence at 8 P.M. from barges anchored off Cristobal Point and will include the following set pieces—the American Flag, Incandescent Suns, Weird White Falls, Aladdin's Jeweled Tree, Pyric Cascade, Portrait of President Roosevelt, Good Night. In addition there will be thirty-nine separate displays of batteries of rockets, bombs, fire balloons, acrobatic candles, meteorites, shells, etc. During the display of fireworks an illuminated boat parade will take place . . . and a special electrical and searchlight illumination of the ships."

The band concerts, the parades, the circus, the fireworks were for the benefit of the lower silver classes as well as the gold elite, but virtually all of the other entertainment was strictly white American. The sons of Africa periodically stole off into the jungle for a night of voodoo, found solace in cheap rum, mimicked their paleface bosses by staging athletic contests and

241

wild demonstrations of their own. The Europeans and Chinese were left to their own devices. While gold bachelors dined in relative splendor at "hotels" conveniently scattered along the Canal right of way, the Europeans consumed their spaghetti, garlic, lentils, and rice—with a free bottle of wine—in cramped, squalid messes for a total charge of forty cents a day; the West Indians paid twenty-seven cents a day for a diet of salt meat, fish, and canned vegetables at dismal kitchens.

The bothersome formalities of marriage appealed to few of the Negroes, but this lack of conviction did not deter them from taking advantage of matrimonial prerogatives. For such representatives of the silver class there was none of the gold luxury. Couples were assigned to two rooms in long, barnlike buildings with verandas fore and aft. The Commission provided cots and a few articles of spent furniture, and outside on porch railings, row on row, charcoal braziers and lockers of corrugated metal, which served as kitchens. Yet even these refinements were spurned by many of the Jamaicans and Barbadians in favor of freedom and a packing-box shack on the edge of the jungle. As for the bachelors, they were housed in great flophouses with triple-deck canvas cots running end to end along the walls and down the middle, and the only space they could call their own was a few square feet of high shelf above the windows where personal belongings were stowed. Daily the floors of the dormitories were hosed and flushed as carefully as the stables at Culebra.

A newspaper in Rome reported:

Very few of the laborers in the service on the Canal Zone have found reason to complain of the too hard or too prolonged work. The great sleeping rooms are always kept in a very excellent condition. In the kitchens where the Italian laborers are not in the majority, we do not always find an Italian cook, but this defect, the most regrettable, has always been eliminated when complaint is brought to the proper authorities. The food, to which Dr. Lomonaco has given particular and rigorous attention, was always found to be good, healthful and abundant. Now, why should not Panama be—I do not mean a fabulous Eldorado—but a good field adapted to the development of the activity of our countrymen where the labor is well paid, the climate mild, and the treatment humane?

In the last analysis the Zone was a little federation of labor camps, not unlike the temporary construction communities along the railroad routes of the Northwest, where no one had reason to expect local franchise, equal rights, or the refinements of home. The only important difference was in government management, and because of that management, confused participants and investigators alike conceived of it in terms of a permanent United States community. No mass of American citizens away from home on a peacetime construction job ever had it so good. By all known work-camp standards of the early 1900's, they were pampered beyond credulity, and despite the comparative neglect of West Indians and Europeans, they too had never encountered such benevolent paternalism. As one sensible employee pointed out to his disgruntled colleagues, the only real drawback was separation "from the great main current of American life; when the work here is completed, we must return to a community in which we will be strangers."

But for gold employees the Commission was doing everything in its power to minimize the differences in social life between Panama and Mississippi, Panama and Pennsylvania. That effort was the excuse for extravagance in entertainment and the expensive transfer of so many features of the home town. The Canal communities would always have the "Commission" stamp in the style of architecture, for Cape Cod cottages and Southern Colonial would have been as out of place in the tropics as they would have been impracticable and costly, but every substantial town on the Isthmus had its American church and American school, its fraternal lodge and Y.M.C.A., its American Commissary and "hotel."

Like American precincts, the Zone also had its jails and an overflowing penitentiary. Five hundred arrests a month was a fair

243

average, and the offenses were anything from murder and rape to forgery and assault. In a four-week period a hundred arrests for drunkenness alone were common. So many criminals from the States got the naïve notion of the Canal's being an ideal sanctuary that a law-abiding Tennesseean considered the police derelict in not having a posse of bloodhounds. "The authorities in my native state," he volunteered, "adopted this method years ago and still use it for recapturing escaped convicts and in detecting the perpetrator of some heinous crime. A good bloodhound rarely fails to uncover his quarry provided the scent is not too cold. I do not own any dogs but merely offer this as a suggestion."

The proponent of bloodhounds got an immediate reply: "Two full-blooded Cuban-Texas bloodhounds arrived on the United Fruit Company's steamer from New Orleans on Friday and were sent immediately to the warden of the penitentiary at Culebra."

Yet when police records leaked out, criminologists unhesitatingly stepped to the defense of the Commission with statistics showing that the Zone police were no busier than those of any American city with a comparable population. In fact, visitors more and more acclaimed the fine *esprit de corps* among the workers. An officious investigator from the National Civic Federation—another woman—penetrated the Zone with a fastidious eye, overlooked the evidences of sin and uncivil behavior, and topped her long list of Isthmian faults with the complaint that the men were cruelly exposed to cold shower baths. Lack of hot water—where the taps ran at 79°—was the worst shortcoming she could find.

Visitors were treated far too hospitably. From attendance at dances, banquets, and baseball games they got the wrong impression. The secret was getting out that life at the Isthmus wasn't nearly as miserable as it had been pictured. Few, however, dared suggest any curtailment in the social program. The combination of work and revelry was what produced the good spirit. "Operations are now being conducted like those of a victorious army," concluded a visiting editor. "The whole construction army seems to be happy and contented, confident in the successful outcome of the work, and taking a just pride in their share of it."

No two communities were alike in their display of industry and victory. Gatun had the air of a teeming village rising out of a disrupted, defiled land; Gorgona was an expanse of noisy foundries, repair shops, mills, and boiler plants; Las Cascadas, with its acres of rail yards and engine houses, looked like the center of a lively transportation system—which it was; the hillsides of Culebra, above the Cut, covered with neat administrative buildings, had the appearance of headquarters for a vast army camp; and at either end of the Canal were the enormous waterfronts of Cristobal and Balboa which could have been mistaken for a section of Marseilles or Málaga.

There were finger bowls, strawberries, and string quartets in the Zone, but the Colonel never let them stand in the way of digging and concrete laying. Autocratic though he was, Goethals was a superb commander and administrator in an enterprise concerned with human engineering as well as civil. A great many witticisms had been expended on the Colonel and the Army discipline he represented, but as Canal-diggers came to understand his mysterious ways, they were ready to retract any barbs they had cast. He wore well. Now they were comparing him with the renowned British field marshal Kitchener of Khartoum—"the Kitchener of the Canal."

245

XIII

"TWO DOZEN NEW GRAVES STAND READY"

PANAMA was on exhibition during the winter of 1912–1913. The work had reached a culmination, with the lock walls near their full height and Culebra Cut near its lowest depth—a naked construction job of awe-inspiring grandeur. Those months provided the last opportunity that anyone would have to see the Canal in the raw, for shortly the yawning ditch would be nothing more than a scenic waterway, the basin between Gatun and the Cut a majestic lake, and the titanic walls of Gatun, Pedro Miguel, and Miraflores squat aisles of masonry protruding above fluctuating water levels. The wonder of Panama was manifest in its construction rather than in its completion, and volunteer press agents the world over were anxiously spreading the word.

The marvelous dredges were still sucking silt out of the channels and pouring it on the banks through pipes a half-mile long. Steel forms, behind which the monolith walls of concrete took shape, still towered in the lock chambers, looking like ponderous stage flats six stories high, yet so mobile that they could readily be drawn on rails from one position to another, so precise that the face of each wall section exactly matched the next. At Gatun the cableways whined overhead; at Miraflores the Rube Goldberg cranes crunched and screamed; in the Cut trains capered over the 130 miles of track, rolling up and down the terraces and along the floor, playfully hooting at each other as they passed.

Then in addition to all this spectacle, the colossal gates were being hoisted into place, and the deafening rat-tat of riveters fastening sheets of steel to skeleton frames brought a new staccato to the tumult of industry on the Isthmus. Atop the lock walls another rail line was being built, in anticipation of a day, not too far distant, when locomotives would be hauling ships along the waterway; and every few hundred feet were massive pillars from which would glare sharp lights to guide those ships through at night.

This was the time to see the Canal at its best—the last chance. It was a big moment in history that could never again be recaptured. The outlines of the stupendous task, under way since 1882, were clearly visible in retrospect, and the design for the completed Canal as clear in prospect. Every kind of mechanical contraption invented for Panama was operating at peak performance; it was the height of a noble battle between man and nature, with victory in sight.

For years tourists had been annoying the engineers and the bosses, poking into places where they didn't belong, dodging trains, asking clumsy questions, casually strolling over danger zones just as dynamite blasts were about to be touched off. They had come in hundreds during the early years; the dry season of 1910 brought twelve thousand; 1911, fifteen thousand; 1912, twenty thousand—not including Congressmen. More than twice that number of visitors were expected between January and May of 1913, and now the government encouraged their coming. Goethals prepared for them by taking on a corps of glib guides, building observation platforms at strategic points, erecting a new hotel—the Washington—in Colón, even converting a few expendable Lidgerwood dirt cars into sightseeing trains.

"The sightseeing business, which has reached large proportions and is expected to increase still further, is a necessity of the situation," came the official announcement. "There is danger in allowing people to wander unguided about the locks, where the structural steel work is in progress and there is a chance of falling; or on the dam at Gatun where trains are moving to and fro; or in the Culebra Cut where trains and dynamite blasts are a constant menace. The sightseeing business has therefore been systematized and its conduct is a regular part of the work."

Goethals didn't exactly create a new department of sightseeing, but he came close to it. A spacious warehouse near the Tivoli Hotel at Ancon was converted into a tourist station, and inside it was constructed an amphitheater overlooking a handsome table relief of the whole Canal Zone, working models of the locks, and a "professor" to do the explaining. The schedule for a special "Seeing-the-Canal" train was announced, with a trip over the Pacific Division and Culebra Cut on Mondays, Wednesdays, and Fridays, Gatun on Tusedays, Thursdays, and Saturdays. To supplement the lecturing of the guides, huge billboards were strung up along the banks and bluffs of the Cut "as indices of progress in excavation and to show the level at which the water will stand when the Canal is in operation." On steam shovels appeared great placards giving their elevation— and the figures on them were changed daily as the machinery moved into lower levels. With the display of signs and billboards, the Canal began to take on the aspect of a cut in the Boston Post Road.

"There is no better way to see the Canal than on the trips of the sightseeing train, and none that requires so little time," appealed the advocate of this new commercialism. "In any consecutive week days, it is possible to see the entire work. The train moves slowly through Culebra Cut, and about the locks and Gatun Dam while the guide explains in clear and authoritative manner all phases of the work, and answers all questions."

Thirty-seven ocean liners, booked to capacity, were ready to make the sight-seeing assault. United Fruit was not only adding two new ships to the Colón run but also was chartering special cruises. Peninsular and Occidental inaugurated a regular bi-

249

weekly service between Key West and Colón. White Star, Red Cross, and North German Lloyd ships of the fourteen-thousand-ton class announced stopovers at the Isthmus as part of extensive Caribbean tours. And other British, German, and American companies that had been docking regularly at Colón for a decade scheduled extra cruises. Only France seemed to have lost interest in Panama.

Owners of private yachts were studying Caribbean charts. Park Avenue residents who favored trips to Greece, Egypt, and the French Riviera made reservations this year at Hotel Tivoli. From Boston was coming a big delegation of Chamber of Commerce celebrities; from Cincinnati by way of New Orleans, a society of brewers; from St. Paul, a host of Minnesota shriners. En route to Panama was a cross section of the United States, including the Mississippi Valley Medical Association, the National Grain Dealers Association, the Nashville Board of Trade, the National Laundrymen's Association, the Louisville Chamber of Commerce. Then the Navy Department almost doubled the most extravagant expectations in tourist traffic by deciding that the bluejackets had earned a junket: "It is planned to have the entire Atlantic fleet of the United States Navy visit the Isthmus during January and February in order that the officers and men may see the Canal before its completion. There will be thirteen to fourteen battleships, each with a crew of about one thousand. They will come in four divisions, remaining four or five days. On each of the days one thousand men will be taken over the work. A cable message from Washington announces that the Department of the Navy also contemplates sending twenty oil-burning torpedo destroyers to Colón in groups of five during January and February."

Such a spectacular show of armor called for a preliminary mission of peace from the Commander-in-Chief. So on the night before Christmas, 1912, the tourist season was officially opened with the arrival of the U.S.S. *Arkansas*, convoyed by the *Delaware*. On board for a hurried forty-eight-hour call was that

250

most habitual of Canal visitors, William Howard Taft, the peaceful President with a message from the Prince of Peace. He wanted once more to reassure the politicos of Central America that the intentions of the United States were amiable and honorable, wanted to spend Christmas in the field with his army of diggers, and incidentally wanted one more look at the Canal while it was still in the rough.

An enthusiast from California who was also a guest for the holidays at the Hotel Tivoli wrote:

Canal or no canal, a trip to Panama is the ideal journey for Christmas. What shall I say of Panama City on the full-orbed evening of Christmas? Venetian palaces seemed to crown the hills and crowd the narrow echoing streets, every window twinkling with an extra holiday light, for it is not only the night of the sacred festival, but the President of the great Republic to the North has come to town. . . . Tinkling mandolins and twanging guitars make the aromatic charm of the moonlight on the flowers and royal palms to become sensible, as it were to the hearing. Panaman beauties, crowned with wonderful flowering headpieces, but bare as to their tawny feet, patter and chatter on the pavement of the latticed courts, or from myriad overswung balconies. . . . I shall carry always this picture of Panama from its old sea wall on the full-moon Christmas night of 1912.

President Taft had seen the Canal on many occasions and could hardly view it with the same sensitivity as the Californian who joined him next day for the sightseeing jaunt. "It is a good railroad by which one plunges into the wilderness; a new line entirely on the east bank of the Canal has been just completed at a cost of $200,000 a mile. . . . The railroad is just a tunnel through the jungle. Most noticeable were the gorgeous blossoms of lignum vitae, purple and yellow in splendor; . . orchids in the most opulent variety feed on the trees that crowd and struggle for fuller life in the dark swamps, fighting their way to the sunshine. To Californians who are used to a four-day trip across the

251

continent, it is a marvelous thing to cross from ocean to ocean in two hours and a quarter to the minute."

Gatun Lake, "shaped roughly like a sting ray," particularly caught the imagination of the visitor from the Far West. "Its broad head or body is twenty-three miles long; its tail, nine miles long, cuts a narrow slash through the continental divide, straight for the Pacific—a most stupendous achievement. Photographs are lamely inadequate; they want the proper perspective, and are unimpressive. The reality is like the forges of Vulcan, the gorges of Cyclops, the furrows that Thor might have dug in Valhalla. In a few months the water will be wholly on, and the splendor of Herculean labors covered forever; today and today only, the Canal is the wonderful sight of the world, a grand canyon hollowed out by man to harness Neptune."

To create this wonderful sight, Taft had fought as hard as anyone—the battle of the home front, a battle of politics and diplomacy, and he was still at it. He had conferences with the President of Panama, brief sessions with the Commission, took time out for another banquet in his own honor, but his real interest now was that of spectator, like that of the thousands of tourists he was preceding. He was a boy again, thrilled by the antics of steam shovels, cranes, and locomotives—a Christmas show put on especially for him, his Christmas present of 1912. The steam shovels were the most fun: "With their gleaming rows of steel teeth and their strenuous capacity for business, they might be nicknamed 'Teddies,' if only they wore glasses."

"One of the steam shovels," reported a bystander, "to the sound of Presidential applause, picked up a regular Taft boulder of some nine or ten tons, reserved for his special amusement, and deposited it on the waiting flat car with the precision of a golfer teeing his ball. Each behemoth was neatly labeled for Presidential inspection, showing its relation to the ultimate base. Some bore signs like 'This Shovel on Canal Bottom'; while others ranged all the way up to 'Thirty-three Feet Above Canal Bottom.' "

Taft saw at work the biggest army of laborers that had yet invaded the Isthmus—over forty thousand, and he observed "all departments of this vast army in full action, from the heavy artillery of the steam shovels whose smoke clouds the valley, and the resounding battering rams within the gigantic steel lock chambers to the needle-guns of the air drills, and the random picket with his oil-gun shooting mosquitoes. Ceaselessly and endlessly roll the transportation trains, half of them conveying the vanquished forces of earth to a grave in the Atlantic, the other half headed for the Pacific." Even Culebra cooperated in the Christmas demonstrations by spilling another few hundred thousand cubic yards into the Cut "as though for the President's delectation."

"The Canal gives an emphatic impression of rapidly nearing completion," concluded the Yuletide observers of 1912. "Culebra Cut is in line with the schedule for next September, while of the three sets of locks, Miraflores is 94 percent and Pedro Miguel 99 per cent finished. The chief forces of mechanical construction are engaged with the giant locks at Gatun, three in number, with their enormous emergency dams, but this work also is highly advanced (being 93 per cent completed), and will be finished long before the Cut is scooped clean. . . . President Taft has never done anything better than his effort to sanction and advance the benevolent despotism that rules and should rule the Canal Zone. If a foolish Senate endeavors to balk him and to hinder the progress of this splendid American achievement, in order to play peanut politics, there should be instant and stinging rebuke."

The day after Christmas Taft bid farewell to his wonderful Panama playground and was off to Key West and Washington for his final struggle with the peanut politicians. The tourist season was on.

Milling hordes began to descend upon Colón and Cristobal immediately after New Year's. The servant force at Hotel Tivoli was doubled, and although the New Washington at Colón was far from completed, half of it had to be opened, unpainted and partly furnished, to take care of the overflow of guests. Guides and railroad conductors became the colonels and captains over the army of invasion. Sightseers were herded onto crowded trains, herded into lecture rooms, and herded onto platforms at vantage points above Miraflores, Gatun, and the Cut. The patter of guides was the gospel of the Canal: "You are now overlooking the world-famous Culebra Cut. The construction tracks of this division total 132.7 miles. Its track length and equipment exceeds that of a great majority of the railroads of the United States. There are 1270 railway systems on the Northern American continent and in Cuba. Seventy-eight per cent, or 998, have less track mileage than that of Culebra Cut. Its maintenance force numbers 1923 men. The tonnage of traffic per mile is reputed to be in excess of that of any other commercial railroad in the world."

Then there was the spiel at Pedro Miguel, shouted above the clatter and blast of the rivet setters: "The gate contractors now have a force of four thousand men at work, over four hundred of whom are white skilled mechanics. The skeleton of steel girders that you see is only the framework. A watertight veneer of steel covering, called leaves, is riveted to the girders. At present the erectors are working on all but four of the forty leaves at Pedro Miguel. There are ninety-two leaves to the forty-six gates on all the Canal locks. They will require the reaming of 5,750,-000 rivet holes and the driving of 5,750,000 rivets."

Skeptical correspondents arrived knowing that the magnitude of the job had been overplayed by sentimental enthusiasts, and determined to cut it back to size. They took the trip on Goethals' "Seeing-the-Canal" car, wandered off by themselves to make their own observations, and returned to their typewriters to eclipse the most grandiose descriptions they had read:

The Panama Canal will stand out as one of the most noteworthy contributions that the Teutonic race has made to the material improvement of the world. The Canal is a triumph, not of men's hands, but of machinery. Regiments of steam shovels attack the banks, exhibiting a grotesque appearance of animal intelligence in their be-havior. An iron grabber is lowered by a crane, it pauses as if to examine the ground before it in search of a good bite, opens a pair of enormous jaws, takes a grab, and swinging round, empties its mouthful in a railway truck. The material is loosened for the shovels by blasts of dynamite, and all the day through the air is shaken by explosives. Over a hundred and fifty trains run seawards each day loaded with spoil. The bed of the Canal is ribboned with railway tracks, which are shifted as required by special track-lifting machines. The masonry work of the locks is laid without hands. High latticed towers—grinding mills and cranes combined—overhang the wall that is being built up. They take up stone and cement by the truck-load, mix them and grind them—in fact digest them—and swinging the concrete out in cages, gently and accurately deposit it between the moulding boards. How sharp is the contrast between the elaborate steam machinery and the hand-labor of the *fellahin* who patiently dug out the Suez Canal!

A British skeptic was astounded by the thousands of globe-trotters who had arrived before him and marveled at "the elabo-rate arrangements made for their education by special sight seeing trains, by appreciative guides, by courses of lectures," He too wanted to dispel some of the hokum about the great under-taking, but the words didn't come. The best he could do was to call attention obliquely to the extravagance and the strictly national character of the Zone economy: "The expenditure is on a lavish scale, but the money that is drawn from the American taxpayer is, however, for the most part returned to them. Practi-cally the whole of the machinery is of American manufacture; the food is American; the stores that are sold in the shops are mainly American; and the only money that is lost to the States is that which is saved by the foreign laborers."

Everyone took his own prejudices with him to Panama and usually found something to support them. A naturalist scorned the feats of excavation and construction, and went paddling on Gatun Lake to inspect the acres of floating bog islands that rising waters lifted from the bottom, and to hunt butterflies and orchids in the treetops protruding above the lake surface. And another tourist went back to New York after being exposed to all the grandeur of Culebra and the bewildering mechanism of Miraflores to report the greatest marvel of all: "I saw on the cars of the Panama Railroad what I have never seen in the States: a little ingenious trap-box near the tank of cold, filtered water, with the generous legend, 'Sanitary Cup—Pull One!' There they were for the pulling." Those free drinking cups were the most appreciated of all the Colonel's symbols of hospitality.

The heyday of tourism came on January 13 with the arrival of the first battleships of the Atlantic fleet, and for more than three weeks it appeared that entertaining the Navy took precedence over building the Canal they came to see. Clerks from administration offices were released to swell the corps of guides, and fifteen trains were withdrawn from regular service to transport the men and officers. The Canal Commission wanted to put on a demonstration of mass hospitality that would never be forgotten—and they succeeded. Open house was declared for all the Y.M.C.A.'s, and dues-paying members defaulted their privileges as the Navy took over. Colored club attendants were drafted as waiters who worked half the night making ham sandwiches—twenty-six thousand sandwiches—and then parceled them out the next day along with barrels of lemonade and bushels of bananas on the train ride across the Isthmus. It went on day after day, night after night, for almost a month.

The visitors were impressed with the Canal, but gobs on shore leave had to have a little variety in their entertainment. A Filipino band from the U.S.S. *Georgia* landed and made a sensational hit with a ragtime concert. Bands from the *Virginia*, *Nebraska*, *Idaho*, and *Ohio* wanted to get in on the competition and came ashore to give clubhouse concerts almost as successful. Not to be outdone in the battle of music, the *Minnesota*, the *Utah*, and the *Michigan* went on parade with their brass instruments. That led to athletic challenges, and no ship could leave port until its basketball team had tilted with a "Y" five. From midmorning until the last lighter left the Cristobal docks for offshore anchorages late at night, the Colón waterfront, the special information bureaus, the wharves, and the streets teamed with the United States Navy. In search of honkytonk adventure, gullible groups paid extortionate fees for horse and livery rides across the border or motor-cab trips to the immoral back alleys of Colón. When the last of the battleships and destroyers had disappeared over the horizon on February 8, old-time Canalers breathed with relief; the place was theirs again.

The visit of the Fleet brought to light the mercenary dealings of local cab services, and Goethals was quick to act. Ceilings were placed on taxi tariffs and chauffeurs held to a maximum charge of six dollars an hour for a six-passenger vehicle. The motor car was beginning to invade the Isthmus. In the whole Canal operation there was not a single motor truck in use. Whenever material or personnel had to be transported in quantity, a track was laid. Mules and horses did what little drayage was necessary where locomotives didn't go, and livery stables or private equipages served the elite who preferred not to walk. It was not a great problem, for there was no highway across the Isthmus, and only a few roads and trails radiated from the principal towns.

But back in the States the gasoline-propelled vehicle was becoming less of a novelty, and the fashion was spreading south —with all manner of restrictions. Drivers were now compelled "to carry and prominently display between the hours of 6 P.M. and 5 A.M. . . . two bright front or head lights, one on either side, and one red light in the rear." They were forbidden to drive "at a speed exceeding fifteen miles an hour on straight roads, or at a speed exceeding eight miles an hour when approaching curves, forks, or crossroads"—with a maximum penalty of $100 and thirty days' imprisonment for any violation. A registration fee of $25 a year was charged to owners of pleasure cars, and a dollar extra for the metal card that had to be "carried in a conspicuous place at the rear, bearing thereon in large numerals, the number of the license," while operators of commercial cabs were assessed a formidable $125 for registration.

It was a lot of law for a total of thirteen automobiles and one "motor wagon" owned by Zone residents, and had the earmarks of legislative restraint of trade for chauffeurs in the Republic of Panama, for they were charged the same fees and subjected to the same restrictions when they crossed the border from Colón or Panama City. Foresightedly, however, Goethals recognized the coming of a motor-car era and started a program of building macadam roads. They were a military necessity and a tourist necessity.

In April, 1913, came an even bigger travel thrill than the automobile. At Panama City arrived Robert G. Fowler, renowned California aviator, with the announced plan of making a nonstop flight the full width of the Isthmus. For three weeks he barnstormed about Balboa, stirring up interest in his undertaking and waiting for just the right weather conditions for the historic flight in his hydrobiplane. Bulletins of his success were issued from day to day: *April 12—Over Panama and vicinity, without passenger; time in air 15 minutes. . . . April 13—Over Panama and vicinity, with passenger and camera; time in air five minutes. Compelled to descend on account of poor gasoline. . . . April 25—Over Panama and Ancon, without passenger; time in air 15 minutes. . . . April 25—Over Panama, islands in the bay, Naos Island breakwater, Pacific entrance and up the Canal as far as Miraflores with passenger and camera. Picture film became exhausted.*

At last, on April 27, he had a break in the weather and decided to make the plunge. With a capacity load of gasoline, a passenger, and a camera, he roared over Balboa, sighted Miraflores below, and headed north. Photographing the Canal from the air was one of the objects of the great expedition, and over Culebra Cut he boldly made a complete circle while his photographer ground away to film the yawning chasm. Below, he saw men wildly waving him on to victory and the puffs of steam from saluting steam shovels. To catch the expanse of Gatun Lake he rose to a breath-taking altitude of 1800 feet. Over Gamboa he ran into a drenching rain squall; the motor coughed and the camera went into hiding, but the eighty-horsepower motor came through the squall functioning smoothly and raced on across the continent. The pilot dipped to an altitude of 400 feet over Gatun, and then with fast-diminishing fuel supply headed down the home stretch of canal toward Limon Bay.

"The trip over the Canal was uneventful," he reported, "with the exception of the descent at Cristobal. The supply of gasoline became exhausted on nearing the journey's end, and the glide failed to carry the machine to deep water. It landed among the rocks off Pier 11."

The flying machine had beaten the steamship in a first trip across the Isthmus—time for the forty miles, one hour and thirty-five minutes.

For the sightseeing season of 1913 tourists were treated to a series of disasters far more grim than the puncturing of airman Fowler's hydrobiplane pontoons. Those with the discernment to take in more than the spectacle, to read more than the big signs, to listen to the hardships of West Indians as attentively as the glamorous patter of guides, could realize some of the harshness of the Panama struggle. At Toro Point, from which the long finger of the Colón Breakwater reached out, two sections of married quarters went up in flames and a half-dozen-upper-floor occupants barely escaped with their lives when ladders on which they were escaping the conflagration collapsed. Sparks from a locomotive set fire to a lumber yard at Balboa; the heat from the burning lumber burst a four-inch oil pipe and a brook of burning oil crept down a railroad siding, setting fire to a train of box cars as it went.

On Gatun Lake the launch *Manzanillo,* carrying a group of surveyors, mysteriously caught fire off shore and exploded. Three chainmen managed to swim to a tree protruding from the water and clung to branches until rescued, but skipper Esau Johnson, painfully burned, didn't make it. Three men were killed and nineteen seriously injured when over twenty thousand pounds of dynamite went up in another premature explosion south of Miraflores locks, and like most of the dynamite accidents, no cause could ever be found. These were not unusual incidents; every day brought more like them.

North of Empire the Obispo Diversion Channel, built to keep out of the Canal the brooks and tributaries of an area ten miles square, broke through the banks, inundated Culebra Cut, and raised havoc for three days, but the tourists scarcely noticed the little emergency. One night the sudden sliding of some eight thousand cubic yards of sea mole carried away the piles under a long section of pier at Balboa, toppling two huge unloading cranes, demolishing the cargo sheds, and sinking the twenty-seven-hundred-ton freighter *Newport* moored alongside. It all happened within two minutes, a waterfront policeman claimed. And the next morning the wreckage looked as though a bomb had struck —a completely collapsed pier, with only the funnel and wheelhouse superstructure of the *Newport* visible above water at high tide, all crowned with a tangle of broken cranes.

More poignant than the property disasters was the loss of life among the West Indians—tragedies that rarely came to the attention of sightseers. The death of George Atchison, Jamaican, check Number 44899, brushed off the side of a trestle at Empire by a passing train, was typical. There was no obituary nor memorial for him, just a single-line recital of the facts in the *Canal Record,* as though he hadn't quite attained human status. Nor was there any more fitting notice for Samuel Thomas of Montserrat, check Number 465185, who died in excruciating agony, caught in the pulleys of a mud scow; nor for Edwin Carrington of Barbados, trapped under a house when the jacks gave way; nor for William Lennon, crushed between a locomotive crane and a staircase at the west wall of Miraflores Locks; nor Joseph Velox of St. Vincent, who was asphyxiated while heroically trying to rescue Jonathan Bentley from the bottom of an airless seventy-five-foot caisson pit.

One touring journalist chose to pay tribute to "The Canal Diggers Who Will Never Come Back," went the rounds of the cemeteries, investigated the hospitals, and discovered that the mortality was close to five hundred a year. She wrote:

There is a noticeable silence about the constantly occurring deaths, especially those by accident. A hospital car is carried on every train, and it is a common thing to see a stretcher, or two, or three, taken out of this car at Panama, upon which lies prostrate a human form; sometimes animate with only a foot or arm or head wrapped in bloody bandages; sometimes covered by a sheet. Once in a while the monotonous noisy hum on the crowded station platform is rent by a wail or shriek as the stretcher is met by some waiting friend or loved one. Then the crowd gathers silently around—orderly, unexcited, simply interested in watching the wife or mother at the side of the grim figure on the stretcher and listening to her weeping. But presently with the systematic despatch that characterizes the whole organization, the stretcher is placed on the hospital ambulance and driven away, and the crowd quietly disperses. The matter has been of too common occurrence even to arouse comment. One would never dream amid all the canal enthusiasm and energy and the sort of joyousness that prevails among the workers, that every day on an average ends more than one life. Two dozen new graves stand ready all the time at Ancon cemetery.

The most conspicuous disasters and setbacks continued to be those in Culebra Cut. Almost every week, in the dry season now, as well as the wet, a new avalanche poured down the banks, slides of a mere 250,000 cubic yards, slides of 900,000 yards, slides a quarter-mile long, and convulsions that thrust the bottom up another thirty feet. The Culebra clubhouse, resting squarely on a break, was being dismantled "in order to lighten the weight upon the west bank of the Canal at this point." On January 19 Cucaracha started acting up again and sent a rock bluff three hundred feet high onto the tracks below. "It is estimated that the break will add not less than 1,000,000 cubic yards to the amount which will have to be removed," declared the engineers. Then at the height of the tourist season, on the night of March 12, came a thundering big slide opposite Culebra. Two steam shovels were overturned and every track, except one, on the Canal floor was buried.

It looked as though the digging could go on interminably. Contending with the everlasting slides called for an uncommon faith and an uncommon philosophy; and the answer from head-quarters was always vaguely the same: "Because the development and extent of the slides cannot be accurately estimated, excavation through the Cut will be prosecuted with vigor. The slides call for no other treatment than unremitting excavation."

But despite the catastrophes no tourist was ever permitted to doubt that ships would be sailing from the Atlantic to the Pacific on January 1, 1915—the date first set by Chief Engineer Stevens. In anticipation of that deadline, work forces were already being given termination notices. As labor in one section was completed, a whole village was quickly torn down and erased from the map. The rock crushing plant at Porto Bello was abandoned; the Gorgona shops were stripped and moved to a more permanent location at Balboa. Churches here and there were closing their doors; fire departments were trimmed down; the I.C.C. Band gave its last concert on February 26, 1913, and quietly folded; the Canal Zone Federation of Women's Clubs held a final "general meeting" on January 25 and ordered that the Club would go out of existence in April because "the forthcoming changes in the canal force would remove the majority of the members from the Isthmus."

None of these subtle changes in Canal life was obvious to visitors. Forty thousand men were still at work. But every tourist sensed that he was witnessing the culmination of a great victory. "When the tourists and the eminent scientists, the congressmen and the rest of them come down after the water is in the ditch, they'll wonder how we managed to spend all the money," remarked a Gatun engineer to a passing tourist. "Next year the vast water tunnels, the intricate electrical mechanisms, and the monolithic steel lock gates will be submerged. And in 1915 the scars of the steam shovels where cuts have been made will be healed and covered over with the irrepressible tropical greenery, disguising the difficulties of their making. In a year or two it will all appear to have been that way since the beginning of time."

The indescribable "difficulties" were what the sightseers of 1913 were viewing. "Culebra Cut is more than evidence of heroic human endeavor," concluded a spectator. "It belongs by rights to the catalogue of geologic events. . . . Those locks are more than tons of concrete and iron, more even than a monument to the labors and loves of our mechanics and engineers. They are the gate to that pathway of which Columbus dreamed and for which Hudson died. They are the answer of courage and faith to doubt and unbelief. In them are the blood and sinew of a great and hopeful Nation, the fulfillment of ancient ideals and the promise of a larger growth to come. I came to the locks with the joyousness of new adventure. I left with the feeling that follows a service in a great cathedral."

XIV

"THERE, IT'S ALL OVER.
GAMBOA IS BUSTED"

CANAL history had been a long record of disappointments in meeting dates and deadlines for completion. In May, 1879, a French international congress of engineers confidently predicted the job could be done within twelve years. From that total de Lesseps airily subtracted four years, and then to expedite his promotion campaign trimmed off two more. At an acrimonious meeting of his stockholders in July, 1883, while a half-dozen clumsy excavators were nibbling into the Great Divide and men were dying like flies, he still insisted that ships would be crossing the Isthmus in 1888.

With the bankruptcy of the first construction company, and with the fadeaway of the fervent promoter, the Compagnie Nouvelle took a more conservative view and talked of another six years for a lock canal—completion in 1900. Chief Engineer Wallace, voicing high American hopes and privately thinking in terms of a sea-level route, wanted to allow two years for preparations, two for contingencies, and six for excavation. And finally John F. Stevens, after sizing up the situation realistically, had the professional self-assurance to give January 1, 1915, as a definite deadline. Goethals ran into problems that Stevens could never have foreseen, but that date was as firmly fixed in his mind as it had been in the mind of his predecessor. He'd beat it if he could.

By the middle of 1913, half the world, it seemed, was putting pressure on the Colonel for a definite commitment. If the Canal were going to be open before New Year's Day, 1915, they wanted to be in on the secret. A new President, Woodrow Wilson, wanted to know; Secretary of War Garrison wanted to know; solicitous Congressmen felt that they were entitled to the information. Important people all over the world—people who might get an invitation to the opening ceremonies—were eager to make the necessary adjustments on their calendars. From Shanghai to Seattle, from Hamburg to Hampton Roads, shipping companies that scheduled sailings months in advance needed to know. Cagily Goethals stuck to the January 1 date, with an exasperating hint that every effort would be made to complete the work before then. He intended to avoid any boners of the de Lesseps variety. If the waterway were completed in advance, he'd use the extra weeks or months in testing the works on whatever shipping came his way. He couldn't be bothered with social calendars of politicians, and the freight movements of every little transportation company. Keeping up with the movement of the banks of Culebra Cut was more than enough to absorb his attention.

In June, 1913, the Atlantic entrance to the Canal was still blocked below Gatun Locks by a railroad dike. The Pacific entrance was blocked by two barriers south of Miraflores Locks; and at Gamboa, halfway along the Canal, was a third massive embankment, which kept Gatun Lake out of Culebra Cut. But the greatest barricade was at Cucaracha, where steam shovels and excavation gangs were finding it difficult to keep even one set of railroad tracks in the clear. The slide extended along the Canal floor for almost a quarter of a mile.

On the locks practically all of the mass masonry was completed; gangs were busy backfilling and grading, mechanics and electricians were installing operating machines. The construction of the lock gates was well along, and most of the culvert valves were in place. None of the spillways nor dams was quite finished, but another six months would see the heaviest work out of the way. Almost as many men were employed in erecting superficial gear like lampposts and chain fenders as had been occupied in laying cement. The deciding factor in determining the opening date of the Canal was not going to be Gatun Dam or Miraflores after all; it was the excavation of Culebra Cut.

At this stage the Chief Engineer's formidable problem was to coordinate the thousands of odds and ends, shifting his labor force and equipment about, so that the essentials would be completed in logical sequence at approximately the same time. And the big unknowns in all this were the slides in the Cut. The rock and dirt kept cascading down the banks in fantastic quantity. At Cucaracha there were as many steam shovels as could be conveniently assembled, yet the surface of the hill oozed out as fast as it could be carted away. "Optimists measure the life of the slides in months, the pessimists in centuries," summarized a visitor. Occasionally a loud voice of despair was raised, but Goethals was no pessimist; he was convinced that he could conquer Cucaracha and do it on schedule.

September 25, 1913, was the four-hundredth anniversary of the discovery of the Pacific by Vasco Núñez de Balboa. That would have been the ideal date for the opening of the Canal. Impossible now, of course. But without making too much noise about it, Goethals counted on honoring the Spanish explorer on the four hundred first anniversary of that discovery. Victory was in the air.

During the spring of 1913 steam shovel number 222 ate its way along the ultimate floor level of Culebra Cut toward steam shovel number 230 on the same level. The two met at four-thirty in the afternoon of May 20, opposite Hodges Hill. At last there was one path through the Continental Divide cut to final grade. Jowl to jowl the steam shovels stood for a few minutes while photographers jockeyed for positions to record the event. Jamaicans doffed their hats and yelled. Italians, Barbadians, Americans, and Spaniards joined them. Trains paused in salute. Every steam whistle in the Cut let out blast after blast. The rejoicing

267

went on until quitting time. It was the first of a long series of noisy celebrations that were to mark the piecemeal conquest.

Three months later arrived the big day for letting the Pacific Ocean into the Canal. This was an occasion that every Isthmian would want to witness, so the festivities were scheduled for a Sunday morning—August 31—when work elsewhere would not be interrupted. Over five hundred holes were drilled into the dike a mile south of Miraflores, and twenty tons of dynamite were planted there. Nine-thirty—at low tide—was the hour set for touching it off.

Zone churches that morning had a slim attendance; Catholics and Congregationalists, Methodists and Mohammedans were all assembled in a holiday mood on the hill slopes overlooking the dike. In a magnificent explosion of mud, the twenty tons of dynamite went off at the appointed moment, tearing out a hole a hundred feet wide, and inspiring from the crowd a voluntary roar that drowned the echo of the blast. Then the audience settled down with their bottles and picnic lunches for a long wait. The second part of the show wouldn't be ready until the tide turned.

Just after midday, as the Pacific began to lap the south bank, a lone comedian with a shovel scooped a small trench across the site of the explosion, and the first wash of the Pacific sloshed through. Then it came with a rush. In three-quarters of an hour the foot-wide ditch had expanded to thirty feet, and a tidal wave was pouring inland over a thirty-foot fall. The suction was so great that a barge moored on the ocean side broke loose and was swept into the maelstrom, parting a heavy steel cable which had been strung across the gap. Within an hour and a half after the flood had started, the rush of water had scoured out a gap four hundred feet wide. Then the fall became less and less spectacular; the surface leveled off. The Pacific and the water of the Canal as far as Miraflores were one.

There was enough celebrating that Sunday to take care of a corresponding event two days later on the Atlantic side. Unceremoniously the rails across the Canal north of Gatun were taken up and dredges began consuming the 180,000 cubic yards of temporary fill. For months there had been a gap in that dike, with a removable span across it, so there was no sudden release of the Caribbean. But with the rail spur removed, hereafter traffic across the Atlantic end of the Canal would have to be by barge or cableway. The channel from the Atlantic to Gatun was open. Gamboa and the slides were the only remaining mass impediments to navigation.

On September 5 the sight-seeing train made its last round through Culebra Cut. The tracks were to be ripped out—all tracks, an entire railroad system of 130 miles. Goethals had decided that the final excavation would be done by dredge after water had been let in. During the next month those nine miles of muddy canyon looked like a battlefield from which a long-entrenched legion was hastily retreating. Broken cranes, tired steam shovels, rusted locomotives were hauled out. Any equipment that could not be salvaged quickly was to be destroyed. An orderly evacuation it was, but daily the deserted ditch appeared more haunted and stricken. From end to end it was strewn with debris where thousands upon thousands had worked for years. Seepage of the rising lake behind Gamboa dike was providing just enough water to make the Canal floor a mucky wallow. Day and night, bonfires of railroad ties and abandoned materials filled the chasm with rancid smoke. And as if to take advantage of the retreat, Cucaracha slumped farther into a vacated area, a solid wall completely closing the Cut.

On October 1 four great pipes built under Gamboa dike were opened and a wall of brown water flushed down the Canal floor. It could flow only as far as Cucaracha, but it was estimated that the section would be filled to the level of Gatun Lake within ten days; then both Gamboa and Cucaracha would be blown out. Removal of these last barriers called for the most dramatic celebration of all—one in which the home front could participate as well as the Canal front. It was to be a major display of fireworks and waterworks—a thousand holes plugged with dynamite, each some thirty-five feet deep, explosive packed into five miles of iron pipe, the total length of the holes alone in lineal feet amounting to almost eight miles.

But Gamboa wasn't allowed to steal the Panama show entirely. Goethals casually announced on September 24 that "as far as operating machinery is concerned, connections could be made in half a day which would allow the passage of a vessel through the sides of the locks for which the gates are ready." Forty-eight hours later he backed up his announcement with action. The sea gates at Gatun swung open just as men were leaving work for the day. Into the massive chamber steamed the tug *Gatun* with flags flying and whistles blowing. It was an unheralded event, and to those who happened to be on the spot it occurred as naturally as though the Canal had been in operation for a decade. Resounding cheers went up from the crowd that quickly thronged along the walls. The lower operating gates were closed and the tug slowly rose in a swirl of water. Into the middle lock, and then into the upper one, the tug cautiously slid. Before dark she was safely moored in Gatun Lake. Though the valve controls still had to be operated locally, rather than through the automatic central panel, the triple locks of Gatun were an assured success. Those who had been blustering for years about the impracticability of raising a ship in a lockage of eighty-five feet were silenced by that two-hour trial.

But the fatalists had one more argument that wasn't yet settled —the question of earthquakes. During the construction period there had been occasional tremors, but none of consequence. To refute the earthquake bugaboo, Stevens had repeatedly pointed out the flat-arch bridge in Old Panama which had stood for four centuries. Yet now, as though the wisdom of building the Canal were being tested belatedly by higher authority, on October 1, 1913, four days after the gates of Gatun first admitted a ship, a violent shudder passed over the Isthmus, followed by another and another. The needles of a seismograph at Ancon were thrown off the scale paper, but an intensity of 7 or 8 was estimated for the epicenter—a shock far worse than the San Francisco quake of 1906. As the terrifying vibrations continued for over an hour, they gave pause even to the lighthearted optimists who knew that no earthquake could damage the Canal.

Word filtered through the next day that a church tower at Los Santos, only a hundred miles up the Pacific coast, had been toppled by the shock, government buildings wrecked, and private dwellings severely damaged. In Panama City stone structures were cracked, and the offshore wires of the Central and South American Cable Company were broken. Canal masonry and dams were hastily checked and the official report announced: "There has been no damage whatever to any part of the Canal work." The experience, however was disquieting. If an earthquake would topple a church tower within a hundred miles of the Zone and crack structural walls in Panama City, what could another do to millions of dollars' worth of masonry at Miraflores, Pedro Miguel, and Gatun?

Every effort was made to minimize the seriousness of the threat, but as minor earth shudders continued during the following days, Goethals dispatched his geologist across the Bay of Panama to investigate the region where the disturbance was calculated to be centered. Word was sent back shortly that "the greater part of the houses in Tonosí have been damaged and many roofs have fallen in. Two distilleries have been destroyed, as well as the ovens in the bakeries. There have been numerous slides in the neighboring mountains, and cracks have opened in the ground in all the valley of Tonosí. None of the hills, however, have sunk. The inhabitants are alarmed, and are living in tents. Small shocks are experienced daily, accompanied by a rumbling like thunder."

This indeed was information that could not be brushed off with an air of indifference.

But the seismic warnings in no way dampened enthusiasm for the big explosion at Gamboa. Unofficially, October 10 was a holiday. No one would be penalized for playing hooky in the afternoon. Special trains from both Colón and Panama were scheduled to converge on Gamboa just before two o'clock. And early in the morning a motley convoy of thirteen vessels—tugs, barges, a floating piledriver, a pipe-line suction dredge, two dump scows, an old French ladder dredge, pontoons, and motor launches—assembled in the Canal below Gatun. They carried everything from drills and dynamite to piles and a few hundred tons of coal, the equipment needed for a final marine onslaught in Culebra Cut, but they also took aboard anyone who wanted free passage through Gatun Locks to Gamboa. The armada could barely squeeze into the lock chambers, and with all the crowding for position, it took three hours for the lift to the Lake. Then they were off to Gamboa.

Canal Is Opened by Wilson's Finger, the New York *Times* incongruously headlined on October 11. In one of the marvelous manifestations of 1913 science, the President of the United States had relayed an electric signal over the land lines from Washington to Galveston, Texas, over the submarine cables and the trans-Isthmian cables to Gamboa, and in seconds touched off the explosion which cast aside the last imposing barrier that kept ships from plying between the Atlantic and the Pacific. Among contemporaries the phenomenon was compared to the miracle of Moses in parting the seas for passage of the children of Israel.

The *Times* account read:

With an explosion which shook the surrounding hills and threw huge rocks into the air, eight tons of dynamite were set off this afternoon by President Wilson touching a button in Washington, more than 4,000 miles away. Gamboa Dike, the last obstruction in the Panama Canal, was swept away and the dream of the centuries became a reality.

When President Wilson finished his lunch today, he sauntered from the White House across the terrace to his office in the Executive Building, went to his desk and touched a button as if to summon his stenographer or a messenger. This simple act detonated the dynamite stowed in Gamboa Dike and caused the greatest spectacle in the history of construction of the world's greatest engineering work. "There, it's all over," smiled the President, "Gamboa is busted."

The blast cut a clear opening of 125 feet. Engineers had erred, however, in calculating how much water should have passed from the Lake into the Cut during the ten preceding days. There was still a difference of six feet. Immediately following the explosion, a mighty six-foot wave curled into the canyon, sweeping a solid wall of debris before it. Riding the crest in reckless sport dashed a native canoe—a cayuca—and close behind two American launches, headed for Miraflores. But the launches got only as far as Cucaracha. Dynamite charges there failed to budge the sodden mass. In less than two hours the Canal was navigable all the way to Cucaracha, but the water stopped there, lapping a barricade more massive than the dike that had been blown up.

The Gamboa explosion, and the shout that went up from the thousands of Canalers assembled on the hilltops above the Cut, did echo around the world. Everywhere the dike was accepted as the last impediment to navigation. As if the Canal were already in operation, the London *Daily News* went so far as to issue the congratulatory message:

The Panama Canal will stand for all time as a monument to the engineering skill of the American Nation in general and of Colonel Goethals in particular.

Gamboa was "busted," but any spectator on the Isthmus knew that the struggle was not "all over." Next day the dredge flotilla moved in and began the monotonous drudgery of cleaning up the dike and attacking Cucaracha. No one on the job dared predict how many months it would take to conquer the slide. Instead of the endless lines of trains that had sped up and down the Cut, plodding tugs with strings of dump barges became the major evidence of activity.

It was essential that dredges be brought in from the Pacific side, and to float them to Cucaracha, water would have to be admitted from Gatun Lake and a ditch had to be dug across the slide. Tons of dynamite were exploded in trying repeatedly to blast a passage, but the soggy paste merely oozed back into the gutters after the explosions. Dynamiting was abandoned, and hundreds of men went to work with shovels to clear a trench. Knee deep in sludge they worked around the clock on eight-hour shifts, three shifts in twenty-four, and made little impression. Sluicing with hoses in addition to the shoveling was tried. The materials yielded a little, very little.

After a week of this ineffective experimentation, dynamite was tried again, enormous charges, "charges of such violence that houses along the Canal from Pedro Miguel to Empire rocked on their foundations as in an earthquake, and articles were thrown from shelves." "Futile," reported the engineers. "The use of dynamite is scarcely more satisfactory than in the previous efforts. The nature of the material is such that it merely slumps back into place, or more of it is pushed forward by the slide to fill the hole made by an explosion."

Finally it was the mighty Chagres that came to the rescue. An afternoon deluge brought floods to the river. The water poured into Gatun Lake, and the Lake backed up to Cucaracha. In three days the level rose as many feet. That was the needed waterhead. A small stream was coaxed across the slide. It turned into a cascade, carrying tons of silt and rock with it. The center of the barrier began to disintegrate, and within a few hours water in the channel to the south was at the level of Gatun Lake.

Triumphantly the first procession of dredges passed through the locks at Miraflores and Pedro Miguel on October 25, and they were soon at work on the Pacific end of the slide. Steam shovels were again put to work on terraces at the top of the hill to relieve the weight from above, and an elaborate sluice system was developed to wash away the back of the hill. But not until the middle of December, when a channel wide enough for passage of dredges and barges had been cut, did it appear that the Cockroach was going to submit to taming.

274

Elsewhere along the line of the Canal, everything was taking on an appearance of the final stages of completion. Finishing touches were being put on the locks; buoys were anchored in Gatun Lake to mark the navigation channel; far back in the hills a dozen miles southwest of Gatun an earth dike was being erected across "Caño Saddle"—the one remaining spot where Gatun Lake might spill over into the Caribbean; the last evacuees were leaving flooded villages like Bas Obispo and Matachín, and to take their places plans were in the making for constructing the most beautiful city in Central America—Balboa.

With the completion of each big operation more men were laid off. By January, 1914, they were leaving the Isthmus at the rate of five hundred a week. Some nine thousand had taken off during the preceding four months, and already the sudden influx of unemployed labor from Panama was being felt in the States.

Word had gotten around that Detroit was the place to head for, and from the automobile city came the distraught message:

Detroit is flooded with the unemployed. Employees on the Isthmus should be advised that they must compete with Canadian job seekers. . . . We petition you to warn any who may be inclined to come this way for a job. It isn't here for them. There are five men in Detroit for every job today. Our advice to wage earners is to keep away from Detroit.

From other cities came similar inhospitable dispatches. The Panama veterans weren't wanted anywhere. At last gold employees began to realize that the congenial days of the Zone were drawing to a close and a long vacation from every kind of employment might await them at home. They didn't want to leave. They couldn't face the realities. It wasn't that they wished any ill fortune to their benevolent despot—but if only an earthquake would level the whole business so that they could start in all over again!

To ease the transition back to normal life, the Colonel announced in February that there would be a 25 per cent cut in compensation and that everyone would soon have to pay rent for quarters. Moreover, the whole system of liberal allowances and fringe benefits would be abolished within two months, when a permanent Zone government took over and the Chief Engineer and Commission Chairman assumed the title of Governor.

The cutback in openhandedness was extended even to tourists, and advance notice was given that they would not be as welcome during the dry season of 1914 as they had been the year before. But the notice was disregarded by both the public and the steamship companies, and as the season for sight-seeing approached, the caveat was politely rescinded. More visitors than ever would be coming, and they had to be treated graciously. The Hotel Tivoli was again expanded, a new "Seeing-the-Canal" train schedule set up, and a sight-seeing barge launched on Gatun Lake.

The trip on this luxury ark, remodeled from a five-hundred-ton dump barge, highlighted a visit to the Canal in 1914. It was gaily decorated and as gaily advertised: "The structure is modeled after that of the sightseeing cars; its floor is raised at the after end to a height of eight feet nine inches, and gradually descends to about two feet at the forward end, so that the occupants of the rear seats can overlook those in front without obstruction to the view. . . . The roof is covered with sailcloth painted and sanded. For the protection of those who prefer to ride on the roof, a double railing has been built around the outer edge. A passageway extends through the center with rows of wooden seats on either side. Seating accommodations have been provided for 276 passengers. The barge is equipped with the usual marine safeguards, including life preservers . . . and toilet facilities."

No one ever begrudged Goethals the dollar and a half paid for a round trip from Gatun to Gamboa and back. Besides a glimpse of the Cut, the excursionists had close-up views of tree-tops full of orchids, wild life marooned on what had once been the tops of inaccessible jungle hills, and exotic floating islands wafted here and there by capricious tropical breezes. The train

trip across the Isthmus lost its appeal without the detour into
Culebra Cut, and the boat excursion almost made up for it. The
spillway gates at Gatun were closed in February, bringing the
Lake up to its full height of eighty-five feet, and the excursion
route offered a preview of what liner passengers would soon be
seeing.

Aquatics champion Alfred Brown was the star tourist that
season. Not content with a bird's-eye view of the Canal from a
perch on the sight-seers' loft, he swam the thirty miles from Gatun
to Balboa, defying crocodiles, water snakes, and hungry dredges.
Sixteen hours, thirty-five minutes was the official time, and a
record for the books: no man ever before had swum from the
Atlantic to the Pacific. But the feat was spoiled by Cucaracha.
At that point Al had to turn amphibious and wade across the mud.

As the tourist season drew to a close, on April 1, 1914,
Goethals dropped his title of Commission Chairman and without
a hint of inaugural splendor became the first Governor of the
Panama Canal. Nor could he be labeled "the Colonel" any longer,
for under political pressure in Washington, the Senate had con-
firmed his promotion to Major General. And the new titles seemed
to give him added incentive for completing the Canal in a hurry.
Back in January, the *Alexander La Valley,* an ancient crane boat
inherited from the French, had been the first vessel to make the
trip from ocean to ocean. Now the drab old tug *Mariner,* towing
barges number 11 and number 15, made what was quietly announced as the "first direct voyage from ocean to ocean by way
of the Canal." There was no blowing of whistles nor any display
of triumph. The American-Hawaiian freighter *Alaskan* had put
in at Balboa with twelve thousand tons of sugar and two hundred
tons of canned pineapples, and required transport of its cargo
across the Isthmus due to the interruption of traffic on the
Tehuantepec railroad in southern Mexico. The Governor gave
assent to the request. The Canal was in business. During the rest
of May and into June a lighter service was operated on regular
schedule between Colón and Balboa, and the announcement was

proudly made on June 10 that the Canal had already earned $7356.12.

The harassed Governor was making progress on every front, and he was confident now that he would be able to pay tribute to Balboa on September 25, but nature wasn't budging a notch to help him. The slides were more or less under control, no freshet had caused a serious washout in months, so on May 27 it was the earthquake scare again. There were still a great many men of wisdom who were sure that Gatun Dam wouldn't survive a serious shock. And that shock came at ten twenty-five on the night of May 27. Perhaps it was no more severe than the tremor of October 1, but it was of a "different character, having more of a vertical motion and continuing for a longer period." During the previous fall thirty-two movements were recorded on the Ancon seismograph in a period of less than two weeks, yet none of them was like the shock of May 27. This had an ominous quality.

All pens were again thrown off the recording instruments, so the exact intensity of the quake remained unknown, but no time was lost the next morning in making a meticulous examination of every piece of Canal construction. The report that came through a few days later reassuringly disguised any alarm the technicians felt: "A careful survey made of the Canal structures shows that no damage was caused to the locks, dams, and spillways. The shop buildings and permanent quarters likewise escaped uninjured, the damage to Canal property apparently being confined to the new administration building at Balboa where some of the concrete blocks and stucco were cracked and six marble slabs partly set in one of the lavatories, were thrown to the floor and broken. The movement had no apparent effect on Cucaracha slide, but on the morning after the shock, a small additional slide developed on the north side of Gold Hill. The walls on one or two buildings in the city of Panama developed fissures."

"Were these shocks working up to a violently destructive one?"

employees scheduled for early sailings back to the States inquired hopefully.

If Governor Goethals had any qualms about Panama earthquakes, other than terror of public expression on what might happen to Gatun Dam and the locks, he did not show it. He had just been appointed chairman of a committee authorized by President Wilson to spend $25,000 on fitting ceremonies for the opening of the Canal. The thing to do was to get it over with as soon as possible, before there were any more setbacks or threatening quakes. On June 8 he sent a Panama Railroad Steamship liner, the *Allianca*, through the Gatun Locks and out again on a test run—"the first ocean-going passenger vessel to enter or pass the locks." Every movement of a dozen valves and gates was timed and logged to the second. Behind scenes waged a bitter battle among the engineers over relative responsibility of captains and pilots during lockage, over ship propulsion versus locomotive propulsion, but the *Allianca* re-entered Limon Bay without a scratch; the mechanism worked perfectly.

Goethals was almost ready. Every day was filled with last-minute preparations; second and third coats of paint were being applied; the pilots had to be fitted out in special uniforms, machinery tested and retested, arguments among subordinate engineers settled, laborers still digging away at Cucaracha cheered on.

"The whole course of life and thought upon the Canal Zone has been affected by the unexpected increase in the landslides," exaggerated a British scientist, Dr. Vaughan Cornish, after a three weeks' tour. "The officials are frankly bored. Most of them have completed their tasks but the Canal cannot be used. . . . The most animated scene on the Canal today is down in the Cut itself at the foot of Cucaracha slide. . . . They are worked in double shifts twenty-four hours out of the twenty-four, that they may be ready for the ceremonial opening next New Year's Day. The American people have waited ten years for that day, and they mean to make the spectacle one of the most imposing that the world has ever seen."

But Goethals had fooled even the notable Dr. Cornish on his dates. Late in July, orders came through from the Secretary of War in Washington that the Canal was to be opened to traffic on August 15. They weren't going to pay formal homage to Balboa after all.

There had to be a dress rehearsal for the opening ceremonies, and since the *Cristobal* was handy, this old cement carrier, which had ferried countless tons of Canal equipment from New York to the Isthmus, was accorded the honor of stand-in. At seven in the morning of August 3, she pulled away from the dock at Cristobal; at six-thirty that evening she anchored off Balboa. "The voyage was without operating incident, other than some minor difficulties with towing locomotives at Gatun and Pedro Miguel Locks," was the official report.

A few long-time Canal employees and engineers were the principal passengers on this historic crossing, and the guest with the warmest sentiment was none other than Bunau-Varilla, who for weeks had been hanging around waiting to be honored on the great occasion. August 3, 1914, was also the day on which newspapers the world over were broadcasting the fateful alarm: *GERMANY INVADES FRANCE*. The man who laid claim to hatching the plot of turning over the Isthmus to the United States learned the news while in transit and recorded his own reactions.

During the thirty-four years [sic] which lapsed from 1885 to 1914, two ambitions filled my brain and my heart. What I desired more than any other material or moral satisfaction was, first, to see the immortal creation of the French genius at Panama finally completed for the utility and the service of civilization; second, to see France washing the slate of history with Prussian blood. . . . By an extraordinary coincidence the glorious war of 1914 began on the very same day that the first ocean steamer passed from the Atlantic to the Pacific.

280

The war in Europe, indeed, put an entirely new complexion on affairs in the Zone. The United States intended to stay out of it, but if it should spread to America, the Canal would be "the most important military possession of the United States, the most vital spot strategically in the whole world."

Governor Goethals was also General Goethals, and he did not need civilian promptings to make him aware of the strategic importance of the Canal. He had been quietly importing cannon among the cranes, dredges, and steam shovels. Before tighter security measures muzzled the press, one reporter reassured the public with full details: "The armament which protects the two ends of the Canal consists of one sixteen-inch, ten fourteen-inch, twelve six-inch rifled cannon, all mounted on disappearing gun-carriages, and twenty-eight twelve-inch mortars of a new and powerful type. The sixteen-inch cannon is more effective than any now carried on any ship afloat. . . . The purpose of these large rifled cannon is to send a heavy shell at 'direct-fire" with such terrific force that it will tear through the side of an approaching battleship. They can shoot through over eleven inches of the best steel armor at nearly nine miles distance. . . . A shot from one of the twelve-inch mortars will pierce any battleship deck in existence." The Canal was invulnerable.

BIG ARMIES READY ON 248-MILE BATTLE FRONT—GERMANS TO STRIKE ALLIES NEAR BRUSSELS—FRENCH MOVE TO ENGAGE FOE AT STRASSBURG—RUSSIA PROMISES POLAND AUTONOMY. Those were far more world-shaking headlines than anything occurring at Panama on August 15, 1914. Goethals appeared to be arranging a family picnic while the countryside about him was going up in flames. But the Isthmus was not to be deprived of another fiesta. Actually this was to be only the "official" opening; the "formal" opening would come later.

The *Ancon*, twin of the *Cristobal*, was chosen as the honored vessel for the ceremonies. All the other previous voyages across the Isthmus were to be overlooked. The *Ancon* was to make the the first recognized run. Slicked up in a new coat of paint, her

officers looking thoroughly uncomfortable in their starched
whites, the venerable tramp ship lay ready at her Cristobal
pier in the early morning. A special train from Panama City
wheezed alongside just before seven o'clock, and some two
hundred dignitaries filed from the cars to the gangway. President
Porras of the Republic of Panama was there, accompanied by
his cabinet and other Panamanian officials, members of the
diplomatic corps and the resident consuls general, officers of the
Tenth Infantry and Coast Artillery Corps, and a few Canal
officials who had survived the shake-up in Zone government. The
absence of top United States notables was shocking. For Isthmian
affairs of far less import there had always been a Roosevelt, a
Taft, or a sprinkling of Congressmen. Even Governor Goethals
declined to go aboard; he preferred to witness the voyage from
the tracks in his "Yellow Peril."

At the forepeak of the *Ancon* waved the ensign of the Republic
of Panama, at the mainmast head the house pennant of the
Panama Steamship fleet, on the jackstaff the flag of the United
States, and from the foremast the flag of the American Peace
Society. The trip was to symbolize the peaceful objectives of the
Panama Canal. Only a few of the passengers knew that below
decks were two huge pieces of artillery for the Pacific batteries.

Exactly at ten minutes past seven, the hawsers were released
and the *Ancon* pulled away from her pier, while the Panama
National Band and the regimental band of the Tenth United
States Infantry joined in a strident rendition of "The Star
Spangled Banner," but the music was irreverently drowned by
cheering thousands and the blasts of scores of ships in the
harbor waiting for the *Ancon* to complete her voyage so that
they too could make a dash to the Pacific.

In order to qualify for a complete voyage, the ship steamed
out to the end of the Colón breakwater and then headed back.
At eight o'clock she entered the Gatun Locks; an hour and a
quarter later she was in the open water of Gatun Lake. Governor
Goethals waved her off and putt-putted down the railroad tracks

in his "Peril" toward Pedro Miguel. At eleven-fifteen the *Ancon* slowed for the entrance into Culebra Cut, where more thousands of spectators lustily cheered her passage. She nosed past Cucaracha just after noon, reached Pedro Miguel at twelve fifty-six, and passed into Miraflores Lake twenty-three minutes later. With Goethals anxiously standing by, she was eased through Miraflores Lock at one fifty-six, entered the sea channel at three-thirty, and completed the official trip off the tip of Naos Breakwater at four-thirty. All along the route passengers caught occasional glimpses of the Governor flying down the tracks in his private vehicle or giving quiet orders as the ship went through the locks. He was waiting at the Balboa pier with two thousand others when the good ship anchored off shore just after five o'clock.

People had been talking prematurely about Panama dreams coming true for years. Officially, that dream didn't materialize until four-thirty in the afternoon of August 15.

The word was flashed around the world: "The Panama Canal is open to the commerce of the world. Henceforth ships may pass to and fro through that great waterway," announced the New York *Times* under a modest headline on page fourteen. International events had crowded into the background "the greatest marvel of the old and the new world."

"This unostentatious dedicatory act may be considered a more appropriate celebration of a triumph of the arts of peace than if it had been associated with martial pomp and an array of destroyers and battleships," consoled the Philadelphia *Record*. Other newspapers echoed variations on the same theme: "The purpose of the Canal is to strengthen the bonds of peaceful commerce, but today commerce stands paralysed and peace has flown. . . . The practical completion of this great achievement wins little attention from a world intent upon the war news from Belgium and Alsace. . . . Americans should find a solemn pride in the thought that they have added much to a world from which other nations are taking so much away."

283

For a few weeks Panama hymns, psalms, and songs appeared in the literary magazines:

> Thou, thou didst give our hand the might
> To hew the hemisphere in twain
> And level for these waters bright
> The mountains with the main:
> In freedom let the great ships go
> On freedom's errand, sea to sea,—
> The oceans rise, the hills bend low,
> Servants of liberty.

Officially the Canal was open for these commercial "errands of freedom," but the grand formal opening had yet to come. Six months after the *Ancon's* passage, Governor Goethals received the blunt message that "the President had directed the formal opening of the Canal to be postponed probably until some time after the first of July 1915." The perfunctory proclamation finally issued by Wilson on July 12, 1920, never quite satisfied Central American fiesta lovers.

Four centuries after the Spanish explorers were censured for conceiving wild dreams of digging a ditch across the continent, they were exonerated by Stevens and Goethals; the French dreamers received token exoneration, too. And after so much persiflage about the bountiful equipment from France, even the mystery of the snow shovels was finally solved. They weren't snow shovels at all. Those awkward wooden implements were intended for handling ashes in the boiler pits of steam shovels. They were just the thing. Much better than the heavy scoops the Yankees used.

There were countless heroes of Panama—both real and self-nominated—and it wasn't always possible to tell the two kinds apart. They ranged all the way from Bunau-Varilla and Admiral Walker, the man who mapped the American route, to the

crippled Miguel and the clerks who sold finger bowls at the
Colon Commissary. Because he saw the job through to completion, George Washington Goethals was popularly enshrined
as "the genius of the Canal," and may always be lauded as such,
though it was Adolph Godin de Lépinay who first blueprinted a
waterbridge across the Divide and John F. Stevens who was its
basic architect; and no one can ever judge how much of the
credit heaped upon Goethals really belongs to Dr. Gorgas, to
engineers like Sibert, Hodges, Williamson, and Rourke, or to
statesmen like Roosevelt, Hay, Moore, Taft, and Root.

American gold employees got their rewards in good pay,
respectable quarters, Canal medals with service bars, and
recognition as members of permanent organizations like the
Society of the Chagres and the Association of Panama Canal
Builders. In the distribution of honors somehow the silver
employees from the West Indies, Europe and the Orient were
overlooked entirely. They had no one to champion their claim to
recognition. They did the menial jobs, and they weren't always
bright. Hundreds of them lost their lives in dank pits, in the
confusion of wheels, in mis-timed dynamite blasts—the unknown
dead of the Panama struggle. For the silver laborers there was no
memorial and scant thanks, yet without them the *Ancon* would
not have crossed the Isthmus on August 15, 1914.

Maurice H. Thatcher, Zone civil administrator for three years
under Colonel Goethals, recognized an inequity in the apportion-
ment of honors, and in 1928 while serving as representative in
Congress, introduced a bill calling for the erection of a Panama
Canal Memorial on the Isthmus. The twenty-fifth anniversary
of the opening of the waterway was approaching, and he maintained that the time at last was ripe for constructing a "great
work of art as well as a great work of memorialization" which
would give recognition to the toil and sacrifice of all who
participated in the endeavor, without regard for race or nation,
eminence or lowliness.

Governor Thatcher visualized a monumental structure with

285

an assembly hall suitable for international gatherings or Pan American congresses, and adjoining museum galleries in which the Canal story of over four centuries would be graphically illustrated in sculpture, pictures, frescoes, and models. It would be a depository for archives from the days of the early European explorers through the American occupation. On the floor of the House he pleaded for a memorial that would commemorate events and benefactors "commencing with the discovery of the Isthmian shores by Columbus, following with the discovery of the Pacific Ocean by Balboa; thence descending through the centuries of colonization and occupation by the Spanish, on through the days of Panama Railroad construction and the discovery of gold in California, with the resulting trans-Isthmian travel; thence through the years of the French effort, down to the final hour of American success and the uniting of the two great oceans." The whole was to stand as a symbol of what could be accomplished through peace and good will among nations, and would glorify the motto of the Canal enterprise— "The land divided, the world united."

But Congressmen weren't particularly interested; nor was the public interested. The twenty-fifth anniversary passed without affirmative action, and unless there were some impulsive burst of interest in the Canal, it was likely too that the semicentennial would pass without appropriate memorialization.

Perhaps the spectacle of World War I stole the show in 1914 and never gave the United States public an opportunity to appreciate what they had accomplished on the Isthmus; perhaps the way in which the Zone was appropriated touched the American conscience and brought a reluctance to give the achievement due recognition; perhaps the Canal was just too big or too far removed for popular comprehension.

In 1914 the Canal was acclaimed around the globe as "the greatest engineering feat of the ages," the American masterwork, the most generous boon to world trade that any nation had ever conceived for the benefit of all nations. Other scientific marvels soon began to overshadow the significance of the Panama achievement, but some of the more savory superlatives are not yet outdated.

The United States rallied to a noble challenge in 1904. The country has another challenge now: the old Canal is gradually becoming inadequate, and if the present rate of increase in shipping through the Cut continues, the waterway will be obsolescent in less than two decades. That leaves all too short a time to remodel the masterwork.

We may return, alas, to Ferdinand de Lesseps' vision of a "Straits of Panama," or to a happier arrangement of the Pacific locks as visualized by John F. Stevens; we may decide on piecemeal reconstruction—but the decision cannot be delayed for long. Although the age of interplanetary traffic may be in the offing, an older age of intercontinental traffic will still be with us. The Panama Crusade isn't over yet. We've got to start digging again.

Chronology

1501   First European, Rodrigo de Bastidas of Seville, explored Panama area.

1502   Christopher Columbus, on fourth American voyage, explored Atlantic coast of Isthmus.

1510   First European settlements made at Santa María la Antigua and Nombre de Dios.

1513   September 25. Pacific Ocean discovered by Vasco Nuñez de Balboa from Darién mountain top.

1515   Isthmus raided by Pedro Arias de Ávila (Pedrarias) for gold.

1516   Panama City chartered by Pedrarias, who ruthlessly raided the Isthmus in search of gold.

1527   Valleys of Chagres and Rio Grande explored by Hernando de la Serna and new route established across Isthmus—"The Spanish Gateway to the South Sea."

1529   Alvaro Saavedra, associate of Cortés, drafted first plans for canal across the Isthmus.

1530   Las Cruces trail constructed across Isthmus from Fort San Lorenzo to Panama City.

1534   Charles V of Spain directed that survey be made for ship canal between Chagres River and Pacific Ocean.

1540   Camino Real built from Old Panama to Porto Bello and Nombre de Dios. Over this paved road millions in gold from Peru and western Mexico were later transported.

1592   Nombre de Dios captured by Sir Francis Drake.

1597   Porto Bello established as major American commercial center with annual trade fair which continued for over a century.

1621   Severe earthquake on Isthmus.

1671   January 28. Panama City looted and burned by buccaneer Sir Henry Morgan.

1673   Panama City rebuilt on present site.

1701   William Patterson, founder of the Bank of England, who established Scotch colony on Isthmus, urged construction of canal.

1739   Panama area incorporated in viceroyalty of New Granada.

1812   Capital of New Granada temporarily transferred from Bogotá to Panama City.

1814   Preliminary attempts of Spain to start canal across Panama thwarted by revolt of her colonies.

1821   Panama severed political connection with Spain and joined "Republic of Greater Colombia."

1825   Republic of the United States of Central America made overtures to the United States for aid in constructing a canal.

1826   On invitation of Simón Bolívar, delegates from young American republics met for historic Congress of Panama.

1831   New Granada became independent republic, incorporating Panama as a state.

1838   May 30. New Granada granted private French company a concession for construction of macadamized roads, railroads and canals across the Isthmus.

1839   By request of President Van Buren, John L. Stephens explored both Nicaragua and Panama routes for canal and recommended Nicaragua.

1841   Panama seceded from New Granada and maintained independence for thirteen months.

1846   Treaty between United States and New Granada gave United States transportation concessions across Isthmus in return for guarantee to protect sovereignty of New Granada.

1847   Panama Railroad Company organized.

1848   January 24. Gold discovered at Sutter's Mill, California, bringing tide of emigrants to Isthmus.

1848   United States Congress authorized contracts for steamship lines from New York and New Orleans to Chagres, and from Panama City to California and Oregon.

1848   December 28. Exclusive concession granted by New Granada to private American company for transit system across Isthmus, with free choice of making it part steamer, part rail, part macadamized road.

1849   February 24. Panama *Star* (later *Star and Herald*) first published in Panama City.

1849   April 7. Panama Railroad Company incorporated under laws of the State of New York.

1850   May. Ground broken on Manzanillo Island (Colón) for Panama Railroad.

1850   July 5. Under Clayton-Bulwer treaty, United States and Great Britain agreed that neither nation would attempt to obtain exclusive control over a canal and guaranteed its neutrality.

1852   February 29. Atlantic terminus of Panama Railroad named "Aspinwall."

1853   Panama temporarily seceded from New Granada.

1855   January 28. First transcontinental train run from Aspinwall to Panama City.

1855   Daily service over unfinished Panama Railroad inaugurated.

1856   September 19. United States Marines landed to protect Panama Railroad following race riot.

1859   January 1. Panama Railroad completed for total length of forty-seven miles.

1861   New Granada adopted name of United States of Colombia.

1869   Diplomatic agreement between United States and Colombia for rights to build a canal rejected by Colombia Senate.

1869   November 17. Opening of Suez Canal focused international attention on an Isthmian canal.

1872   United States Congress authorized appointment of Interoceanic Canal Commission to determine most practicable route for waterway between the Atlantic and the Pacific.

1875   Ferdinand de Lesseps proposed a sea-level canal at Panama before Geographic Society of Paris.

1876   February 7. United States Interoceanic Canal Commission recommended Nicaragua route via San Juan River.

1876   Société Civile Internationale du Canal Interocéanique organized in Paris to make surveys and explorations for Panama Canal.

1878   March 20. Lucien Napoléon Bonaparte Wyse completed negotiations with Colombia for canal concession between Limon Bay and Panama City.

1879   May. One hundred and thirty-five delegates to Congrès Internationale d'Etudes du Canal Interocéanique met in Paris. Proposal of Adolphe Godin de Lépiney for lock canal rejected by de Lesseps.

1879   June 25. United States Congress resolved that any attempt of of a European power to establish a ship canal across the Isthmus would be considered "a manifestation of an unfriendly disposition toward the United States."

1879   August 17. Compagnie Universelle du Canal Interocéanique de Panama organized with Ferdinand de Lesseps as President.

1880   January 1. Canal digging ceremoniously inaugurated by de Lesseps in Bay of Panama.

1880   January 10. Excavation of Culebra Cut inaugurated by de Lesseps.

1880   March. De Lesseps made unsuccessful canal-promotion tour of the United States.

1880   April 24. Nicaragua granted ninety-nine-year concession to American group to build a canal, competing with French effort.

1880   American engineer, James B. Eads, designed plans for a railroad to convey ships across Isthmus over Tehuantepec route.

1881   January 29. First French construction gangs arrived at Colón.

1881   June. First deaths from yellow fever among Canal employees.

1881   August. Compagnie Universelle gained control of Panama Railroad at price of over $25,000,000.

1882   January 20. Second formal French inauguration of excavation in Culebra Cut.

1882   September 7-11. Series of severe earthquake shocks damaged railroad and canal buildings.

1882   September 17. Ancon hospital dedicated.

1883   March 1. Second visit of de Lesseps to Panama.

1885   May 18. Colón burned during a Panama revolution.

1885   Philippe Bunau-Varilla appointed canal engineer.

1886   Bunau-Varilla relieved.

1886   Status of Panama changed from Colombia state to a "department" with government by federal appointees.

1886   Nicaragua Canal Association, private New York corporation, formed to build canal across Nicaragua, following failure of United States Senate to ratify treaty providing for canal construction on San Juan route.

1887   French canal plan changed from sea-level to lock type.

1888   December 14. Compagnie Universelle went into receivership.

1888   Convention of Constantinople agreed that Suez Canal should always remain free and open in time of war or peace to all military or commercial vessels without distinction of flag—

a basic treaty on canal internationalization often applied to Panama.

1889   February 20. Maritime Canal Company of Nicaragua incorporated by United States Congress.

1889   May 8. Maritime Canal Company began four-year effort to construct canal over San Juan route.

1889   May 15. French company suspended work on Panama Canal.

1890   Colombian government ordered that "Aspinwall" be dropped as city name for Colón.

1894   October 21. Compagnie Nouvelle du Canal de Panama incorporated to replace Compagnie Universelle.

1895   March 2. Nicaraguan Canal Board authorized by Congress to make surveys for completing canal started by Maritime Canal Company.

1898   Five-year revolt against Colombia started in Panama.

1899   March 3. First United States Isthmian Canal Commission created to examine all practicable routes across the Isthmus.

1899   June 10. Rear Admiral John G. Walker appointed chairman of Canal Commission.

1900   November 13. Isthmian Canal Commission unanimously recommended Nicaragua route for canal.

1901   Hay-Pauncefote Treaty conceded to the United States the right to build and control an Isthmian canal independent of Great Britain, and established rules for free and open navigation for vessels of commerce and war.

1901   November 16. Nicaragua Canal Board reported estimated cost of San Juan canal at $189,864,062 against $144,233,358 for completing Panama Canal.

1902   January 4. Compagnie Nouvelle agreed to sale of canal properties for $40,000,000.

1902   January 18. Isthmian Canal Commission reversed decision favoring Nicaragua route and advised adoption of Panama route if satisfactory terms could be obtained from Compagnie Nouvelle.

1902 June 28. Under Spooner Act, Congress granted broad powers to the President to construct Panama Canal, with alternative of using the Nicaragua route.

1902 November 21. "War of the Thousand Days" ended in Colombia.

1903 March 17. United States Senate ratified Hay-Herran Treaty which would grant construction rights and canal zone of six-mile width in return for payment of $10,000,000 to Colombia and annuity of $250,000.

1903 August 12. Hay-Herran Treaty rejected by Colombia.

1903 November 3. Revolt in Panama and declaration of independence.

1903 November 6. Government of Panama recognized by United States.

1903 November 18. Signing of Hay–Bunau-Varilla Treaty granted United States occupation of Canal Zone in perpetuity for payment of $10,000,000 and $250,000 annuity.

1903 December 2. New treaty ratified by Panama.

1904 February 27. Hay–Bunau-Varilla Treaty proclaimed by President, U. S. guaranteeing independence of Republic of Panama.

1904 March 3. Isthmian Canal Commission under chairmanship of Rear Admiral John G. Walker, took office.

1904 April 5. Canal Commission arrived in Colón for inspection tour.

1904 May 4. Acquisition Day. French canal property transferred to United States.

1904 May 17. General George W. Davis arrived at Canal Zone as first Governor.

1904 June 1. John F. Wallace assumed office of Chief Engineer.

1904   November 11. First American steam shovel put in operation at Culebra Cut.

1904   November 27. Secretary of War Taft arrived at Colón for first visit.

1905   February. Yellow fever epidemic started.

1905   March 4. President Roosevelt requested resignation of first Isthmian Canal Commission.

1905   April 1. Second Canal Commission appointed, Theodore P. Shonts, Chairman.

1905   June 24. International Board of Consulting Engineers appointed by President Roosevelt to recommend most desirable type of canal, General Davis chairman.

1905   June 28. Wallace resigned as Chief Engineer.

1905   July 1. John F. Stevens appointed Chief Engineer.

1905   August 1. Excavation in Culebra Cut temporarily halted by Stevens.

1905   November 2. Taft, with George W. Goethals as guest, visited Isthmus.

1906   February 5. International Board of Consulting Engineers submitted report to I.C.C. recommending sea-level canal.

1906   June 29. Congressional Act calling for lock canal signed by President.

1906   Summer. Drought in Colón.

1906   October. Excavation started for Gatun Locks.

1906   November 14–18. Visit of President Roosevelt.

1907   March 4. John F. Stevens appointed the first Chairman and Chief Engineer of the Isthmian Canal Commission.

1907   April 1. Third Canal Commission appointed. Colonel Goethals replaced Stevens as Chief Engineer and was also appointed Chairman of the Canal Commission and Governor—"The Czar of the Canal Zone."

1907   June 1. Relocation of Panama Railroad line started.

1907 September 4. First publication of *Canal Record*, official I.C.C. weekly.

1907 October 4. Cucaracha slide of 500,000 cubic yards buried steam shovels in Cut.

1907 October 12. Canal Zone Women's Clubs organized.

1907 December 20. Sosa Hill abandoned as site for Pacific locks and dam.

1908 Gamboa dike built.

1908 January 20. Plans for locks changed from width of 100 to 110 feet.

1908 July 15. Reorganization under Atlantic, Central, and Pacific Divisions completed.

1908 October 23. Widening of base channel in Culebra Cut from 200 to 300 feet authorized.

1908 November 21. Section of rock toe at Gatun Dam sank twenty feet, starting sensational stories in American press.

1908 December 12. Thirty-six killed and forty severely injured in premature explosion at Bas Obispo.

1908 December 24. Pumping of hydraulic fill started construction of Gatun Dam proper.

1908 Highest record for excavation in any one year set—37,000,000 cubic yards.

1909 January 29. President-elect Taft arrived in Colón for ten-day inspection tour.

1909 March 2. Rock crushing plant put into operation at Porto Bello.

1909 March. Highest record for excavation in single month set— 4,062,632 cubic yards.

1909 April 30. La Boca renamed Balboa.

1909 May 2. Death of former president Amador.

1909 July 28. Gatun Lock cableways put into operation.

1909 August 24. Concrete construction at Gatun Locks started.

1909   September 1. Concrete construction at Pedro Miguel Locks started.

1909   November 16. First great break at Culebra occurred, extending for a mile on west bank of Canal.

1909   November. Continuous rains (42.50 inches recorded at Cristobal during month) disrupted canal work and caused slides in Culebra estimated at two million cubic yards.

1909   December 29. Record for twenty-four-hour rainfall on Isthmus established at Porto Bello—10.86 inches.

1910   March 15. Berm and chamber cranes put in operation at Pedro Miguel.

1910   April 23. Clearing of ship channel from Gatun to Culebra Cut completed.

1910   April 25. West diversion at Gatun closed, bringing Gatun Lake into existence.

1910   May 17. Slide of half-million cubic yards at Cucaracha filled Canal for nine hundred feet, covering all railroad tracks.

1910   May 30. Concrete construction at Miraflores Locks started.

1910   August 8. Trestle for eleven-thousand-foot Colón breakwater started.

1910   October 22. Sixteen flat cars, two locomotives, and two steam shovels buried by sudden slide at Cucaracha.

1910   November 14. President Taft arrived for four-day visit.

1910   November 23. Manufacture of forty-six gates for Canal locks started in Pittsburgh.

1910   December 13. Great slide on east bank of Canal opposite Las Cascadas brought total slide area there to 7.6 acres.

1911   March 8. Excavation for Gatun Locks completed.

1911   March 8. Channel at Pacific entrance completed from deep water to Balboa.

1911   May 12. Construction of gates at Gatun Locks started.

1911   November 29. All-time record for rainfall established at

Porto Bello where 2.46 inches fell in three minutes (total for night "shower" 7.6 inches).

1912 January 31. Slides below Culebra village necessitated decision to move twenty-nine buildings from Canal edge.

1912 February 15. Relocated line of Panama Railroad between Gatun and Gamboa placed in operation.

1912 March 20. Attempts to surface Culebra slide areas with cement abandoned.

1912 March 29. New Hotel Washington opened at Colón Beach.

1912 May 25. Relocated Panama Railroad completed.

1912 August 6. Upper guard gates at Gatun Locks first closed to raise level of Gatun Lake.

1912 August 17. Wharf at Balboa collapsed.

1912 August 24. Law providing for opening, maintaining, defense, and operation of Canal signed by President Taft.

1912 August 28. Eight-hundred-foot section of Gatun Dam settled twenty feet.

1912 November 6. Railroad trestle to Naos Island completed.

1912 December 1. Miraflores Dam completed.

1912 December 15. Gatun Dam completed.

1913 January 17. Railroad transportation in Culebra Cut stalled by slide of 400,000 cubic yards at Cucaracha.

1913 January 20. Three-hundred-foot rock bluff south of Gold Hill fell into Canal, carrying half-million cubic yards.

1913 April 27. First crossing of Canal Zone by flying machine.

1913 May 17. Concrete construction on Miraflores Locks completed.

1913 May 18. Dike near Corozal blown up, letting waters of Pacific into Canal channel.

1913 May 21. Masonry for Gatun Locks completed.

1913 August 31. Miraflores dike, last remaining barrier at Pacific end of Canal, dynamited.

1913   September 2. Canal entrance to Gatun Locks opened with removal of railroad tracks across dike north of locks. Passenger service established between Colón and Panama City over relocated railroad line.

1913   September 10. Culebra Cut cleared of machinery preparatory to flooding.

1913   September 26. Seagoing tug *Gatun* first vessel to pass through Gatun Locks.

1913   October 1–15. Severe earthquake followed by series of forty tremors.

1913   October 9. Thirteen utility vessels raised from Atlantic channel to Gatun Lake.

1913   October 10. Gamboa dike blown up, flooding Culebra Cut.

1913   October 14. First lockage at Pacific terminal when tug *Miraflores* with three barges and launch were raised to Miraflores Lake.

1913   October 20. Channel cut across Cucaracha slide, completing water "bridge" across Isthmus.

1913   October 26. Dredging of last barriers in Culebra Cut started.

1914   January 7. *Alexander La Valley*, French crane boat, made first passage through the Canal.

1914   January 27. Orders for permanent Zone government issued by President Wilson.

1914   February 4. Gatun Lake level raised to full height of eighty-five feet.

1914   April 1. Goethals became first Governor of Canal Zone; I.C.C. terminated.

1914   April 6. Under Thomson-Urritia Treaty, Colombia recognized the U. S. title to the Panama Canal and Railroad.

1914   May 18. Commercial service through the Canal inaugurated with lightering of sugar cargo on fleet of twelve barges.

1914   May 27. Earthquake damaged buildings in Balboa and Panama City.

1914   June 8. Panama Railroad Steamship *Allianca* passed through Gatun Locks to Gatun Lake.

1914   July 15. Canal headquarters transferred from Culebra and Cristobal to permanent administration building at Balboa.

1914   August 3. Test voyage of *Cristobal* through Canal.

1914   August 15. Canal opened to traffic with passage of *Ancon* from ocean to ocean.

1914   August 18. Peruvian destroyer first warship to pass through Canal.

1914   October 14. Slide of 725,000 cubic yards north of Gold Hill closed Canal for a week.

1914   October 31. Second slide, after opening, closed Canal for four days.

1915   March 4. Slide north of Gold Hill closed Canal for six days.

1915   August 7. Slide at Culebra closed Canal for five days.

1915   September 4. Slide closed Canal for six days.

1915   September 18. Slide of twenty million cubic yards closed Canal for seven months.

1920   July 12. Canal formally opened by proclamation of President Wilson.

1921   April 20. United States Senate ratified treaty granting Colombia indemnity of $25,000,000.

1921   June 30. Construction account for Canal closed, showing total cost (excluding defense installations) at $386,910,-301.04.

1922   March 30. Long-delayed Thomson-Urritia Treaty proclaimed.

1924   July 9. Diplomatic relations between Colombia and Panama established.

1931   November 9. Slides blocked ships except those of shallow draft for a week.

1932   Thatcher Ferry and Highway, essential link in Inter-American highway, completed.

1935   Concrete dam across Chagres River at Alhajuela completed, providing reserve storage of 22,000,000 cubic feet in Madden Lake twenty-two miles square.

1936   March 2. Under the Hull-Alfaro Treaty of Friendship and Cooperation, the United States increased the Canal annuity from $250,000 to $430,000, and withdrew guarantee of Panamanian independence. (Not proclaimed until July 27, 1939.)

1939   August 15. On silver anniversary of Canal opening, S. S. *Ancon* reenacted voyage through Canal.

1939   "Third Locks Project" authorized by Congress at cost of $277,000,000.

1939   Agreement made between the United States and Panama for construction of Boyd-Roosevelt highway across the Isthmus.

1940   July 1. Construction started on "Third Locks Project", providing for construction of new set of locks with chambers 140 feet wide and 1200 long.

1942   Third Locks Project suspended due to urgent need of manpower and materials for World War II.

1943   May 20. "Terminal Lake-Third Locks Plan", comprehensive plan for major operational improvement of the Canal, presented by Commander Miles P. DuVal, Jr.

1943   Trans-Isthmian highway opened.

1945   December 28. Governor of the Panama Canal directed by Congress to investigate means for increasing capacity and security of the Canal to meet future needs of interoceanic commerce and national defense.

1946   October. Zone administration ordered end to gold and silver segregation system.

1947   November. Governor of Panama Canal submitted report recommending that existing waterway be converted into sea-level canal at cost then estimated at $2,483,000,000.

1947   December 1. Governor's report recommending "Sea-Level

Project" transmitted by President Truman to Congress without presidential approval, comment, or recommendation.

1951   April 26. Transit of 150,000th ocean-going commercial vessel through Canal.

1951   July 1. Entire Canal enterprise reorganized by Congress and placed on a self-sustaining basis under The Panama Canal Company, a corporate agency of the United States Government whose Board of Directors is appointed by the Secretary of the Army.

1954   April. Major rockslide into Culebra Cut averted by removal of two and a half million cubic yards from slope of Contractors Hill, where wide seams had opened.

1954   July. East half of Canal blocked temporarily by Cucaracha slide.

1955   January 25. Under Eisenhower-Remon Treaty, annuity to Panama increased to $1,930,000, and valuable properties connected with Canal surrendered to Panama without compensation to the U. S.

1955   June 30. Net investment of the United States in the Canal proper evaluated at $368,004,765, exclusive of fortifications and defense bases.

1956   July 26. "Nationalization" of Suez focused world attention on Panama Canal.

1957   March. International Round Table Conference on Interoceanic Canals, meeting in Panama, without U. S. representation, agreed to further revision of Canal treaties, with aim of securing larger compensation for Panama and eventual denunciation of perpetuity clauses in the Hay-Bunau-Varilla Treaty.

1957   October 4. Transit of 200,000th commercial vessel through Canal.

Reference Sources

Foreword. "Something Worth Bragging Aboot." P. 12—"Haughty announcement": *London Daily Express* (UP), April 13, 1957. P. 12—President de la Guardia's response: letter to author. P. 14—Buying back the Canal: *Congressional Record* (Representative Sullivan) August 5, 1957, p. 12412. Pp. 16-17—Wells' statement: ibid., May 29, 1957, p. 7135. P. 17—Argument for sea-level Canal: *The Panama Canal. The Sea-Level Project and National Security* (Report of the Special Committee on the Panama Canal of the National Rivers and Harbors Congress 1956. U.S. Government Printing Office. Washington, 1956), p. 1. P. 17—Vulnerability to atomic attack: Bradley, Willis W., "What of the Panama Canal," *Congressional Record*, April 21, 1948, p. A2451. Pp. 17-18—Governor Thatcher's comment: "Address Before the Panama Canal Society, May 12, 1956," *Congressional Record*, May 29, 1956. P. 19—Taft's address: *Canal Record*, February 24, 1909, p. 204. P. 20—Scottish engineer's comment: *Scribner's Magazine*, July 1921, p. 33.

Chapter I. "I Took the Isthmus, Started the Canal." P. 26—"Enough rifles and cartridges": New York *Times*, November 5, 1903, p. 2. P. 27—"Attempt of a stronger nation": Pringle, H. F., *Theodore Roosevelt* (Harvest edition, Harcourt, Brace and Co., 1956), p. 208. Pp. 27-28—Roosevelt's name-calling: ibid., pp. 219, 220. Hill, H. C., *Roosevelt and the Caribbean* (University of Chicago Press, 1927), p. 67. P. 28—Movement of Naval vessels: New York *Times*, November 1, 1903, p. 8; November 3, 1903, p. 12. P. 29—*Nashville* sailing: ibid., November 1, 1903, p. 4. P. 29—News from Baranquilla: ibid., November 2, 1903, p. 7. P. 29—"I took the Isthmus": Charter Day Address, Berkeley, California, March 23, 1911, San Francisco *Chronicle*, March 24, 1911, p. 2. P. 29—Bunau-Varilla's assertion: Bunau-Varilla, Philippe, *From Panama to Verdun* (Dorrance and Co., Philadelphia, 1940), pp. 110-111. P. 30—Moore and

Reference Sources

Cromwell: Mack, Gerstle, *The Land Divided* (Knopf, 1944) p. 455.
P. 30—Editorial: New York *Times,* November 5, 1903, p. 8. P. 31—
Complaint of Consul General: ibid., November 10, 1903, p. 2. P. 32—
Comment of Assistant Secretary: ibid., November 5, 1903, p. 2. P. 32
—"I should be delighted": *Works of Theodore Roosevelt* (Memorial
Edition Charles Scribner's Sons, N.Y., 1923-1926), XXIII, p. 322. P. 33—
Orders to *Nashville:* Miner, D. C., *The Fight for the Panama Route*
(Columbia University Press, 1940), pp. 361-362. P. 34—Rumor re.
Bunau-Varilla: Bunau-Varilla, *Panama: The Creation, Destruction and
Resurrection* (Constable and Co. Ltd., London, 1913), p. 227. P. 36—
Le Matin: Bunau-Varilla, *Great Adventure of Panama* (Doubleday, 1920),
pp. 177, 178. P. 37—Beer's report: Bunau-Varilla, *Panama: The Creation,
Destruction and Resurrection,* p. 290. P. 38—"Smile as sweetly": Miner,
op. cit., p. 77. Pp. 39-40—Cromwell and Lindo conferences: Johnson,
W. F., *Four Centuries of the Panama Canal* (Holt, 1907), pp. 166-168.
Pp. 40-41—Bunau-Varilla's version: Bunau-Varilla, *Panama: The Cre-
ation, Destruction and Resurrection,* pp. 291, 292. P. 41—"Not to be
caught napping": Bunau-Varilla, *Great Adventure of Panama,* p. 209.
Pp. 41-42—Conferences with Bunau-Varilla: Bunau-Varilla, ibid., p. 183;
From Panama to Verdun, pp. 128, 134, 135.

Chapter II. "But It Is the Hour of Siesta." P. 47—Persistent rumors: New
York *Times,* November 4, 1903, p. 1. P. 47—"Better advice": ibid., November 5, 1903, p. 2. P. 48—Concession terms to railroad: Lower, I. E.,
Acquisition of the Panama Canal (Ms. Library, University of California),
p. 28. P. 52—Account of siesta: Johnson, op. cit., pp. 173-176. Pp. 53-54
—Report from Colón: New York *Times,* November 4, 1903, p. 1. P. 54—
Orders to *Maine:* ibid., November 7, 1903. P. 54—Reply to Cromwell's
partner: ibid., November 6, 1903, p. 2. P. 54—*Mayflower:* ibid., November 7, 1903, p. 2. P. 56—*Bogota*'s departure: ibid., November 5, 1903,
p. 2. P. 57—Navy's threat: ibid. P. 57—Hubbard's note to Prefect: ibid.,
p. 1. P. 58—*Times'* optimistic cable: ibid. P. 60—Amador's address:
Pringle, op. cit., pp. 230-231. P. 60—Declaration of Independence: John-
son, op. cit., pp. 405-406. Pp. 60-61—Message to Bunau-Varilla: Bunau-
Varilla, *From Panama to Verdun,* p. 150. P. 61—Paris reaction: New
York *Times,* November 9, 1903, p. 2. P. 61—Panama demonstrations:
ibid., November 8, 1903, p. 2; November 7, p. 1. Pp. 61-62—Comment of
Secretary of State: ibid., November 7, 1903, p. 1. P. 62—Protests: ibid.,
November 5, 1903, p. 1; November 6, p. 8; November 9, p. 6. P. 63—
Congressional investigation: ibid., December 18, 1908. P. 63—"Indecent
haste": *Nation,* November 13, 1903 (Editorial), p. 398. P. 63—Com-

mentator: Hill, op. cit., pp. 66, 67. P. 63—President's footwork: Wood, F. S., *Roosevelt as We Knew Him* (Winston, 1927), pp. 66, 67.

Chapter III. "Shell of Rust Covered with Paint." Pp. 65-66—Tarantula and snake stories: Bunau-Varilla, *Panama: The Creation, Destruction and Resurrection,* pp. 55, 56. P. 67—Bunau-Varilla's deal: Bunau-Varilla, *From Panama to Verdun,* pp. 157, 158. P. 68—"Life dies and death lives": Lambert, Ernest, "Panama—Story of a Colossal Bubble," *Forum,* March, 1893, p. 12. P. 68—"When the trade winds die": "What We Inherit from the Panama Canal," *Scientific American,* July 23, 1904, p. 58. P. 72— Promotion bandwagon: Panama *Star,* December 24, 1853, as quoted by DuVal, M. P., *And the Mountains Will Move* (Stanford University Press, Palo Alto, 1947), p. 24. P. 73—Congressional threat: DuVal, op. cit., p. 42. Pp. 73-74—De Lesseps' speech: *Canal Record,* July 29, 1908, p. 383. P. 74—"The Canal will be made": Robinson, Tracy, *Panama— A Personal Record of Forty-Six Years, 1861-1907,* (*Star and Herald,* Panama, 1907), p. 140. P. 74—Speech of *Herald* Correspondent: *Canal Record,* July 29, 1908, p. 383. P. 74—De Lesseps' description: Robinson, op. cit., pp. 139, 141. P. 76—Liquor: Bishop, J. B., *Panama Gateway* (Scribners, New York, 1913), p. 88. Pp. 76-77—$300,000-story: Johnson, op. cit., pp. 102, 103. Pp. 77-78—1891 observations: "Ruins of Panama Canal," *Scientific American,* August 1, 1891, p. 68. P. 78—"Reading notices": "Panama Corruption Fund," *Nation,* December 29, 1892, p. 492. Pp. 78-79—Graveyard inheritance: *Scientific American,* July 23, 1904, p. 58. Pp. 79-80—Disintegration and waste: ibid. P. 80—Pay-offs to bankers and government officials: "Panama Scandal," *Review of Reviews,* January 1893, p. 659.

Chapter IV. "Tell Them I'm Going to Make the Dirt Fly." Pp. 83-84— Roosevelt scripture: *Works of Theodore Roosevelt* (National Edition, Scribners, 1926), XIV, p. 291, XIX, p. 424, XIII, p. 331. *Presidential Addresses and State Papers,* Vol. IV, (Review of Reviews Co. New York, 1910) p. 392. Pp. 84-85—Criticism of Roosevelt: "Haste and Repentance," *Nation,* November 13, 1903, p. 398. P. 85—"Instead of debating": *Works of Theodore Roosevelt,* XII, p. 545. P. 85—"What this nation will insist upon": DuVal, op. cit., p. 130. P. 85—"Utmost practical speed": "Panama Muddle," *Nation,* November 23, 1905, p. 416. P. 85—"Push the work": "Makers of the Panama Canal," *Outlook,* April 2, 1904, p. 835. P. 88—Colon "Blot": Weir, H. C., *Conquest of the Isthmus* (Putnam's, 1909), p. 69. P. 88—Senator Morgan's comment: New York *Times,* November 7, 1903, p. 1. P. 89—Panama City: Johnson, op. cit., pp. 370, 375.

P. 90—Philip II story: ibid., p. 33. P. 95—"Dirt Fly": *Nation,* November 23, 1905, op. cit., p. 412. P. 96—Panama laborers: Sibert, W. L. and Stevens, J. F., *Construction of the Panama Canal* (Appleton, N.Y., 1915), p. 110. P. 97—Quarters at Ancon Hospital: *Canal Record,* September 11, 1907, p. 15. Pp. 98-100—Barrett's article: "Progress at Panama," *Independent,* January 25, 1905, p. 430. P. 100—Taft's acclamation: Johnson, op. cit., p. 265.

Chapter V. "Nobody's Here for His Health." P. 102—Newcomer in Colon: Lyle, E. P., "Real Conditions at Panama," *World's Work,* November 1905, pp. 6878 ff. P. 103—Room equipment, ibid. P. 103—"Nobody's here for his health": Slosson, E. E. and Richardson, Gardner, "Life in the Canal Zone," *Independent,* March 22, 1906, pp. 653-660. P. 105—Water quotas: Linehan, B. E., "The Panama Canal," *Catholic World,* May 1905, pp. 176-184. Pp. 105-06—Lumber deliveries: Slosson and Richardson, op. cit., p. 654. P. 106—Washington graft: ibid., p. 659. P. 106—"Serious difficulty": Linehan, op. cit., p. 179. P. 106—"No place for a white man": Lyle, op. cit., p. 6879. P. 107—Prophylactic: Slosson and Richardson, "The *Independent*'s Report on Panama," *Independent,* March 15, 1906, p. 589. P. 107—Feminine deficiencies: Slosson and Richardson, "Life in the Canal Zone," op. cit., p. 660. P. 107—Colon saloons: Linehan, op. cit., p. 180. Pp. 107-08—Foreman's accommodations: ibid., p. 177. Pp. 108-09 —Negro complainant: Bigelow, Poultney, "Our Mismanagement in Panama," *Independent,* January 4, 1906, p. 12. P. 109—Requisition route: Lyle, op. cit. P. 109—Order for drink: Linehan, op. cit., p. 178. P. 109— Hinges: Bates, Lindon W., *Retrieval at Panama* (Privately printed, 1907), p. 30. Pp. 109-10—Dirt is not flying: Lyle, op. cit. P. 110—Shipping confusion: Slosson and Richardson, "Life in the Canal Zone," op. cit., p. 653. P. 110—*Post* and *Picayune: Literary Digest,* April 8, 1905, p. 497. P. 111 —Wallace checked and thwarted: Slosson and Richardson, "Life in the Canal Zone," op. cit., p. 653. P. 112—Walker to Gorgas: DuVal, op. cit., p. 147. P. 113—Criticism of Commission: "Real Situation in Panama," *Independent,* February 9, 1905, pp. 307-314. Pp. 113-14—Taft's endorsement: Linehan, op. cit., p. 177.

Chapter VI. "Nobody Was Working But the Ants and the Typists." P. 118 —"Nobody was working": Carr, J. F., "Panama Canal. The Chief Engineer and His Work," *Outlook,* June 2, 1906, p. 266. P. 118—Comment on acceptance: Webster, H. J., "John F. Stevens," *American Magazine,* October 1905, p. 678. P. 119—Stevens' conversation with T.R.: Stevens, J. F., "Address on the Panama Canal," July 13, 1927, *Transactions,*

American Society of Civil Engineers (1927), #1650, pp. 949, 950. P. 120
—Stevens' first observations: ibid., p. 950. P. 122—Three diseases: Bishop,
Farnum, *Panama, Past and Present* (Century, New York, 1913), p. 159.
P. 123—Stevens' experience with Indians: Webster, op. cit., p. 676. P. 123
—"Canny Maine Yankee": Carr, op. cit., p. 265. P. 124—Collisions:
Haskin, F. J., *The Panama Canal* (Doubleday, 1914), p. 136. P. 124—
"Digging is the least thing": Lyle, op. cit., p. 6878. P. 126—Stevens'
tirade: Stevens, op. cit., p. 952. P. 126—Magoon on yellow fever: John-
son, op. cit., p. 330. P. 126—Tonnage of sulphur and insecticide: Gorgas,
W. C., *Sanitation in Panama* (Appleton, 1915), p. 151. P. 127—Negro
home: Franck, H. A., *Zone Policeman 88* (Century, 1913), p. 40. P. 127
—"Holding what had been accomplished": Gorgas, op. cit., p. 156. P. 129
—Mortality statistics: ibid., pp. 149, 158. P. 130—Stevens' bungalow:
Carr, op. cit., p. 266. P. 130—Stevens under flat car: Slosson and Richardson, "Life in the Canal Zone," op. cit., p. 657. P. 130—Day's work: Carr,
op. cit., p. 265. Pp. 130-31—Stevens' replies: ibid., p. 266. P. 131—"One
man to grapple": ibid., pp. 265, 266.

Chapter VII. "It Was Lovely to See the Orchids." P. 134—Query of Board
member: *Report of the Board of Consulting Engineers for the Panama
Canal* (1906), pp. 293, 294. Pp. 134-35—"Deluge of plans": Sibert and
Stevens, op. cit., p. 76. P. 135—Rock crushing plant: ibid., p. 84. P. 136—
Stevens on overwork: *Report of the Board*, op. cit., pp. 284, 294. P. 136
—President's charge: ibid., p. 12. P. 137—"Great cracks": Slosson and
Richardson, "Life in the Canal Zone," op. cit., p. 659. P. 137—"Hand to
the plow": Carr, op. cit., p. 268. Pp. 138-39—Bigelow article: *Independ-
ent*, January 4, 1906, pp. 9-21. Pp. 139-40—Board Resolution: *Report of
the Board*, op. cit., p. 14. P. 140—Stevens' letter: ibid., p. XXI. P. 141—
President's endorsement: ibid., p. IV. P. 142—Stevens' criticism of sea-
level canal: Sibert and Stevens, op. cit., pp. 29, 30, 36. P. 143—Shrewd
calculations: ibid., p. 81. P. 144—"Keynote": Stevens, op. cit., p. 958.
P. 145—"Cloud across the sky": *Report of the Board*, op. cit., p. 287.
P. 145—"Sub rosa negotiations": Stevens, op. cit., p. 959. Pp. 149-50—
Letter to Kermit: *Works of Theodore Roosevelt* (Memorial edition) XXI,
p. 576. P. 150—Letter to Theodore Roosevelt, Jr.: ibid., (National edition), XIX, p. 519. P. 150—"Fulfilled promise": Stevens, op. cit., pp. 949,
960. P. 150—"Biggest scandal": Carr, op. cit., p. 270. P. 151—"Personal
reasons": Stevens, op. cit., p. 961.

Chapter VIII. "You Received My Orders." P. 153—Roosevelt's proposal:
Bishop, *Panama Gateway*, p. 176. P. 154—President's note and Goethals'

response: Bishop, J. B. and Farnum, *Goethals, Genius of the Panama Canal* (Harper, New York, 1930), p. 141. P. 155—Roosevelt's conversation with Goethals: ibid. (quoted indirectly). P. 155—"Plain straight duty": ibid., p. 149. P. 155—Minneapolis *Journal* quote: *Literary Digest,* March 16, 1907, p. 410. Pp. 155-56—New York *Times* quote: Bishop, J. B. and F., op. cit., pp. 147, 148. P. 156—Editorial: *Independent,* March 7, 1907, pp. 571, 572. P. 157—"Sewer gas": Bishop, J. B. and F., op. cit., p. 148. P. 157—Panama *Star and Herald* quote: ibid., p. 154 (March 3, 1907). P. 158—"Culebra's cut to the heart": DuVal, op. cit., p. 263. P. 158—"Don't talk": ibid. P. 158—Petition: ibid. P. 160— Goethals' speech: ibid., p. 268 (Panama *Star and Herald,* March 19, 1907). P. 161—"The magnitude of the work": Bishop, J. B. and F., op. cit., pp. 150-153. P. 161—Goethals' surmise on Stevens: ibid., p. 151. P. 161—"Details": ibid., p. 166. P. 161—Stevens' inhospitability: ibid., p. 150. P. 162—"Laws are made to be obeyed": ibid., p. 157. P. 162— Goethals' reactions to Congressmen: ibid., p. 158. P. 163—"Captain, I am ready": DuVal, op. cit., p. 272. P. 164—"See the Colonel" and jingle: Abbot, W. J., *Panama and the Canal in Picture and Prose* (Syndicate Publishing Co., New York, 1913), p. 161. P. 165—Baseball and builder's stories: ibid., pp. 166, 167, 168. P. 166—Stevens to strikers: DuVal, op. cit., p. 249. P. 167—"Yellow peril": Bishop, J. B. and F., op. cit., p. 228. P. 167—Health officer story: ibid., p. 165. P. 168—*Canal Record* purpose: *Canal Record,* September 4, 1907, p. 1. P. 168—Caimito Mulato: ibid., November 20, 1907, p. 89 and Weir, op. cit., p. 8. Pp. 168-69—Cement bags: *Canal Record,* December 7, 1910, p. 113. P. 169—Tribute with historical insight: DuVal, op. cit., p. 265. P. 169—"All over but the shouting": *Canal Record,* April 1, 1908, p. 245.

Chapter IX. "Thinks Gatun Dam Safe." P. 171—Stevens' rebuke: *Engineering News,* February 21, 1907, p. 220. Pp. 172-73—Zone labor: Franck, op. cit., pp. 100, 118, 119. P. 173—Dynamite accident: *Canal Record,* July 28, 1909, p. 378. P. 175—"Open cut": Sibert and Stevens, op. cit., p. 230. P. 176—"Upstream flow": New York *Times,* December 20, 1908, Part V, p. 2. Pp. 178-79—Engineer's explanation to Congressmen: Minter, J. E., *The Chagres: River of Westward Passage* (Rinehart and Co., N.Y., 1948), p. 364. P. 179—"Superincumbant load": *Scientific American,* May 25, 1907, p. 94. Pp. 179-80—"Storm center": ibid. P. 180 —Schedule anecdote: Minter, op. cit., p. 361. Pp. 181-82—Material for concrete work: *Canal Record,* April 7, 1909, p. 253. P. 183—"Collapse of Gatun Dam": *Engineering News,* December 3, 1908, p. 617. P. 183— Boston *Transcript:* November 24, 1908, p. 1. P. 184—London *Times:*

November 25, 1908, p. 7. P. 184—*Figaro:* New York *Times:* December 14, 1908, p. 1. P. 184—"Whole matter better be dropped": *Engineering News,* December 31, 1908, p. 751. P. 184—San Francisco *Chronicle:* November 25, 1908, p. 2. P. 184—Goethals' cable: New York *Times,* November 26, 1908, p. 1. P. 184—"Thinks Gatun Dam Safe": ibid., November 25, 1908, p. 4. Pp. 184-85—Page-1 sensation: ibid., December 19, 1908, p. 1. P. 185—*Times* feature: ibid., December 20, 1908, Part V, p. 2. P. 185—Stevens' letter: *Engineering News,* December 31, 1908, p. 751. P. 186—Authoritative statement: ibid., December 24, 1908, p. 717. P. 186 —*Canal Record:* January 6, 1909, p. 147. P. 188—Sibert's conjecture: Sibert and Stevens, op. cit., p. 233. P. 188—Collapse of retaining wall: ibid., p. 234. P. 189—Taft's speech: *Canal Record:* February 24, 1909, p. 204.

Chapter X. "Culebra Cut Was a Hell's Gorge." P. 191—"Probable total": Bishop, J. B., op. cit., p. 185. P. 193—False start at Panama: Robinson, Tracy, op. cit., pp. 146, 147. P. 193—*Bulletin* report: Bishop, op. cit., p. 73. Pp. 193-94—Celebration of January 20, 1882: *Canal Record,* July 14, 1909, p. 362. Pp. 196-97—Halfway mark: ibid., October 27, 1909, p. 68. P. 198—Visitor's impressions: Bishop, op. cit., p. 195. Pp. 198-99— Sounds and color: Abbot, op. cit., pp. 210, 211. Pp. 201-02—Explosion reports: *Canal Record:* June 3, 1908, p. 314; August 25, 1909, p. 411; October 14, 1908, p. 51; December 16, 1908, p. 125. Pp. 202-03— Miguel's ascension: Abbot, op. cit., p. 209. P. 203—Dry slide: *Scientific American,* November 9, 1912, p. 390. P. 204—Humping: Sibert and Stevens, op. cit., p. 278. P. 205—Oxidation: *Canal Record,* March 6, 1912, p. 225. Pp. 206-07—Slide of November 16, 1909: ibid., November 24, 1909, pp. 98, 99. P. 207—Reassurance on Culebra slide: ibid., May 18, 1910, p. 297. P. 207—"Hell's Gorge": Bishop, J. B. and F., op. cit., p. 208.

Chapter XI. "Miraflores and Pedro Miguel Were Sleeping Peacefully." P. 210—Stevens at hearing: *U.S. Senate Committee on Interoceanic Canals. Report of Hearings,* 1906, #18, Volume 1, pp. 289, 327, 328. P. 210—Taft on Sosa Hill: *Report of the Board of Consulting Engineers,* February 19, 1906, p. VII. P. 211—Board report: *Canal Record,* December 25, 1907, p. 132; *Engineering News,* May 9, 1907, p. 522. Pp. 213-14 —Goethals' letter to Taft: *Canal Record,* December 25, 1907, p. 132. P. 214—Notes of Progress: ibid., p. 129. Pp. 215-16—Executive order: ibid., January 22, 1908, p. 162. P. 216—Feature stories: ibid., March 24, 1909, p. 236; May 12, 1909, p. 294. P. 217—La Boca to Balboa: ibid., May 5, 1909, p. 281. Pp. 217-18—Pennell: *Joseph Pennell's Pictures of*

the Panama Canal (J. B. Lippincott Co., Philadelphia, 1913), pp. XVIII,
XXII. P. 219—Production capacity of cranes: *Canal Record,* January 4,
1911, p. 149. P. 220—Roosevelt on tourism: ibid., September 14, 1910,
p. 21. P. 221—Gongs: ibid., January 11, 1911, p. 155. P. 222—French
Cemeteries: Jewell, L. P., "The Canal Diggers Who Will Never Come
Back," *Colliers,* October 4, 1913, p. 20. Pp. 224-25—Taft speeches: *Canal
Record,* November 23, 1910, pp. 99, 100.

Chapter XII. "The Real Good that Women Are Doing Here." P. 228—
White employees are gold: *Canal Record,* March 25, 1908, p. 233. P. 228
—Furniture: ibid., September 4, 1907, p. 6. P. 229—Fulmination: Franck,
op. cit., pp. 219, 220. Pp. 230-31—"Bachelor is a bachelor": ibid., pp. 86,
87. P. 231—Paraiso insomniac: *Canal Record,* January 15, 1908, p. 154.
P. 231—Bachelor quarters: ibid., January 29, 1908, p. 172; March 4,
1908, p. 214. P. 231—Bearup's reply: ibid., January 29, 1908, p. 172.
P. 232—Allegation: Abbot, op. cit., p. 341. P. 233—Applications: *Canal
Record,* October 9, 1907, p. 42. P. 234—Commissary bureaucracy: ibid.,
November 6, 1907, p. 75. P. 235—Pies: ibid., May 6, 1908, p. 281. P. 235
—Strawberries: ibid., May 6, 1908, p. 280; May 13, 1908, p. 288.
Pp. 235-36—Miss Boswell: ibid., October 2, 1907, p. 37; October 16,
1907, p. 50. P. 237—Need for social diversion: ibid., October 30, 1907,
p. 68; November 13, 1907, p. 84. P. 237—Texas celebration: ibid., Sep-
tember 25, 1907, p. 31. P. 238—IORM: ibid., October 16, 1907, p. 52;
February 26, 1908, p. 204. P. 239—Ancon Association: ibid., January 1,
1908, p. 141. P. 240—High diver: ibid., January 8, 1908, p. 151. P. 240—
Walking race: ibid., December 4, 1907, p. 111. P. 241—Circus: ibid.,
January 1, 1908, p. 139. P. 241—Greased pole: ibid., January 1, 1908,
p. 349. Pp. 242-43—Rome news quote: (*Gazzetta del Populo*) ibid.,
February 12, 1908, p. 190. P. 244—Bloodhounds: ibid., February 12,
1908, p. 187. Pp. 244-45—"Victorious army": ibid., July 1, 1908, p. 346.
P. 245—"Kitchener of the Canal": Sherer, J. A. B., "Christmas in Panama," *Independent,* January 16, 1913, p. 136.

Chapter XIII. "Two Dozen New Graves Stand Ready." Pp. 248-49—
Sightseeing business: *Canal Record,* December 18, 1912, p. 133. P. 249
—Billboards: ibid., January 1, 1913, p. 149. P. 249—"No better way to
see the Canal": ibid., December 18, 1912, p. 133. P. 250—Atlantic fleet
visit: ibid., December 25, 1912, p. 141. P. 251—"Canal or no canal":
Sherer, op. cit., pp. 129-136. Pp. 251-53—Taft's visit: ibid. P. 254—Guide
at Culebra: *Canal Record,* July 23, 1913, p. 409. P. 254—Guide at Pedro
Miguel: ibid., December 4, 1912, p. 117. Pp. 254-55—Skeptical corre-

spondent: Fuller, Bampfylde, *Nineteenth Century,* July 1913, pp. 68-77. P. 255—Britisher's observation: ibid. Pp. 257-58—Motor laws: *Canal Record,* February 5, 1908, p. 178; December 7, 1910, p. 118; September 11, 1912, p. 17. Pp. 258-59—Hydrobiplane flight: ibid., April 30, 1913, p. 297. Pp. 259-61—Canal victims: Jewell, op. cit., p. 20. P. 261—Culebra clubhouse: *Canal Record,* September 11, 1912, p. 17. P. 262—Cucaracha slide: ibid., January 22, 1913, p. 173. P. 262—"Unremitting excavation": ibid., October 2, 1912, p. 49. Pp. 262-63—"Tourists and eminent scientists": Putnam, G. P., "Canal Today," *Sunset,* October 1912, p. 383. P. 263—"Heroic human endeavor": "Spectator," *Outlook,* October 11, 1913, pp. 324-326.

Chapter XIV. "It's All Over. Gamboa Is Busted." P. 267—Optimists and pessimists: Cornish, Vaughan, "Scenes of Panama Canal," *Living Age,* September 24, 1914, p. 779. P. 270—Half-day notice: *Canal Record,* September 24, 1913, p. 37. Pp. 270-71—Earthquake report: ibid., October 8, 1913, p. 53. P. 271—Tonisí destruction: ibid., October 15, 1913, p. 74. P. 272—"Canal is Opened": New York *Times,* October 11, 1913, p. 9. P. 273—London *Times:* ibid. P. 274—"Charges of such violence": *Canal Record:* October 22, 1913, p. 77. P. 275—Detroit message: ibid., January 7, 1914, p. 182. P. 277—First direct voyage: ibid., May 20, 1914, p. 373. P. 278—"Different character": ibid., June 3, 1914, p. 397. P. 278—Survey report: ibid. P. 279—*Allianca:* ibid., June 10, 1914, p. 410. Pp. 279-80— Cornish quote: Cornish, op. cit., p. 780. P. 280—Bunau-Varilla's reactions: Bunau-Varilla, *Great Adventure of Panama,* p. 260, 261. P. 281— Important military possession: Blakeslee, G. H., "Future of the Panama Canal," *Outlook,* August 25, 1915, pp. 966-976. P. 281—Armament details: ibid. P. 281—World War I headlines: New York *Times,* August 16, 1914, p. 1. P. 283—"Greatest marvel": Bunau-Varilla, *Great Adventure of Panama,* p. 261. P. 283—Newspaper comments: *Literary Digest,* August 29, 1914, p. 335. P. 284—Poem: Stafford, W. P., "Panama Hymn," *Atlantic Monthly,* December 1913, p. 790. P. 284—Formal opening postponement: *Canal Record,* February 10, 1915, p. 231. Pp. 285-86— Panama Canal Memorial: H.R. 13706 (1928); *Remarks of Honorable Maurice H. Thatcher of Kentucky* (U.S. Government Printing Office, Washington, 1928).

Index

315

Index

Index